THE BOOK OF THE INN

The George Inn, Glastonbury.

The George Inn, Glastonbury
From a woodcut by Robert Gibbings

THE BOOK OF THE INN

being two hundred pictures of the
english inn from the earliest
times to the coming of
the railway hotel

selected and edited by
THOMAS BURKE

London
Constable & Co Ltd
1927

PRINTED IN GREAT BRITAIN BY THE WHITEFRIARS PRESS, LTD.,
LONDON AND TONBRIDGE.

TO

All Virtuous and Illustrious Hosts and Hostesses,

Whose Lives are Dedicate to the Noble Art of
Innkeeping,

This Book Wishes

Honour, Health, and Prosperity ;

And

To All Travellers

It Wishes

Good Roads, free of East Winds and Magneto Trouble,
and, at Their Inns, Honest Usage and
Fair Reckonings.

The Editor.

PREFACE

WELCOME !

THE Christian Church began in the stable of an inn, and to this day the inn figures in our minds as the material counterpart of the Church. It succours and fortifies the mortal, in time of need, as the Church succours and fortifies the immortal. It is the stage of a pilgrimage. We find there refuge and solace ; sleep for weariness, meat and wine for hunger, chance company and the brotherhood of men. In almost every old village of England the church spire or tower denotes the position of the inn. For centuries they have stood together, complementing each other in a beautiful wedding of spirit and sense ; and, despite the conspiracies of certain evil-disposed persons to sever them, they still stand. Should we abolish the inn, we might as well prepare to abolish the Church, for when men have forgotten how to rejoice they will have forgotten how to pray.

No institution of English life has gathered about it so lustrous an accumulation of story. Being at the heart of life our inns are for ever young ; and they carry their dower of story and association with the centuries as lightly as the youth of the past carried his staff of forest oak from their yards, or the youth of to-day carries his golf-clubs. Throughout literature and history they recur, and their very names and signs are the poetry of travel. They have lived in the stream of daily life these six centuries, among the simple and among the great. They have known common festival and portentous assembly. Whatever in the state fell or shifted, they remained ; being in turn resting-places, council chambers, courts and moot-halls. Defeated kings have surrendered within their walls ; princes have lain in hiding or have faced their assailants ; commissioners have fought great causes across their tables. At all times, since their beginning, they have been the centre of the life of their times, and in their rooms our fathers before us have sat and talked, or tarried a little between great enterprises ; have feasted, despaired, been happy.

The very word " inn " lights up the mind as its actual windows light up a dark and rainy road. Call it " Railway Hotel," and the mind receives nothing but draught and grit. It is the random opening of the whole volume of adventure. Here pilgrimages begin, journeys end, strange acquaintance is made, and lovers meet or part ; and from the pillow that receives your head, and will to-morrow night receive the head of a traveller in hardware, rises store of legend and a pageant of the ages. All other houses have their times of peace ; the inn knows no rest from movement. To-day, as three hundred years ago, men come at night, furtively, it seems, bent upon romantic business. Their muffled steps break into your first sleep. All night the passages rustle with them. At any hour the yard bell may ring, and night-porter or Boots must open and admit to the house a creature of whom he knows nothing save that he comes as a traveller and will depart as Number Fifteen. That is one of the hundred pleasures of the inn—the sinking of one's identity. Our names are with us all our lives, and, jealous as we are of them, there are times when we are heartily sick of them, and long to escape them. The inn is the only place (save prison)

where we may throw them off with our coats, and become
for a space Mister Nobody or Number Fifteen ; where
William Jones, owner of a small villa, may lose his daily
self and be a lord.

For the best of our inns have the nobility of the great
houses—Hatfield, Knole, Penshurst, Wilton—but without their arctic seclusion. The doors of the inn are open
to us all. For the price of bed-and-breakfast the humblest
of us may pass through their arches when he will, and
enjoy the dignity of their chambers, their mullioned
windows, raftered roofs and Tudor staircases, and the
comforts of their tables. A night in a good inn gives
repose a quality of stimulus. Sleep and food have here a
flavour that is absent from sleep and food at a friend's
house. The inn waits at the end of the journey as
certainly as your friend's house ; yet its shelter and food
come always with an agreeable sensation of accident and
surprise. Too, you have at your inn all that your friend
can give you, with many more conveniences and a wider
range of entertainment ; and with all this you are yet at
the full centre of fluid life. In your friend's house you
are shut away, but in the inn you are a looker-on at goings
and comings ; you are in contact with the present and
you touch hands with the wraiths of the past and the substantial mementoes of their days ; and from your seat in
the lounge you view the world as through a loophole of
retreat. I begrudge my sixpence or shilling for the
inspection of the mansions of the great, with their Keep
Off the Grass and Please Do Not Touch ; I consider
five pounds a trifle for the privilege of spending a night
at the George of Glastonbury, the Feathers of Ludlow,
the Lygon Arms of Broadway, or the Spread Eagle of
Thame, where I am free to look and touch, and to walk

unhindered up lordly staircases and to command a retinue
of servitors. The ordinary Englishman's home is not in
any sense—and never was—his castle. An officer or
bailiff with the proper warrant may enter it when he
chooses. But the Englishman's inn—say, the Angel, at
Grantham, or the King Arthur, at Tintagel—is a castle,
and every sojourner is its lord. He may feel its traditions
in his blood as certainly as the children of a great house
feel the traditions of their territory.

Your old inn is a many-pointed star, at each point
touching great event or pleasing anecdote. A single inn
may evoke memories of Izaak Walton, Charles I., Walter
Scott, Drunken Barnaby, Bolingbroke, George Borrow,
Jonathan Swift ; and all these memories and traditions
are yours. Isn't it worth five pounds to sit down to dinner
with that company, or to trip over that same unseen stair
in the dark passages that sent Celia Feinnes to her hands
and knees ? Or to use that room at The Angel, Grantham, where Richard signed Buckingham's death-warrant
in 1483 ; or sleep in that oaken four-poster at the
Saracen's Head, Southwell, where Charles slept his last
night of freedom before surrendering to the Scotch ; or to
sleep in the rooms where slept those shadowy but urgently-
living creatures of our novelists ? It would be cheap at
five pounds, but it may actually be enjoyed for about
fifteen shillings.

To many travellers, though, an inn is an inn—a
stopping-place for bed or refreshment, and nothing more.
It is infuriating to meet in the coffee room of some noble
old hostelry a company of motorists who know nothing
of the house's history, and who might just as well be
stopping at the Regent Palace or the Metropole—where
they rightly belong. These are the people who break

the heart of the intelligent inn-keeper and discourage all his pride in his house. He goes into it, knowing something of its story and giving his mind to preserving its character with the loving care that the young squire bestows upon the family mansion. And his patrons have either never heard of his house, or, when told its history, receive it with a polite " Oh, really ! " I was never nearer doing murder than I was one day in the lounge of The Lion, at Buckden. I had an apprehension, when he entered, that he would say it ; and he did. He looked round the panelled walls. He looked at the great stone fireplace. He looked at the oaken ceiling that centred in a carven rose dated 1587. He turned to his wife : " Ha ! This is an old-fashioned place—eh ? " " Yes, rather. *Quite Dickensian !* "

To get the full savour of an old inn you should come to it at night, and best of all a winter night, or twilight, when the mists are rising and the soul is low, and a log fire and a dinner seem to be the twin stars of human aspiration. All of us know those moments, and that is why inns were made—to stand upon the pilgrim's way with an understanding smile for the pilgrim's weakness. They are a sign to us to shed austerity and vigilance, and to meet and mingle with our fellows ; to turn from our various occasions, lofty or low, and to ease our common needs and common anxieties in kindly communion. It has been said, once for all, and you will find it in this book : "Nothing has yet been contrived by man by which so much happiness is provided as by a good tavern or inn."

Most of my selections, which I have chosen from a range of English literature beginning with William Langland and ending with Anthony Trollope, and touching every point of the many-pointed star, reflect this happiness.

Only here and there does a shadow fall. But the inn, admirable institution that it is, cannot expect to have it all its own way. Because it catches us in our softer and weary moments, when we are too grateful for its happening, it must not think that imperfections pass unperceived. There is much yet for the inn-keeper to learn, and, as a good-natured friend of the modern inn, I cannot stand by and watch it sink under a flood of praise. We were told that the revival of road-travel was to bring the inn back to life, and to bring it back in finer and fuller form. There are some fifty inns in England, kept by enlightened hosts and hostesses, which deserve every epithet of praise. There are hundreds of others that are still living in the late eighteenth century ; and many have come back to no more than faint breathing. In one point there has been little change since the days of Smollett. Snobbery still rules the inn. Arrive in a car, and you are received with some interest. Arrive on foot or by train, and you are given merely the icy edge of civility. At an inn in Berkshire recently, when I was walking, I received a precisely similar reception to those mentioned by Pastor Moritz and de Quincey. I was flatly told that I could not have a room ; that their rooms were reserved for motorists ; and I was politely directed to a public-house across the way—where, I may add, I was given a clean bright room, bath, supper, breakfast and brisk attention for nine-and-sixpence.

I think the imperfections of the modern inn are mainly due to the motorists. Motorists, as a class, live in a state of hurry. They are always anxious to go on. They do not travel ; they buzz from place to place ; and they put up with treatment and food that they are too hasty to examine, and that the slower and more critical commercial traveller would not suffer for a moment.   Take those inns bearing the insignia of certain motor associations.   I used to think that those letters on an inn front meant that the inn was all that an inn should be ; but after recent experiences, I am beginning to wonder what was in the mind of the official when he gave the recommendation.   I can indicate a dozen inns bearing these signs that I would not recommend to the most hardened and casual traveller. Do these associations, I wonder, ever pay secret and surprise visits to their recommended hotels ?   I can hardly think they do.   There is a village within fifty miles of London which has two hotels.   One is a Trust House— bright, beautifully appointed, and full of life.   The other, bearing the sign of a motorists' association, is the sort of place you might find in a village of Western Ireland— decayed, slapdash, and obviously surprised to get a customer, and having nothing to offer him but bedrooms with peeling wall-paper and meals out of a tin.   Some of the most wretched meals I have ever looked at (I couldn't eat them) have been put before me at hotels bearing the motor signs ; and I can only believe that the inspecting officials of these organisations are very easily pleased, or that they do not inspect at all, or, when they do, they give notice of their coming.

Where, I wonder, do some of these inns find their cooks ? Why are their kitchens run like a Ford car— replenished day by day from standardised stores ?   Why do they never do as even the humblest housewife does— vary the menu according to the season ?   I know of but one inn in England where the kitchen is inspired.   It is a village inn, some twenty miles from Oxford, kept by an artist.   Here unusual soups are served, and the *entrée* and sweet are always a surprise—some delightful invention of the moment ; and you sit to every meal sure only of one thing : that whatever is coming to the table will not be an hotel meal. It will be as good a meal as you could get in the most exclusive London restaurant, and it will be something wholly different from the meal of yesterday or the day before. If one inn can do this, why cannot the others ? Why must we always have, winter and summer, soup, fish, joint, vegetables, sweets and cheese ; the same two joints ; the same old sweets ; and the everlasting tomato soup ?

I lately took an American friend, paying his first visit to England, to a famous old inn on the Bath Road, which he had wished to visit. The inn had a stone front and an Oriel window. It had a long yard with a gallery hung with creeper. There were old bells, old blunderbusses, old oak doors and bolts. Twenty motors were parked in its yard. Beyond the yard a gate led to a garden. We looked into the garden, and saw a long chicken-run, a vegetable garden, and a fruit garden. There were currants, red and black, gooseberries, peas, beans, strawberries. My friend was elated. He was charmed with the structure and age of the house, and he spoke of omelettes, and fried chicken and fresh peas. We entered and asked for lunch. An apathetic girl, of the housemaid type, showed us to a table, handed us a stained menu, and went away. The eternal menu. The month was July, the weather was of the *old* July kind, and we were offered tomato soup, fried plaice, roast beef, potatoes, cabbage, fruit salad, cheese and coffee. However, remembering the garden, I had hopes that the fruit salad would compensate for the rest of the bill. But it was not so. The tomato soup of Ye Olde Soldier's Heade was fresh from ye packet. The plaice was not so fresh, and evilly cooked,

The beef was fresh from the Argentine, the potatoes were of the consistency of old bullets, and the cabbage was a compressed brown mass. But when I remembered the fruit salad they might have given us from that garden ; when I remembered how easy it is in one's own home to cut oranges in quarters and mix with grapes, cherries, bananas, apples ; and when I saw what they placed before me—the also-everlasting plate of juice with a piece of tinned pineapple, a piece of tinned apricot, and two hard prunes—I thrust it away and apologised to my friend. The cheese came—two hard lumps that must have left Canada a year before. The coffee came—freshly made by somebody who had once kept a London coffee-stall. The bill came—five shillings each.

But when I again apologised my friend smiled, and waved it away. " No, no—that's all right. I thur'ly enjoyed that. This is what I came to see. I'll have something to tell the folks when I get home. I've seen the real thing. This dingy dining-room, this dirty cloth —those old oak panels—that fine old gallery—that fly-blown waitress—this bit of waxy cheese—this eating rubbish out of a tin when you've got a Garden of Eden on the premises—these things, friend Burke, are England ! "

Will inn-keepers who read this book and appreciate the piquant morsels of prose in which the English inn is commemorated—particularly that morsel which is the Dedication—will they kindly note that I wanted to contradict my friend and that I couldn't ? And will they kindly take a look over their houses and their kitchens, and make it possible for me to do so ?

T. B.

CONTENTS

A LODGING FOR THE NIGHT

MINE HOST AND HOSTESS

PAGE

ARRIVAL AND DEPARTURE

CONTENTS

CHAMBERMAID, OSTLER, DRAWER

ADVENTURE AND ENCOUNTER

TAKING MINE EASE

CONTENTS

A LODGING FOR THE NIGHT

From thence towards London Bridge, on the same side, be many fair inns for receipt of travellers, by these signs, The Spurre, Christopher, Bill, Queene's Head, Tabarde, George, Harte, Kinge's Head, etc. Amongst the which, the most ancient is the Tabarde, so called of the sign, which, as we now term it, is of a jacket, or sleeveless coat, whole before, open on both sides, with a square collar, winged at the shoulders; for the inn of the tabard, Geoffrey Chaucer, esquire, the most famous poet of England, writeth in commendation thereof.

John Stow.

> *We climb'd the hills, when starry night arose,*
> *And Axminster affords a kind repose.*
> *The maid, subdu'd by fees, her trunk unlocks,*
> *And gives the cleanly aid of dowlas smocks.*
> *Meantime our shirts her busy fingers rub,*
> *While the soap lathers o'er the foaming tub.*
> *We rise; our beards demand the barber's art;*
> *A female enters and performs the part.*

John Gay.

The hall a very grove of dead game and dangling joints of mutton; and in one corner an illustrious larder, with glass doors developing cold fowls and noble joints. And tarts wherein the raspberry jam coyly withdrew itself, as such a precious creature should, behind a lattice-work of pastry.

Charles Dickens.

WE read of Innkeepers that they were of ancient
time.

Our Saviour in the Gospel commends the use of Inns.
Yea, Christ himself by his own presence did sanctify the
use of Inns by eating his passover there.

In Acts xxviii there is express mention of an Inn with
approbation and liking.

Common experience sheweth all men what use there
is of inns for ease of travellers, that their bodies, which are
the members of Christ, and Temples of the holy ghost
appointed to a glorious resurrection, may be refreshed
after wearisome labour.

It must not be accounted a small matter to afford house
room, lodging, rest and food to the comforts of God's
children.

Rules for Inn-keepers

Though your house (as an Inn) be open for all men to
come unto, yet account honest men your best guests ;
ever hold their company better than their rooms.

Amongst honest men, let such as be religious withal, be
most welcome. The feet of the Saints are blessed, and
often leave blessings behind them.

Of religious and godly men let faithful Ministers have
heartiest entertainment. The feet of such as bring glad
tidings of peace and good things, oh, how beautiful are

they. Be not so glad of your gain as that you may pleasure such.

Because your guests be God's children, and their bodies the members of Christ, let their usage for meat, lodging, diet and sleep be such as becomes such worthy personages.

In serving and loving your guests, remember you do serve and love God, who takes all as done to himself which for his sake is done to his.

Content yourselves with an honest gain, so using your guests as they may have an appetite to return to you when they are gone from you.

Make choice of good servants, such as know God and make conscience of their ways ; for these are likeliest to be true, faithful, diligent, and cheerful in their service ; also such will best please your best guests, and will not justly offend your worst. Moreover, God will cause your business to prosper best in the hands of such.

Give your servants no evil example in word or deed, bear not with their lying, deceit, swearing, profaning of the Sabbath, or wantonness. Cause them to keep the Lord's day holy, going to the Church by turns ; examine them how they profit by Sermons, love such servants best, as most love God's word.

Rules for Guests

Use an Inn not as your own house, but as an Inn ; not to dwell in, but to rest for such time as ye have just and needful occasion, and then to return to your own families.

Remember ye are in the world as in an Inn to tarry for a short space ; and then to be gone hence.

At night when ye come to your Inn thank God for your Preservation ; next morning pray for a good Journey.

Eat and drink for necessity and strength ; not for lust.

At table let your talk be powder'd with the salt of heavenly wisdom, as your meat is season'd with material and earthly salt.

Above all abhor all oaths, cursing and blasphemy, for God will not hold him guiltless which taketh his name in vain.

Old Broadside.

THE PILGRIM'S INN

CHRISTIANA then wished for an inn to refresh herself and her children, because they were weary. Then said Mr. Honest, There is one a little before us, where a very honourable disciple (one Gaius) dwells. So they all concluded to turn in thither ; and the rather, because the old gentleman gave him so good a report. So when they came to the door, they went in, not knocking, for folks use not to knock at the door of an inn. Then they called for the master of the house, and he came to them ; so they asked if they might lie there that night ?

Gaius : Yes, gentlemen, if you be true men, for my house is for none but pilgrims. Then was Christiana, Mercy, and the boys, the more glad, for that the inn-keeper was a lover of pilgrims. So they called for rooms, and he showed them one for Christiana and her children, and Mercy, and another for Mr. Great-heart and the old gentleman.

Then said Mr. Great-heart, Good Gaius, what hast thou for supper ? for these pilgrims have come far to-day, and are weary.

It is late, said Gaius, so we cannot conveniently go out to seek food ; but such as we have, you shall be welcome to, if that will content you.

Great-heart : We will be content with what thou hast in the house ; forasmuch as I have proved thee, thou art never destitute of that which is convenient.

Then he went down and spake to the cook, whose name was Taste-that-which-is-good, to get ready supper for so many pilgrims. This done, he comes up again, saying, Come, my good friends, you are welcome to me ; and I am glad that I have a house to entertain you ; and while supper is making ready, if you please, let us entertain one another with some good discourse.

John Bunyan.

IN PRAISE OF THE INN

THOSE townes that we call thorowfares have great and sumptuous innes builded in them for the receiving of such travellers and strangers as passe to and fro. The manner of harbouring wherein, is not like that of some other countries, in which the host or goodman of the house doth challenge a lordlie authoritie over his guests, but clean otherwise, sith every man may use his inne as his owne house in England, and have for his monie how great or how little varietie of vittals, and what other service himselfe shall thinke expedient to call for. Our innes are also verie well furnished with naperie ; bedding and tapestrie especiallie with naperie ; for beside the linen used at the tables, which is commonlie washed dailie, is such and so much as belongeth unto the estate and calling of the guest. Each commer is sure to lie in cleane sheets, wherein no man hath beene lodged since they came from the landresse. If the traveller have an horse, his bed doth cost him nothing, but if he go on foot he is sure to paie a pennie for the same ; but whether he be horseman or footman if his chamber be once appointed he may carie the kaie with him, as of his own house so long as he lodgeth there. If he lose ought whilst he abideth in the inne, the host is bound by a general custome to restore the damage, so that there is no greater securitie anie where for travellers than in the greatest innes of England. Their horses in like sort are walked, dressed and looked unto by certaine hostelers or hired servants, appointed at the charges of the goodman of the house, who in hope of extraordinarie reward will deale verie diligentlie after outward appearance in this their function and calling.

Each owner of them contendeth with other for good-nesse of entertainment of their guests, as about finesse and change of linen, furniture of bedding, beautie of roomes, service at the table, costlinesse of plate, strengthe of drinke, varietie of wines, or well using of horses. Finallie there is not so much omitted among them as the gorgeousness of their verie signes at their doores, wherein some do con-sume thirtie or fortie pounds, a mere vanitie in mine opinion, but so vaine will they needs be, and that not onelie to give some outward token of the inne keeper's wealth, but also to procure good guests to the frequenting of their houses in hope there to be well used.

William Harrison.

AN UNEASY NIGHT

SO, leaving my wife, I begun a journey with them, and with much ado through the fenns, along dikes, where sometimes we were ready to have our horses sink to the belly, we got by night, with a great deal of stir, and hard riding, to Parson's Drove, a heathen place, where I found my uncle and aunt Perkins, and their daughters, poor wretches ! in a sad, poor thatched cottage, like a poor barne, or stable, peeling of hemp, in which I did give myself good content to see their manner of preparing of hemp ; and in a poor condition of habitt took them to our miserable inne, and there, after long stay, and hearing of Frank, their son, the miller, play upon his treble, as he calls it, with which he earnes part of his living, and singing of a country song, we set down to supper ; the whole crew, and Spankes's wife and child, a sad company, of which I was ashamed, supped with us. By and by, newes is brought to us, that one of our horses is stole out of the stable, which proves my uncle's, at which I am inwardly glad—I mean, that it was not mine ; and at this we were at a great loss ; and they doubting a person that lay at next door, a Londoner, some lawyer's clerk, we caused him to be secured in his bed, and other care to be taken to seize the house ; and so, about twelve at night or more, to bed, in a sad, cold, stony chamber ; and a little after I was asleep, they waked me, to tell me that the horse was found, which was good news, and so to sleep, but was bit cruelly, and nobody else of our company, which I wonder at, by the gnatts.

Up, and got our people together ; and after eating a dishe of cold creame, which was my supper last night too, we took leave of our beggarly company, though they seem good people, too.

Samuel Pepys.

IN GOOD COMPANY

PISC. : I will forbear at this time to say any more, because you see yonder come our brother Peter and honest Coridon. . . . Well met, gentlemen ; this is lucky that we meet so just together at this very door. Come, hostess, where are you ? Is supper ready ? Come, first give us drink, and be as quick as you can, for I believe we are all very hungry. Well, brother Peter, and Coridon, to you both ; come, drink, and then tell me what luck of fish ; we two have caught but ten trouts, of which my scholar caught three ; look, here's eight, and a brace we gave away ; we have had a most pleasant day for fishing and talking, and are returned home both weary and hungry, and now meat and rest will be pleasant.

Peter : And Coridon and I have had not an unpleasant day, and yet I have caught but five trouts ; for indeed we went to a good honest ale-house, and there we played at shovel-board half the day ; all the time that it rained we were there, and as merry as they that fished ; and I am glad we are now with a dry house over our heads, for hark how it rains and blows. Come, hostess, give us more ale, and our supper with what haste you may ; and when we have supped let us have your song, Piscator, and the catch that your scholar promised us ; or else Coridon will be dogged. . . .

Pisc. : Come, we will all join together, my host and all, and sing my scholar's catch over again, and then each man drink the other cup, and to bed, and thank God we have a dry house over our heads.

Izaak Walton.

MOLL FLANDERS AT DUNSTABLE

HE came with me as far as Dunstable, within thirty miles of London, and then he told me fate and his own misfortunes obliged him to leave me, and that it was not convenient for him to go to London, for reasons which it was of no value to me to know, and I saw him preparing to go. The stage-coach we were in did not usually stop at Dunstable, but I desiring it for a quarter of an hour, they were content to stand at an inn-door a while, and we went into the house. Being in the inn, I told him I had but one favour more to ask him, and that was, that since he could not go any farther, he would give me leave to stay a week or two in the town with him, that we might in that time think of something to prevent such a ruinous thing to us both as a final separation would be. This was too reasonable a proposal to be denied, so he called the land-lady of the house, and told her his wife was taken ill, and so ill that she could not think of going any farther in a stage-coach, which had tired her almost to death, and asked if she could not get us a lodging for two or three days in a private house, where I might rest me a little. The land-lady, a good sort of a woman, well-bred, and very obliging, came immediately to see me ; told me she had two or three very good rooms in a part of the house quite out of the noise, and if I saw them she did not doubt but I would like them, and I should have one of her maids that would do nothing else but wait on me. This was so very kind that I could not but accept of it ; so we paid the stage-coach, took out our baggage, and resolved to stay here a while.

Here I told him I would live with him now till all my money was spent, but would not let him spend a shilling of his own. We had some kind squabble about it, but I told him it was the last time I was like to enjoy his com-pany, and I desired that he would let me be master in that thing only, and he should govern in everything else.

Daniel Defoe.

TOM JONES' BAD NIGHT

THE Quaker was no sooner assured by this fellow of the birth and low fortune of Jones, than all com-passion for him vanished ; and the honest plain man went home fired with no less indignation than a duke would have felt at receiving an affront from such a person.

The landlord himself conceived an equal disdain for his guest ; so that when Jones rung the bell in order to retire to bed, he was acquainted that he could have no bed there. Besides disdain of the mean condition of his guest, Robin entertained violent suspicion of his intentions, which were, he supposed, to watch some favourable opportunity of robbing the house. In reality, he might have been very well eased of these apprehensions, by the prudent precautions of his wife and daughter, who had already removed everything which was not fixed to the freehold ; but he was by nature suspicious, and had been more particularly so since the loss of his spoon. In short, the dread of being robbed totally absorbed the comfortable consideration that he had nothing to lose.

Jones being assured that he could have no bed, very contentedly betook himself to a great chair made with rushes, when sleep, which had lately shunned his company in much better apartments, generously paid him a visit in his humble cell.

As for the landlord, he was prevented by his fears from retiring to rest. He returned therefore to the kitchen fire, whence he could survey the only door which opened into the parlour, or rather hole, where Jones was seated ; and as for the window to that room, it was impossible for any creature larger than a cat to have made his escape through it. The landlord having taken his seat directly opposite to the door of the parlour, determined to keep guard there the whole night. The guide and another fellow remained long on duty with him, though they neither knew his suspicions, nor had any of their own. The true cause of their watching did, indeed, at length, put an end to it ; for this was no other than the strength and goodness of the beer, of which having tippled a very large quantity, they grew at first very noisy and vociferous, and afterwards fell both asleep.

But it was not in the power of liquor to compose the fears of Robin. He continued still waking in his chair, with his eyes fixed stedfastly on the door which led into the apartment of Mr. Jones, till a violent thundering at his outward gate called him from his seat, and obliged him to open it ; which he had no sooner done than his kitchen was immediately full of gentlemen in red coats, who all rushed upon him in as tumultuous a manner as if they intended to take his little castle by storm.

The landlord was now forced from his post to furnish his numerous guests with beer, which they called for with great eagerness ; and upon his second or third return from the cellar, he saw Mr. Jones standing before the fire in the midst of the soldiers ; for it may easily be believed, that the arrival of so much good company should put an end to any sleep, unless that from which we are to be awakened only by the last trumpet.

The company having now pretty well satisfied their thirst, nothing remained but to pay the reckoning, a circumstance often productive of much mischief and discontent among the inferior rank of gentry, who are apt to find great difficulty in assessing the sum, with exact regard to distributive justice, which directs that every man shall pay according to the quantity which he drinks. This difficulty occurred upon the present occasion ; and it was the greater, as some gentlemen had, in their extreme hurry, marched off, after their first draught, and had entirely forgot to contribute anything towards the said reckoning.

A violent dispute now arose, in which every word may be said to have been deposed upon oath ; for the oaths were at least equal to all the other words spoken. In this controversy the whole company spoke together, and every man seemed wholly bent to extenuate the sum which fell to his share ; so that the most probable conclusion which could be foreseen was, that a large portion of the reckoning would fall to the landlord's share to pay, or (what is much the same thing) would remain unpaid.

The dispute now grew so very warm that it seemed to draw towards a military decision, when Jones, stepping forward, silenced all their clamours at once, by declaring that he would pay the whole reckoning, which indeed amounted to no more than three shillings and four-pence.

This declaration procured Jones the thanks and applause of the whole company. The terms honourable, noble, and worthy gentleman, resounded through the room ; nay, my landlord himself began to have a better opinion of him, and almost to disbelieve the account which the guide had given.

Henry Fielding.

A NIGHT AT HODDESDON

INTO an old inn did this equipage roll,
At a town they call Hodson, the sign of the Bull,
Near a nymph with an urn, that divides the highway,
And into a puddle throws mother of tea.

Come here, my sweet landlady, pray how d'ye do ?
Where is Cicely so cleanly, and Prudence, and Sue ?
And where is the widow that dwelt here below ?
And the ostler that sung about eight years ago ?

And where is your sister, so mild and so dear ?
Whose voice to her maids like a trumpet was clear.
By my troth ! she replies, you grow younger, I think ;
And pray, sir, what wine does the gentleman drink ?

Why now let me die, Sir, or live upon trust,
If I know to which question to answer you first ;
Why things, since I saw you, most strangely have varied,
The ostler is hang'd, and the widow is married.

And Prue left a child for the parish to nurse ;
And Cicely went off with a gentleman's purse ;
And as to my sister, so mild and so dear,
She has lain in the churchyard full many a year.

Well, peace to her ashes ! what signifies grief ?
She roasted red veal, and she powder'd lean beef ;
Full nicely she knew to cook up a fine dish ;
For tough were her pullets, and tender her fish.

For that matter, Sir, be you squire, knight, or lord,
I'll give you whate'er a good inn can afford ;
I should look on myself as unhappily sped,
Did I yield to a sister, or living or dead.

Of mutton a delicate neck and a breast
Shall swim in the water in which they were drest ;
And because you great folks are with rarities taken,
Addle-eggs shall be next course, toss'd up with rank bacon.

Then supper was serv'd, and the sheets they were laid ;
And Morley most lovingly whisper'd the maid.
The maid ! was she handsome ? why truly so-so.
But what Morley whisper'd we never shall know.

Then up rose the heroes as brisk as the sun,
And their horses, like his, were prepared to run.
Now when in the morning Matt ask'd for the score,
John kindly had paid it the evening before.

Their breakfast so warm to be sure they did eat,
A custom in travellers mighty discreet ;
And thus with great friendship and glee they went on,
To find out the place you shall hear of anon.

Matthew Prior.

THE PROSPEROUS INN

HIGH in the street, o'erlooking all the place,
The rampant lion shows his kingly face ;
His ample jaws extend from side to side,
His eyes are glaring, and his nostrils wide ;
In silver shag the sovereign form is dress'd,
A mane horrific sweeps his ample chest.
Yet nothing dreadful to his friends the sight,
But sign and pledge of welcome and delight :
To him the noblest guest the town detains
Flies for repast, and in his court remains ;
Him too the crowd with longing looks admire,
Sigh for his joys and modestly retire.
Here not a comfort shall to them be lost
Who never ask or never feel the cost.
    The ample yards on either side contain
Buildings where order and distinction reign ;
The splendid carriage of the wealthier guest,
The ready chaise and driver smartly dress'd ;
Whiskeys and gigs and curricles are there,
And high-fed prancers many a raw-boned pair.
On all without a lordly host sustains

The care of empire, and observant reigns ;
The parting guest beholds him at his side,
With pomp obsequious, bending in his pride ;
Round all the place his eyes all objects meet,
Attentive, silent, civil and discreet.
O'er all within the lady hostess rules,
Her bar she governs, and her kitchen schools ;
To every guest th' appropriate speech is made,
And every duty with distinction paid ;
Respectful, easy, pleasant or polite—
" Your honour's servant—Mister Smith, good-night."

George Crabbe.

A HOMELY BED

THE night was very dark in which our friends began
their journey ; however, they made such expedition,
that they soon arrived at an inn which was at seven miles'
distance. Here they unanimously consented to pass the
evening, Mr. Adams being now as dry as he was before he
had set out on his embassy.

This inn, which indeed we might call an ale-house, had
not the words, The New Inn, been writ on the sign,
afforded them no better provision than bread and
cheese and ale ; on which, however, they made a very
comfortable meal ; for hunger is better than a French cook.

They had no sooner supped, than Adams, returning
thanks to the Almighty for his food, declared he had ate
his homely commons with much greater satisfaction than
his splendid dinner ; and expressed great contempt for the
folly of mankind, who sacrificed their hopes of heaven to
the acquisition of vast wealth, since so much comfort was
to be found in the humblest state and the lowest provision.
" Very true, sir," says a grave man who sat smoking his

pipe by the fire, and who was a traveller as well as himself. " I have often been as much surprised as you are, when I consider the value which mankind in general set on riches, since every day's experience shows us how little is in their power ; for what, indeed, truly desirable, can they bestow on us ? Can they give beauty to the deformed, strength to the weak, or health to the infirm ? Surely if they could we should not see so many ill-favoured faces haunting the assemblies of the great, nor would such numbers of feeble wretches languish in their coaches and palaces."

Adams now began a long discourse : but as most which he said occurs among many authors who have treated this subject, I shall omit inserting it. During its continuance Joseph and Fanny retired to rest, and the host likewise left the room. When the English parson had concluded, the Romish resumed the discourse, which he continued with great bitterness and invective ; and at last ended by desiring Adams to lend him eighteen-pence to pay his reckoning ; promising if he never paid him, he might be assured of his prayers. The good man answered that eighteen-pence would be too little to carry him any very long journey ; that he had half a guinea in his pocket, which he would divide with him. He then fell to searching his pockets, but could find no money ; for indeed the company with whom he dined had passed one jest upon him which we did not then enumerate, and had picked his pocket of all that treasure which he had so ostentatiously produced.

" Bless me ! " cried Adams, " I have certainly lost it ; I can never have spent it. Sir, as I am a Christain, I had a whole half-guinea in my pocket this morning, and have not now a single halfpenny of it left. Sure the devil must have taken it from me ! "—" Sir," answered the priest smiling, " you need make no excuses ; if you are not willing to lend me the money I am contented."—" Sir," cries Adams, " if I had the greatest sum in the world— aye, if I had ten pounds about me—I would bestow it all to rescue any Christian from distress. I am more vexed at my loss on your account than my own. Was ever anything so unlucky ? Because I have no money in my pocket I shall be suspected to be no Christian."—" I am more unlucky," quoth the other, " if you are as generous as you say ; for really a crown would have made me happy, and conveyed me in plenty to the place I am going, which is not above twenty miles off, and where I can arrive by to-morrow night. I assure you I am not accustomed to travel pennyless. I am but just arrived in England ; and we were forced by a storm in our passage to throw all we had overboard. I don't suspect but this fellow will take my word for the trifle I owe him ; but I hate to appear so mean as to confess myself without a shilling to such people ; for these, and indeed too many others, know little difference in their estimation between a beggar and a thief." However, he thought he should deal better with the host that evening than the next morning : he therefore resolved to set out immediately, notwithstanding the darkness ; and accordingly, as soon as the host returned, he communicated to him the situation of his affairs ; upon which the host, scratching his head, answered, " Why I do not know, master ; if it be so, and you have no money, I must trust, I think, though I had rather always have ready money if I could ; but, marry, you look like so honest a gentleman that I don't fear your paying me if it was twenty times as much." The priest made no reply, but, taking leave of him and Adams as fast as he could, not without confusion, and perhaps with some distrust of Adams's sincerity, departed.

He was no sooner gone than the host fell a shaking his head, and declared, if he had suspected the fellow had no money, he would not have drawn him a single drop of drink, saying he despaired of ever seeing his face again, for that he looked like a confounded rogue. "Rabbit the fellow," cries he, " I thought, by his talking so much about riches, that he had a hundred pounds at least in his pocket." Adams chid him for his suspicions, which, he said, were not becoming a Christian ; and then, without reflecting on his loss, or considering how he himself should depart in the morning, he retired to a very homely bed, as his companions had before ; however, health and fatigue gave them a sweeter repose than is often in the power of velvet and down to bestow.

Henry Fielding.

THE WAYSIDE INN

ALONG the varying road of Life,
In calm content, in toil or strife ;
At morn or noon, by night or day,
As time conducts him on his way,
How oft doth man, by Care oppress'd,
Find in an inn a place of rest ?
Whether intent on worldly views,
He, in deep thought, his way pursues ;
Whether by airy pleasure led,
Or by hope's fond delusions fed,
He bids adieu to home and strays
Through unknown paths and distant ways ;
Where'er his fancy bids him roam,
In every inn he finds a home.

Should fortune change her fav'ring wind,
Though former friends should prove unkind,
Will not an inn his cares beguile,
Where on each face he sees a smile ?
When cold winds blow and tempests lower,
And the rain pours in angry shower,
The dripping traveller looks around,
To see what shelter may be found :
Then on he drives through thick and thin
To the warm shelter of an inn.
Whoe'er would turn their wand'ring feet,
Assur'd the kindest smiles to meet :
Whoe'er would go, and not depart
But with kind wishes from the heart,
O let them quit the world's loud din,
And seek the comforts of an inn.

    'Twas at an inn, in calm repose,
Heedless of human joys or woes,
That Syntax passed a quiet night
In pleasing dreams and slumbers light.
But in the morn the thunder roar'd,
The clouds their streaming torrents pour'd ;
The angry winds impetuous blew,
The rattling casement open flew.
Scar'd at the noise, he rear'd his head ;
Then, starting quickly from his bed,
" Is it," he cried, " the day of doom ? "
As he bestrode the trembling room.
The houses' tops with water stream'd,
The village street a river seem'd :
While at the tempest all amaz'd,
The rustics from their windows gaz'd.
" I'm not," he said, " dispos'd to fear,

But 'tis not time to loiter here ;
I'll change the scene, and quick retire
From flaming flash to kitchen fire ;
Nay, while rude Nature's threats prevail,
I'll lose the storm in toast and ale."

William Combe.

ON TOUR WITH THE DOCTOR

WE dined at an excellent inn at Chapel House, where he expatiated on the felicity of England in its inns and taverns, and triumphed over the French for not having, in any perfection, the tavern life. " There is no private house (said he) in which people can enjoy themselves so well as in a capital tavern. Let there be ever so great plenty of good things, ever so much grandeur, ever so much elegance, ever so much desire that everybody should be easy ; in the nature of things it cannot be: there must always be some degree of care and anxiety. The master of the house is anxious to entertain his guests ; the guests are anxious to be agreeable to him : and no man, but a very impudent dog indeed, can as freely command what is in another man's house as if it were his own. Whereas, at a tavern, there is a general freedom from anxiety. You are sure you are welcome : and the more noise you make, the more trouble you give, the more good things you call for, the welcomer you are. No servants will attend you with the alacrity which waiters do, who are incited by the prospect of an immediate reward in proportion as they please. No, Sir ; there is nothing which has yet been contrived by man by which so much happiness is produced as by a good tavern or inn." He then repeated, with great emotion, Shenstone's lines.

James Boswell.

THE WAGGON-PARTY HALTS FOR THE NIGHT.

ABOUT this time I fell asleep, and enjoyed a comfortable nap, till such time as we arrived at the inn where we put up. Here, having alighted from the waggon, I had an opportunity of viewing the passengers in order as they entered. The first who appeared was a brisk airy girl, about twenty years old, with a silver-laced hat on her head, instead of a cap, a blue stuff riding-suit trimmed with silver, very much tarnished, and a whip in her hand. After her came limping an old man, with a worsted night-cap, buttoned under his chin, and a broad-brimmed hat slouched over it, an old rusty blue cloak tied about his neck, under which appeared a brown surtout, that covered a threadbare coat and waistcoat, and, as we afterwards discerned, a dirty flannel jacket. His eyes were hollow, bleared, and gummy ; his face was shrivelled into a thousand wrinkles, his gums were destitute of teeth, his nose sharp and drooping, his chin peaked and prominent, so that, when he mumped or spoke, they approached one another like a pair of nut-crackers ; he supported himself on an ivory-headed cane ; and his whole figure was a just emblem of winter, famine, and avarice. But how was I surprised, when I beheld the formidable captain in the shape of a little thin creature, about the age of forty, with a long withered visage, very much resembling that of a baboon, through the upper part of which two little grey eyes peeped : he wore his own hair in a queue that reached to his rump, which immoderate length, I suppose, was the occasion of a baldness that appeared on the crown of his head, when he deigned to take off his hat, which was very much of the size and cock of Pistol's. Having laid aside his greatcoat, I could not help admiring the extraordinary make of this man of war : he was about five feet and three inches high, sixteen inches of which went to his face and long scraggy neck ; his thighs were about six inches in length, his legs resembling spindles or drum-sticks, two feet and a half, and his body, which put me in mind of extension without substance, engrossed the remainder ; so that, on the whole, he appeared like a spider or grasshopper erect, and was almost a *vox et præterea nihil.* His dress consisted of a frock of what is called bear-skin, the skirts of which were about half a foot long, an hussar waistcoat, scarlet breeches, reaching half-way down his thigh, worsted stockings, rolled up almost to his groin, and shoes with wooden heels at least two inches high : he carried a sword very near as long as himself in one hand, and with the other conducted his lady, who seemed to be a woman of his own age, and still retained some remains of an agreeable person ; but so ridiculously affected, that, had I not been a novice in the world, I might have easily perceived in her the deplorable vanity and second-hand airs of a lady's woman. We were all assembled in the kitchen, when Captain Weazel (for that was his name) desired a room with a fire for himself and spouse, and told the landlord they would sup by themselves. The inn-keeper replied, that he could not afford them a room by themselves ; and as for supping, he had prepared victuals for the passengers in the waggon, without respect of per-sons ; but if he could prevail on the rest to let him have his choice in a separate manner, he should be very well pleased. This was no sooner said, than all of us declared against the proposal ; and Miss Jenny, our other female passenger, observed, that, if Captain Weazel and his lady had a mind to sup by themselves, they might wait until we should have done. At this hint, the captain put on a martial frown, and looked very big, without speaking ; while his yoke-fellow, with a disdainful toss of her nose, muttered something about " Creature ! " which Miss Jenny overhearing, stept up to her, saying, " None of your names, good Mrs. Abigail. Creature, quotha—I'll assure you, no such creature as you, neither—no ten pound sneaker—no quality coupler."—Here the captain interposed, with a " Damme, madam, what do you mean by that ? "—" Damn you, sir, who are you ? " replied Miss Jenny ; " who made you a captain, you pitiful, trencher-scraping, pimping curler ?—'Sdeath ! the army is come to a fine pass, when such fellows as you get commissions."

In the midst of this quarrel the master of the waggon alighted, who, understanding the cause of the disturbance, and fearing the captain and his lady would take umbrage, and leave his carriage, was at great pains to have everything made up, which he at last accomplished, and we sat down to supper all together.

Tobias Smollett.

THE DECAYING INN

LARGE the domain, but all within combine
To correspond with the dishonour'd sign ;
And all around dilapidates ; you call—
But none replies—they're inattentive all ;
At length a ruin'd stable holds your steed,
While you through large and dirty rooms proceed,
Spacious and cold ; a proof they once had been
In honour—now magnificently mean ;
Till in some small, half-furnish'd room you rest,
Whose dying fires denotes it had a guest.
In those you pass'd where former splendour reigned,

You saw the carpets torn, the paper stain'd ;
Squares of discordant glass in windows fix'd,
And paper oil'd in many a space betwixt ;
A soil'd and broken sconce, a mirror crack'd,
With table underpropp'd, and chairs new-back'd ;
A marble side-slab with ten thousand stains,
And all an ancient tavern's poor remains.
With much entreaty, they your food prepare,
And acid wine afford, with meagre fare ;
Heartless you sup, and when a dozen times
You've read the fractured window's senseless rhymes,
Have been assured that Phoebe Green was fair,
And Peter Jackson took his supper there,
You reach a chilling chamber, where you dread
Damps, hot or cold, from a tremendous bed ;
Late comes your sleep, and you are waken'd soon
By rustling tatters of the old festoon.
O'er this large building, thus by time defac'd,
A servile couple has its owner plac'd,
Who, not unmindful that its style is large,
To lost magnificence adapt their charge.
Few years have passed, since brightly 'cross the way
Lights from each window shot the lengthen'd ray ;
And busy looks in every face were seen,
Through the warm precincts of the reigning Queen ;
There fires inviting blaz'd, and all around
Was heard the tinkling bells' seducing sound ;
The nimble waiters to that sound from far
Sprang to the call, then hasten'd to the bar ;
Where a glad priestess of the temple sway'd,
The most obedient and the most obey'd ;
Rosy and round, adorn'd in crimson vest,
And flaming ribbons at her ample breast :

She, skill'd like Circe, tried her guests to move
With looks of welcome and with words of love.
Her port in bottles stood, a well-stain'd row,
Drawn for the evening from the pipes below ;
Three powerful spirits fill'd a parted case,
Some cordial-bottles stood in secret place ;
Fair acid fruits in nets above were seen,
Her plate was splendid, and her glasses clean ;
Basins and bowls were ready on the stand,
And measures clatter'd in her powerful hand.

George Crabbe.

THE WORSHIP OF APPEARANCES

EVERYTHING seemed to be all alive in this little
village ; there was a party of militia soldiers who
were dancing, singing, and making merry. Immediately
on my entrance into the village, the first house that I saw,
lying on my left was an inn, from which, as usual in
England, a large beam extended across the street to the
opposite house, from which hung dangling an astonishing
large sign, with the name of the proprietor.

" May I stay here to-night ? " I asked with eagerness :
" Why, yes, you may ; " an answer, which, however cold
and surly, made me exceedingly happy.

They showed me into the kitchen, and set me down
to sup at the same table with some soldiers and the servants.
I now, for the first time, found myself in one of those
kitchens which I had so often read of in Fielding's fine
novels ; and which certainly give one, on the whole, a
very accurate idea of English manners.

The chimney in this kitchen, where they were roasting
and boiling, seemed to be taken off from the rest of the
room and enclosed by a wooden partition : the rest of the

apartment was made use of as a sitting and eating room. All round on the sides were shelves with pewter dishes and plates, and the ceiling was well stored with provisions of various kinds, such as sugar-loaves, black-puddings, hams, sausages, flitches of bacon, etc.

While I was eating, a post-chaise drove up : and in a moment both the folding-doors were thrown open, and the whole house set in motion, in order to receive, with all due respect, these guests, who, no doubt, were supposed to be persons of consequence.   The gentlemen alighted however only for a moment, and called for nothing but a couple of pots of beer ; and then drove away again. Notwithstanding, the people of the house behaved to them with all possible attention, for they came in a post-chaise.

Though this was only an ordinary village, and they certainly did not take me for a person of consequence, they yet gave me a carpeted bedroom, and a very good bed.

The next morning I put on clean linen, which I had along with me, and dressed myself as well as I could. And now, when I thus made my appearance, they did not, as they had the evening before, show me into the kitchen, but into the parlour ; a room that seemed to be allotted for strangers, on the ground floor.   I was also now addressed by the most respectful term, *Sir ;* whereas, the evening before I had been called only *Master :* by this latter appellation, I believe, it is usual to address only farmers, and quite common people.

Carl Philip Moritz.

THE SWAN, AT STAFFORD

THE inn, of which I had become an inhabitant, was a place of infinite life and bustle. Travellers of all descriptions, from all the cardinal points, were continually

stopping at it ; and to attend to their wants, and minister
to their convenience, an army of servants, of one description or other, was kept ; waiters, chambermaids, grooms,
postillions, shoe-blacks, cooks, scullions, and what not,
for there was a barber and hair-dresser, who had been at
Paris, and talked French with a cockney accent ; the
French sounding all the better, as no accent is so melodious
as the cockney. Jacks creaked in the kitchens turning
round spits, on which large joints of meat piped and
smoked before great big fires. There was running up
and down stairs, and along galleries, slamming of doors,
cries of " Coming, sir," and " Please to step this way,
ma'am," during eighteen hours of the four-and-twenty.
Truly a very great place for life and bustle was this inn.
And often in after life, when lonely and melancholy, I
have called up the time I spent there, and never failed to
become cheerful from the recollection.

George Borrow.

JEANIE DEANS AT YORK

MRS. BICKERTON, lady of the ascendant of the
Seven Stars, in the Castle-gate, York, was deeply
infected with the unfortunate prejudices of her country.
Indeed, she displayed so much kindness to Jeanie Deans
(because she herself, being a Merse woman, marched with
Mid-Lothian, in which Jeanie was born), showed such
motherly regard to her, and such anxiety for her farther
progress, that Jeanie thought herself safe, though by
temper sufficiently cautious, in communicating her whole
story to her.

Mrs. Bickerton raised her hands and eyes at the recital,
and exhibited much wonder and pity. But she also gave
some effectual good advice. She required to know the

strength of Jeanie's purse, reduced by her deposit at
Libberton, and the necessary expense of her journey, to
about fifteen pounds. " This," she said, " would do
very well, providing she could carry it a' safe to London."

" Safe ? " answered Jeanie ; " I'se warrant my carrying it safe, bating the needful expenses."

" Ay, but highwaymen, lassie," said Mrs. Bickerton ;
" for ye are come into a more civilised, that is to say, a
more roguish country than the north, and how ye are
to get forward, I do not profess to know. . . . But take
my advice, and hide thy gold in thy stays, and keep a
piece or two and some silver, in case thou be'st spoke
withal ; for there's as wud lads haunt within a day's walk
from hence, as on the Braes o' Doun in Perthshire. And,
lass, thou maunna gang staring through Lunnon, asking
wha kens Mrs. Glass at the sign o' the Thistle ; marry,
they would laugh thee to scorn. But gang thou to this
honest man," and she put a direction into Jeanie's hand,
" he kens maist part of the sponsible Scottish folk in the
city, and he will find out your friend for thee."

A neat little supper concluded the evening. The
exported Scotswoman, Mrs. Bickerton by name, ate
heartily of one or two seasoned dishes, drank some sound
old ale, and a glass of stiff negus ; while she gave Jeanie a
history of her gout, admiring how it was possible that she,
whose fathers and mothers for many generations had been
farmers in Lammermuir, could have come by a disorder
so totally unknown to them. Jeanie did not choose to
offend her friendly landlady, by speaking her mind on the
probable origin of this complaint ; but she thought on the
flesh-pots of Egypt, and, in spite of all entreaties to better
fare, made her evening meal upon vegetables, with a glass
of fair water.

Mrs. Bickerton assured her, that the acceptance of any reckoning was entirely out of the question, furnished her with credentials to her correspondent in London, and to several inns upon the road where she had some influence or interest, reminded her of the precautions she should adopt for concealing her money, and as she was to depart early in the morning, took leave of her very affectionately, taking her word that she would visit her on her return to Scotland, and tell her how she had managed, and that *summum bonum* for a gossip, "all how and about it." This Jeanie faithfully promised.

Sir Walter Scott.

THE TRAVELLER'S PURGATORY

A WET Sunday in a country inn !—whoever has had the luck to experience one can alone judge of my situation. The rain pattered against the casements ; the bells tolled for church with a melancholy sound. I went to the windows in quest of something to amuse the eye ; but it seemed as if I had been placed completely out of the reach of all amusement. The windows of my bedroom looked out among tiled roofs and stacks of chimneys, while those of my sitting-room commanded a full view of the stable-yard. I know of nothing more calculated to make a man sick of this world than a stable-yard on a rainy day. The place was littered with wet straw that had been kicked about by travellers and stable-boys. In one corner was a stagnant pool of water, surrounding an island of muck ; there were several half-drowned fowls crowded together under a cart, among which was a miserable, crestfallen cock, drenched out of all life and spirit ; near the cart was a half-dozing cow, chewing the cud, and standing patiently to be rained on, with wreaths of vapour rising from her reeking hide ; a drab of a kitchen wench tramped backwards and forwards through the yard in pattens, looking as sulky as the weather itself ; everything, in short, was comfortless and forlorn, excepting a crew of hardened ducks, assembled like boon companions round a puddle, and making a riotous noise over their liquor.

I was lonely and listless, and wanted amusement. My room soon became insupportable. I abandoned it, and sought what is technically called the travellers' room. This is a public room set apart at most inns for the accommodation of a class of wayfarers, called travellers, or riders ; a kind of commercial knights-errant, who are incessantly scouring the kingdom in gigs, on horseback, or by coach. They are the only successors that I know of at the present day to the knights-errant of yore. They lead the same kind of roving, adventurous life, only changing the lance for a driving-whip, the buckler for a pattern-card, and the coat of mail for an upper Benjamin. As the room of the house, in the good old fighting times, would be hung round at night with the armour of way-worn warriors, such as coats of mail, falchions, and yawning helmets ; so the travellers' room is garnished with the harnessing of their successors, with box-coats, whips of all kinds, spurs, gaiters, and oil-cloth covered hats.

I was in hopes of finding some of these worthies to talk with, but was disappointed. There were, indeed, two or three in the room ; but I could make nothing of them. One was just finishing his breakfast, quarrelling with his bread and butter, and huffing the waiter ; another buttoned on a pair of gaiters, with many execrations at Boots for not having cleaned his shoes well ; a third sat drumming on the table with his fingers and looking at the rain as it streamed down the window-glass ; they all appeared infected by the weather, and disappeared, one after the other, without exchanging a word.

I sauntered to the window, and stood gazing at the people picking their way to church, with petticoats hoisted mid-leg high, and dripping umbrellas. The bell ceased to toll, and the streets became silent. I then amused myself with watching the daughters of a trades-man opposite ; who, being confined to the house for fear of wetting their Sunday finery, played off their charms at the front windows, to fascinate the chance tenants of the inn. They at length were summoned away by a vigilant, vinegar-faced mother, and I had nothing further from without to amuse me.

What was I to do to pass away the long-lived day ? I was sadly nervous and lonely ; and everything about an inn seems calculated to make a dull day ten times duller. Old newspapers, smelling of beer and tobacco-smoke, which I had already read half-a-dozen times. Good-for-nothing books, that were worse than rainy weather. I bored myself to death with an old volume of the *Lady's Magazine*. I read all the commonplace names of ambitious travellers scrawled on the panes of glass ; the eternal families of the Smiths, and the Browns, and the Jacksons, and the Johnsons, and all the other sons ; and I deciphered several scraps of fatiguing inn-window poetry which I have met with in all parts of the world.

It was quite refreshing (if I may be allowed a hack-neyed phrase of the day) when, in the course of the morn-ing, a horn blew, and a stage-coach whirled through the street, with outside passengers stuck all over it, cowering

under cotton umbrellas, and seethed together, and reeking with the streams of wet box-coats and upper
Benjamins.

The sound brought out from their lurking-places a
crew of vagabond boys and vagabond dogs, and the
carroty-headed ostler, and that nondescript animal
yclept Boots, and all the other vagabond race that infest
the purlieus of an inn ; but the bustle was transient ;
the coach again whirled on its way, and boy, and dog,
and ostler, and Boots, all slunk back again to their holes ;
the street again became silent, and the rain continued to
rain on.

Washington Irving.

CONINGSBY'S INN

IT was not the comely and courteous hostess of the
Adelphi Hotel, Manchester, that gave occasion to
these remarks, though she may deserve them, and though
she was most kind to our Coningsby as he came in late at
night very tired, and not in very good humour.

He had travelled the whole day through the great
district of labour, his mind excited by strange sights, and
at length wearied by their multiplication. He had passed
over the plains where iron and coal supersede turf and
corn, dingy as the entrance of Hades, and flaming with
furnaces ; and now he was among illumined factories
with more windows than Italian palaces, and smoking
chimneys taller than Egyptian obelisks. Alone in the
great metropolis of machinery itself, sitting down in a
solitary coffee-room glaring with gas, with no appetite, a
whirling head, and not a plan or purpose for the morrow,
why was he there ? Because a being, whose name even
was unknown to him, had met him in a hedge ale-house

during a thunderstorm, and told him that the Age of Ruins was past.

Remarkable instance of the influence of an individual ; some evidence of the extreme susceptibility of our hero.

Even his bedroom was lit by gas. Wonderful city ! That however could be got rid of. He opened the window. The summer air was sweet even in this land of smoke and toil. He feels a sensation such as in Lisbon or Lima precedes an earthquake. The house appears to quiver. It is a sympathetic affection occasioned by a steam-engine in a neighbouring factory.

Notwithstanding however all these novel incidents, Coningsby slept the deep sleep of youth and health, of a brain, which however occasionally perplexed by thought, had never been harassed by anxiety. He rose early, freshened and in fine spirits. And by the time the devilled chicken and the buttered toast, that mysterious and incomparable luxury, which only can be obtained at an inn, had disappeared, he felt all the delightful excitement of travel.

Benjamin Disraeli.

A HAUNT OF ROMANCE

THE Maypole—by which term from henceforth is meant the house, and not its sign—the Maypole was an old building, with more gable ends than a lazy man would care to count on a sunny day ; huge zigzag chimneys, out of which it seemed as though even smoke could not choose but come in more than naturally fantastic shapes, imparted to it in its tortuous progress ; and vast stables, gloomy, ruinous, and empty. The place was said to have been built in the days of King Henry the Eighth ; and there was a legend, not only that Queen Elizabeth had slept there one night while upon a hunting excursion, to wit, in a certain oak-panelled room with a deep bay window, but that next morning, while standing on a mounting-block before the door with one foot in the stirrup, the Virgin Monarch had then and there boxed and cuffed an unlucky page for some neglect of duty. The matter-of-fact and doubtful folks, of whom there were a few among the Maypole customers, as unluckily there always are in every little community, were inclined to look upon this tradition as rather apocryphal ; but whenever the landlord of that ancient hostelry appealed to the mounting-block itself as evidence, and trium-phantly pointed out that there it stood in the same place to that very day, the doubters never failed to be put down by a large majority, and all true believers exulted as in a victory.

Whether these, and many other stories of the like nature, were true or untrue, the Maypole was really an old house, a very old house, perhaps as old as it claimed to be, and perhaps older, which will sometimes happen with houses of an uncertain, as with ladies of a certain age. Its windows were old diamond-pane lattices, its floors were sunken and uneven, its ceilings blackened by the hand of Time, and heavy with massive beams. Over the doorway was an ancient porch, quaintly and gro-tesquely carved ; and here on summer evenings the more favoured customers smoked and drank—ay, and sang many a good song too, sometimes—reposing on two grim-looking high-backed settles, which, like the twin dragons of some fairy tale, guarded the entrance to the mansion.

In the chimneys of the disused rooms swallows had built their nests for many a long year, and from earliest spring to latest autumn whole colonies of sparrows chirped and twittered in the eaves. There were more pigeons about the dreary stable-yard and outbuildings than anybody but the landlord could reckon up. The wheeling and circling flights of runts, fantails, tumblers, and pouters, were perhaps not quite consistent with the grave and sober character of the building, but the monotonous cooing, which never ceased to be raised by some among them all day long, suited it exactly, and seemed to lull it to rest. With its overhanging stories, drowsy little panes of glass, and front bulging out and projecting over the pathway, the old house looked as if it were nodding in its sleep. Indeed it needed no very great stretch of fancy to detect in it other resemblances to humanity. The bricks of which it was built had originally been a deep dark red, but had grown yellow and discoloured like an old man's skin ; the sturdy timbers had decayed like teeth ; and here and there the ivy, like a warm garment to comfort it in its age, wrapt its green leaves closely round the time-worn walls.   *Charles Dickens.*

SEVENTEENTH CENTURY INNS

ALL the various dangers by which the traveller was beset were greatly increased by darkness. He was therefore commonly desirous of having the shelter of a roof during the night ; and such shelter it was not difficult to obtain. From a very early period the inns of England had been renowned. Our first great poet had described the excellent accommodation which they afforded to the pilgrims of the fourteenth century. Nine and twenty persons, with their horses, found room in the wide chambers and stables of the Tabard in Southwark.

The food was of the best, and the wines such as drew the company on to drink largely. Two hundred years later, under the reign of Elizabeth, William Harrison gave a lively description of the plenty and comfort of the great hostelries. The Continent of Europe, he said, could show nothing like them. There were some in which two or three hundred people, with their horses, could without difficulty be lodged and fed. The bedding, the tapestry, above all, the abundance of clean and fine linen was matter of wonder. Valuable plate was often set on the tables. Nay, there were signs which had cost thirty or forty pounds. In the seventeenth century England abounded with excellent inns of every rank. The traveller sometimes, in a small village, lighted on a public house such as Walton has described, where the brick floor was swept clean, where the walls were stuck round with ballads, where the sheets smelt of lavender, and where a blazing fire, a cup of good ale, and a dish of trouts fresh from the neighbouring brook, were to be procured at small charge. At the larger houses of entertainment were to be found beds hung with silk, choice cookery, and claret equal to the best which was drunk in London. The innkeepers too, it was said, were not like other innkeepers. On the Continent the landlord was the tyrant of those who crossed the threshold. In England he was a servant. Never was an Englishman more at home than when he took his ease in his inn. Even men of fortune, who might in their own mansions have enjoyed every luxury, were often in the habit of passing their evenings in the parlour of some neighbouring house of public entertainment. They seem to have thought that comfort and freedom could in no other place be enjoyed in equal perfection. This feeling continued during many generations to be a national peculiarity. The liberty and jollity of inns long furnished matter to our novelists and dramatists. Johnson declared that a tavern chair was the throne of human felicity ; and Shenstone gently complained that no private roof, however friendly, gave the wanderer so warm a welcome as that which was to be found at an inn.

Many conveniences, which were unknown at Hampton Court and Whitehall in the seventeenth century, are to be found in our modern hotels. Yet on the whole it is certain that the improvement of our houses of public entertainment has by no means kept pace with the improvement of our roads and of our conveyances. Nor is this strange ; for it is evident that, all other circumstances being supposed equal, the inns will be best where the means of locomotion are worst. The quicker the rate of travelling, the less important is it that there should be numerous agreeable resting-places for the traveller. A hundred and sixty years ago a person who came up to the capital from a remote county generally required twelve or fifteen meals, and lodging for five or six nights by the way. If he were a great man, he expected the meals and lodging to be comfortable, and even luxurious. At present we fly from York or Exeter to London by the light of a single winter's day. At present, therefore, a traveller seldom interrupts his journey merely for the sake of rest and refreshment. The consequence is that hundreds of excellent inns have fallen into utter decay. In a short time no good houses of that description will be found, except at places where strangers are likely to be detained by business or pleasure.

Lord Macaulay.

A FOREIGN VIEW

ENGLISHMEN who do not belong to the aristocracy, and are not very rich, usually travel without a servant by the mail or stage coach, which deposits them at the inn. The man who waits on strangers to the coach, cleans their boots, etc., has the universal appellation of Boots. It is, accordingly, Boots who brings your slippers, helps you to pull off your boots, and then departs, first asking at what time you will have, not, as in Germany, your coffee, but your hot water to shave. He appears with it punctually at the appointed hour, and brings your clothes cleanly brushed. The traveller then hastens to dress himself and to return to his beloved coffee-room, where the ingredients of breakfast are richly spread upon the table. To this meal he seems to bring more animation than to any other, and, indeed, I think, more appetite ; for the number of cups of tea, the masses of bread and butter, eggs and cold meat which he devours, awaken silent envy in the breast, or rather in the stomach, of the less capable foreigner. He is now not only permitted, but enjoined (by custom, his gospel) to read. At every cup of tea he unfolds a newspaper of the size of a table-cloth. Not a single speech, crim. con., murder, or other catastrophe, invented by the "accident maker" in London, escapes him.

Like one who would rather die of a surfeit than leave anything uneaten which he had paid for, the systematic Englishman thinks that, having called for a newspaper, he ought not to leave a letter of it unread. By this means his breakfast lasts several hours, and the sixth or seventh cup is drunk cold. I have seen this glorious meal protracted so long that it blended with dinner ; and you will hardly believe me when I assure you that a light supper followed at midnight without the company quitting the table.

Prince Muskau.

PAUL CLIFFORD BENIGHTED

THE footman who had apprised the squire of their misfortune was, unlike most news-tellers, the first to offer consolation.

"There be an excellent public," quoth he, "about half a mile on, where your honour could get horses ; or, mayhap, if Miss Lucy, poor heart, be faint, you may like to stop for the night."

Though a walk of half a mile in a dark night, and under other circumstances, would not have seemed a grateful proposition, yet, at present, when the squire's imagination had only pictured to him the alternatives of passing the night in the carriage, or of crawling on foot to Bath, it seemed but a very insignificant hardship. And tucking his daughter's arm under his own, while in a kind voice he told Clifford to support her on the other side, the squire ordered the footman to lead the way with Clifford's horse, and the coachman to follow or be d——d whichever he pleased. . . .

The servant, who had had previous opportunities of ascertaining the topography of the " public " of which he spake, and who was perhaps tolerably reconciled to his late terror in the anticipation of renewing his intimacy with the " spirits of the past," now directed the attention of our travellers to a small inn just before them. Mine host had not yet retired to repose, and it was not necessary to knock twice before the door was opened.

A bright fire, an officious landlady, a commiserate

landlord, a warm potation, and the promise of excellent beds, all appeared to our squire to make ample amends for the intelligence that the inn was not licensed to let post-horses ; and mine host having promised forthwith to send two stout fellows, a rope, and a cart-horse, to bring the carriage under shelter (for the squire valued the vehicle *because* it was twenty years old), and, moreover, to have the harness repaired, and the horses ready by an early hour the next day, the good humour of Mr. Brandon rose into positive hilarity. Lucy retired under the auspices of the landlady to bed, and the squire having drunk a bowl of bishop, and discovered a thousand new virtues in Clifford, especially that of never interrupting a good story, clapped the captain on the shoulder, and making him promise not to leave the inn till he had seen him again, withdrew also to the repose of his pillow. Clifford remained below, gazing abstractedly on the fire for some time afterwards ; nor was it till the drowsy chambermaid had thrice informed him of the prepared comforts of his bed, that he adjourned to his chamber. Even then it seems that sleep did not visit his eyelids, for a wealthy grazier, who lay in the room below, complained bitterly the next morning of some person walking over-head " in all manner of strides, just for all the world like a happarition in boots."

Lord Lytton.

THE INN KITCHEN

IN the evening we reached a village where I had determined to pass the night. As we drove into the great gateway of the inn I saw on one side the light of a rousing kitchen fire beaming through a window. I entered, and admired, for the hundredth time, that picture of con-

venience, neatness, and broad, honest enjoyment, the
kitchen of an English inn. It was of spacious dimensions,
hung round with copper and tin vessels highly polished,
and decorated here and there with a Christmas green.
Hams, tongues, and flitches of bacon were suspended
from the ceiling ; a smoke-jack made its ceaseless clank-
ing beside the fireplace, and a clock ticked in one corner.
A well-scoured deal table extended along one side of the
kitchen, with a cold round of beef and other hearty
viands upon it, over which two foaming tankards of ale
seemed mounting guard. Travellers of inferior order
were preparing to attack this stout repast, while others
sat smoking and gossiping over their ale on two high-
backed oaken settles beside the fire. Trim housemaids
were hurrying backwards and forwards under the directions of a fresh bustling landlady ; but still seizing an
occasional moment to exchange a flippant word, and have
a rallying laugh with the group round the fire. The
scene completely realised Poor Robin's humble idea of
the comforts of mid-winter,—

> Now trees their leafy hats do bare
> To reverence Winter's silver hair ;
> A handsome hostess, merry host,
> A pot of ale now and a toast,
> Tobacco and a good coal fire,
> Are things this season doth require.
>
> *Washington Irving.*

A TIP FOR TRAVELLERS

I NOW was directed to a public-house where coachmen and guards stopped, and where many travellers
were in the habit of resting. It was getting late, and

almost dark, and I determined not to be shuffled out of this next place by any pretence. I entered a rather handsome bar parlour, where a numerous company was sitting, apparently farmers, who were taking their pipes and glass after the fair or market. I asked the landlady, a smart but unassuming woman, if I could have a bed for the night. From the moment I entered she had been eyeing me over, and seeing, as I suppose, my shoes all dust, and myself, a brown, and not very polished-looking customer, she said she was very sorry, but there was not a bed to spare in the house, so many soldiers had brought billets, they were quite full. I drew my hand across my brows, looked at my feet rather feelingly, and requesting she would serve me with a pint of ale, I sat down. The ale was brought, and I gave it a hearty pull, and then asked for a pipe and tobacco, which were placed before me. My next order was for something to eat, intimating that a chop or a steak, with a hot potato, would be preferred. Meantime, I drank up my ale, and called for another pint, and sat smoking and chatting with the farmers in a quite comfortable way. When they heard I came from Lancaster they made many inquiries as to late events and present prospects, and I told them all they required so far as my information went, and as candidly and fairly as my judgment enabled me, and we became very agreeable company. When my supper was brought in I despatched it with a hearty relish, and then, having ordered some brandy and water, I called the landlady to receive my shot, observing that it was time I should look out for lodgings, for I wished to try what fair means would do first. " Oh," she said, " make yourself comfortable, young man ; you seem to be very good company, and we'll make you a bed somehow or other, you shall see." " Another glass, sir, did you say ? " asked the maid, who stood at her mistress' elbow. I nodded assent, and thus got installed for the night, and had a most excellent lodging.

I have been the more circumstantial in narrating this transaction, inasmuch as it contains a useful intimation to foot travellers. I have never since, save on two occasions, tried the experiment of getting lodgings at a public-house in the way I put the question on this night, and on those occasions I took the plan more from curiosity than from any other motive. A foot traveller, if he is really desirous to obtain lodgings, should never stand asking about them. He should walk into a good room— never into the common tap-room—put his dusty feet under a table, ring the bell pretty smartly, and order something to eat and drink, and not speak in the humblest of tones. He will be served quickly and respectfully— that is, if those two things happen to be understood at the house. After his repast he should take his pipe or cigar, if he be a smoker, and whether he be or not, he should drink, chat, and make himself quite at ease until bed-time, when all he has to do will be to call the chamber-maid and ask her to light him to bed. That will be done as a matter of course, and he will probably have saved himself a tramp round the town in search of lodgings, and probably, after all, the making of his own bed under a manger or in a hay-loft.

Samuel Bamford.

THE PICKWICKIANS AT TOWCESTER

"I SAY," remonstrated Bob Sawyer, looking in at the coach window, as they pulled up before the door of the Saracen's Head, Towcester, " this won't do, you know."

"Bless me," said Mr. Pickwick, just awaking from a nap, "I'm afraid you're wet."

"Oh, you are, are you?" returned Bob. "Yes, I am a little that way. Uncomfortably damp, perhaps."

Bob did look dampish, inasmuch as the rain was streaming from his neck, elbows, cuffs, skirts and knees; and his whole apparel shone so with the wet that it might have been mistaken for a full suit of prepared oil-skin. "I *am* rather wet," said Bob, giving himself a shake, and casting a little hydraulic shower around, like a Newfoundland dog just emerged from the water.

"I think it's quite impossible to go on to-night," interposed Ben.

"Out of the question, sir," remarked Sam Weller, coming to assist in the conference; "it's a cruelty to animals, sir, to ask 'em to do it. There's beds here, sir," said Sam, addressing his master, "everything clean and comfortable. Wery good little dinner, sir, they can get ready in half an hour—pair of fowls, sir, and a weal cutlet; French beans, 'taturs, tart, and tidiness. You'd better stop vere you are, sir, if I might recommend. Take adwice, sir, as the doctor said."

The host of the Saracen's Head opportunely appeared at this moment, to confirm Mr. Weller's statement relative to the accommodations of the establishment, and to back his entreaties with a variety of dismal conjectures regarding the state of the roads, the doubt of fresh horses being to be had at the next stage, the dead certainty of its raining all night, the equally mortal certainty of its clearing up in the morning, and other topics of inducement familiar to innkeepers.

"Well," said Mr. Pickwick; "but I must send a letter to London by some conveyance, so that it may be delivered the very first thing in the morning, or I must go forward at all hazards."

The landlord smiled his delight. Nothing could be easier than for the gentleman to inclose a letter in a sheet of brown paper, and send it on, either by the mail or the night coach from Birmingham. If the gentleman were particularly anxious to have it left as soon as possible, he might write outside, " To be delivered immediately," which was sure to be attended to ; or " pay the bearer half-a-crown extra for instant delivery," which was surer still.

" Very well," said Mr. Pickwick, " then we will stop here."

" Lights in the Sun, John ; make up the fire ; the gentlemen are wet ! " cried the landlord. " This way, gentlemen ; don't trouble yourselves about the postboy now, sir. I'll send him to you when you ring for him, sir. Now, John, the candles."

The candles were brought, the fire was stirred up, and a fresh log of wood thrown on. In ten minutes' time, a waiter was laying the cloth for dinner, the curtains were drawn, the fire was blazing brightly, and everything looked (as everything always does, in all decent English inns) as if the travellers had been expected, and their comforts prepared, for days beforehand.

Charles Dickens.

TOM BROWN AT ISLINGTON

" NOW, sir, time to get up if you please. Tally-ho coach for Leicester 'll be round in half-an-hour, and don't wait for nobody." So spake the Boots of the Peacock Inn, Islington, at half-past two o'clock on the morning of a day in the early part of November 183–, giving Tom at the same time a shake by the shoulder, and then putting down a candle and carrying off his shoes to clean.

Tom and his father had arrived in town from Berkshire the day before, and finding on inquiry that the Birmingham coaches which ran from the city did not pass through Rugby, but deposited their passengers at Dunchurch, a village three miles distant on the main road, where said passengers had to wait for the Oxford and Leicester coach in the evening, or take a post-chaise, had resolved that Tom should travel down by the Tally-ho, which diverged from the main road and passed through Rugby itself. And as the Tally-ho was an early coach, they had driven out to the Peacock to be on the road.

Tom had never been in London, and would have liked to have stopped at the Belle Savage, where they had been put down by the Star, just at dusk, that he might have gone roving about those endless, mysterious, gas-lit streets, which, with their glare and hum and moving crowds, excited him so that he couldn't talk even. But as soon as he found that the Peacock arrangement would get him to Rugby by twelve o'clock in the day, whereas otherwise he wouldn't be there till the evening, all other plans melted away ; his one absorbing aim being to become a public school-boy as fast as possible, and six hours sooner or later seeming to him of the most alarming importance.

Tom and his father had alighted at the Peacock, at about seven in the evening, and having heard with unfeigned joy the paternal order at the bar of steaks and oyster-sauce for supper in half-an-hour, and seen his father seated cosily by the bright fire in the coffee-room, with the paper in his hand, Tom had run out to see about

him, had wondered at all the vehicles passing and repass-
ing, and had fraternised with the boots and ostler, from
whom he ascertained that the Tally-ho was a tip-top
goer, ten miles an hour including stoppages, and so
punctual, that all the road set their clocks by her.

Then being summoned to supper, he had regaled himself in one of the bright little boxes of the Peacock
coffee-room, on the beef-steak and unlimited oyster-
sauce, and brown stout (tasted then for the first time—a
day to be marked for ever by Tom with a white stone) ;
had at first attended to the excellent advice which his
father was bestowing on him from over his glass of
steaming brandy-and-water, and then begun nodding,
from the united effects of the stout, the fire, and the
lecture. Till the Squire observing Tom's state, and
remembering that it was nearly nine o'clock, and that
the Tally-ho left at three, sent the little fellow off to the
chambermaid, with a shake of the hand (Tom having
stipulated in the morning before starting, that kissing
should now cease between them) and a few parting
words. Tom was carried off by the chambermaid in a
brown study, from which he was roused in a clean little
attic, by that buxom person calling him a little darling,
and kissing him as she left the room ; which indignity he
was too much surprised to resent.

Thomas Hughes.

LOST IN HAMPSHIRE

WE got to Headley, the sign of the Holly Bush, just
at dusk, and just as it began to rain. I had neither
eaten nor drunk since eight o'clock in the morning ;
and as it was a nice little public-house, I at first intended
to stay all night, an intention that I afterwards very in-

discreetly gave up. I had laid my plan, which included
the getting to Thursley that night. When, therefore, I
had got some cold bacon and bread, and some milk, I
began to feel ashamed of stopping short of my plan,
especially after having so heroically persevered in the
" stern path," and so disdainfully scorned to go over
Hindhead. I knew that my road lay through a hamlet
called Churt, where they grow such fine bennet-grass
seed. There was a moon ; but there was also a hazy
rain. I had heaths to go over, and I might go into
quags. Wishing to execute my plan, however, I, at last,
brought myself to quit a very comfortable turf-fire, and
to set off in the rain, having bargained to give a man
three shillings to guide me out to the northern foot of
Hindhead. I took care to ascertain that my guide knew
the road perfectly well ; that is to say, I took care to
ascertain it so far as I could, which was, indeed, no farther
than his word would go. Off we set, the guide mounted
on his own or master's horse, and with a white smock
frock, which enabled us to see him clearly. We trotted
on pretty fast for about half an hour : and I perceived,
not without some surprise, that the rain, which I knew to
be coming from the south, met me full in the face, when
it ought, according to my reckoning, to have beat upon
my right cheek. I called to the guide repeatedly to ask
him if he was sure that he was right, to which he always
answered, " Oh ! yes, Sir, I know the road." I did not
like this, " I know the road." At last, after going about
six miles in nearly a southerly direction, the guide turned
short to the left. That brought the rain upon my right
cheek, and, though I could not very well account for the
long stretch to the south, I thought that, at any rate, we
were now in the right track ; and, after going about a

mile in this new direction, I began to ask the guide how much farther we had to go ; for I had got a pretty good soaking, and was rather impatient to see the foot of Hindhead. Just at this time, in raising my head and looking forward as I spoke to the guide, what should I see but a long, high, and steep hanger arising before us, the trees along the top of which I could easily distinguish ! The fact was, we were just getting to the outside of the heath, and were on the brow of a steep hill, which faced this hanging wood. The guide had begun to descend, and I had called for him to stop ; for the hill was so steep that, rain as it did and wet as my saddle must be, I got off my horse in order to walk down. But now, behold, the fellow discovered that he had lost his way ! Where we were I could not even guess. There was but one remedy, and that was to get back, if we could. I became guide now ; and did as Mr. Western is advising the ministers to do, retraced my steps. We went back about half the way that we had come, when we saw two men, who showed us the way we ought to go. At the end of about a mile, we fortunately found the turnpike-road ; not, indeed, at the foot, but on the tip-top of that very Hindhead on which I had so repeatedly vowed I would not go ! We came out on the turnpike some hundred yards on the Liphook side of the buildings called the Hut ; so that we had the whole of three miles of hill to come down at not much better than a foot pace, with a good pelting rain at our backs.

It is odd enough how differently one is affected by the same sight, under different circumstances. At the Holly Bush at Headley there was a room full of fellows in white smock frocks drinking and smoking and talking, and I, who was then dry and warm, moralised within myself on their folly in spending their time in such a way. But, when I got down from Hindhead to the public-house at Road Lane, with my skin soaking and my teeth chattering, I thought just such another group, whom I saw through the window sitting round a good fire with pipes in their mouths, the wisest assembly I had ever set my eyes on. A real Collective Wisdom.

William Cobbett.

MR. JORROCKS AT NEWMARKET

THE Yorkshireman, having an eye to a bed, speedily had Mr. Jorrocks' luggage and his own on the back of a porter on its way to the Rutland Arms, while that worthy citizen followed in a sort of sleepy astonishment at the smallness of the place, inquiring if they were sure they had not stopped at some village by mistake. Two beds had been ordered by two gentlemen who could not get two seats by the mail, which fell to the lot of those who did, and into these our heroes trundled, having arranged to be called by the early exercising hour.

Whether it was from want of his usual night-cap of brandy-and-water, or the fatigues of travelling, or what else, remains unknown, but no sooner was Mr. Jorrocks left alone with his candle, than all at once he was seized with a sudden fit of trepidation, on thinking that he should have been inveigled into such a place as New-market, and the tremor increasing as he pulled four five-pound bank notes out of his watch-pocket, besides a vast of silver, and his great gold watch, he was resolved, should an attempt be made upon his property, to defend it with his life ; and having squeezed the notes into the toe of his boots, and hid the silver in the wash-hand stand, he very deliberately put his watch and the poker under

E 2

the pillow, and set the heavy chest of drawers with two stout chairs and a table against the door, after all which exertions he got into bed and very soon fell sound asleep.

Most of the inmates of the house were up with the lark to the early exercise, and the Yorkshireman was as early as any of them. Having found Mr. Jorrocks' door, he commenced a loud battery against it without awakening the grocer; he then tried to open it, but only succeeded in getting it an inch or two from the post, and after several holloas of "Jorrocks, my man! Mr. Jorrocks! Jorrocks, old boy! Holloa, Jorrocks!" he succeeded in extracting the word "Wot?" from the worthy gentleman as he rolled over in his bed. "Jorrocks!" repeated the Yorkshireman, "it's time to be up." "Wot?" again was the answer. "Time to get up. The morning's breaking." "Let it break," replied he, adding on a mutter, as he turned over again, "it owes me nothing!"

R. S. Surtees.

CASUAL QUARTERS

ON the middle of the down stood a wayside inn; a desolate and villainous-looking lump of lichen-spotted granite, with windows paper-patched, and rotting thatch kept down by stones and straw-bands; and at the back a rambling courtledge of barns and walls, around which pigs and bare-foot children grunted in loving communion of dirt. At the door, rapt apparently in the contemplation of the mountain peaks, which glowed rich orange in the last lingering sunrays, but really watching which way the sheep on the moor were taking, stood the innkeeper, a brawny, sodden-visaged, blear-eyed six feet of brutishness, holding up his hose with one hand, for want of points, and clawing with the other his elf-locks, on which a fair sprinkling of feathers might denote : first, that he was just out of bed, having been out sheep-stealing all the night before ; and, secondly, that by natural genius he had anticipated the opinion of that great apostle of sluttishness, Fridericus Dedekind, and his faithful disciple Dekker, which last speaks thus to all gulls and grobians :—" Consider that as those trees of cobweb lawn, woven by spinners in the fresh May mornings, do dress the curled heads of the mountains, and adorn the swelling bosoms of the valleys ; or as those snowy fleeces, which the naked briar steals from the innocent sheep to make himself a warm winter livery, are, to either of them both, an excellent ornament ; so make thou account, that to have feathers sticking here and there on thy head will embellish thee, and set thy crown out rarely. None dare upbraid thee, that like a beggar thou hast lain on straw, or like a travelling pedlar upon musty flocks ; for those feathers will rise up as witnesses to choke him that says so, and to prove thy bed to have been of the softest down." Even so did those feathers bear witness that the possessor of Rogues' Harbour Inn, on Brent-Tor Down, whatever else he lacked, lacked not geese enough to keep him in soft lying.

Presently he spies Amyas and his party coming slowly over the hill, pricks up his ears, and counts them ; sees Amyas's armour ; shakes his head and grunts ; and then, being a man of few words, utters a sleepy howl—

" Mirooi !—Fushing pooale ! "

A strapping lass — whose only covering (for country-women at work in those days dispensed with the ornament of a gown) is a green bodice and red petticoat, neither of them over ample—brings out his fishing-rod and basket, and the man, having tied up his hose with some ends of string, examines the footlink.

" Don vlies' gone ! "

" May be," says Mary ; " shouldn't hav' left mun out to coort. May be old hen's ate mun off. I see her chocking about a while agone."

The host receives this intelligence with an oath, and replies by a violent blow at Mary's head, which she, accustomed to such slight matters, dodges, and then returns the blow with good effect on the shock head.

Whereon mine host equally accustomed to such slight matters, quietly shambles off, howling as he departs—

" Tell patrico ! "

Mary runs in, combs her hair, slips a pair of stockings and her best gown over her dirt, and awaits the coming guests, who make a few long faces at the " mucksy sort of a place," but prefer to spend the night there than to bivouac close to the enemy's camp.

So the old hen who has swallowed the dun fly is killed, plucked, and roasted, and certain " black Dartmoor mutton " is put on the gridiron, and being compelled to confess the truth by that fiery torment, proclaims itself to all noses as red-deer venison. In the meanwhile Amyas has put his horse and the ponies into a shed, to which he can find neither lock nor key, and therefore returns grumbling, not without fear for his steeds' safety. The baggage is heaped in a corner of the room, and Amyas stretches his legs before a turf fire ; while Yeo, who has his notions about the place, posts himself at the door, and the men are seized with a desire to superintend the cooking, probably to be attributed to the fact that Mary is cook. *Charles Kingsley.*

THE INN AT ITS BEST

THEN (*i.e.*, at the latter end of the eighteenth and
the beginning of the nineteenth century) half an
hour was the minimum of time spent at each change of
horses. Your arrival produced a great bustle of unload-
ing and unharnessing ; as a matter of course you alighted
and went into the inn ; if you sallied out to report progress, after waiting twenty minutes, no signs appeared of
any stir about the stables. The pace was such as the
roads of that day allowed ; never so much as six miles an
hour, except upon a very great road, and then only by
extra payment to the driver. Yet, even under this com-
paratively miserable system, how superior was England,
as a land for the traveller, to all the rest of the world,
Sweden only excepted ! Bad as were the roads, and
defective as were all the arrangements, still you had these
advantages : no town so insignificant, no posting-house
so solitary, but that at all seasons, except a contested
election, it could furnish horses without delay, and
without license to distress the neighbouring farmers. On
the worst road, and on a winter's day, with no more than
a single pair of horses, you generally made out sixty
miles ; even if it were necessary to travel through the
night, you could continue to make way, although more
slowly ; and, finally, if you were of a temper to brook
delay, and did not exact from all persons the haste or
energy of Hotspurs, the whole system in those days was
full of respectability and luxurious ease, and well fitted
to renew the image of the home you had left, if not in its
elegancies, yet in all its substantial comforts. What cosy
old parlours in those days ! Low-roofed, glowing with
ample fires, and fenced from the blasts of doors by

screens, whose foldings were or seemed to be infinite ! What motherly landladies ! won, how readily, to kindness the most lavish by the mere attractions of simplicity and youthful innocence, and finding so much interest in the bare circumstance of being a traveller at a childish age ! Then what blooming young handmaidens ; how different from the knowing and worldly demireps of modern high-roads ! And sometimes grey-headed, faithful waiters, how sincere and how attentive, by comparison with their flippant successors, the eternal " Coming, sir, coming," of our improved generation.

Thomas de Quincey.

A CUMBERLAND INN

THE innkeeper was a fine specimen of a north-country man, or any kind of man. He had a ruddy cheek, a bright eye, a well-knit frame, an immense hand, a cheery outspeaking voice, and a straight, bright, broad look. He had a drawing-room, too, upstairs, which was worth a visit to the Cumberland Fells. The ceiling of this drawing-room was so crossed and recrossed by beams of unequal lengths, radiating from a centre, in a corner, that it looked like a broken star-fish. The room was comfortably and solidly furnished with good mahogany and horsehair. It had a snug fireside, and a couple of well-curtained windows looking out upon the wild country behind the house. What it most developed was an unexpected taste for little ornaments and nick-nacks, of which it contained a most surprising number. They were not very various, consisting in great part of waxen babies with their limbs more or less mutilated, appealing on one leg to the parental affections from under little cupping glasses ; but Uncle Tom was there, in crockery,

receiving theological instructions from Miss Eva, who
grew out of his side like a wen, in an exceedingly rough
state of profile propagandism.   Engravings of Mr.
Hunt's country boy, before and after his pie, were on
the wall, divided by a highly-coloured nautical piece,
the subject of which had all her colours (and more)
flying, and was making great way through a sea of regular
pattern, like a lady's collar.   Everything became a nick-
nack in this curious room.   The copper tea-kettle,
burnished up to the highest point of glory, took his
station on a stand of his own at the greatest possible
distance from the fire-place, and said : " By your
leave, not a kettle but a bijou."   The very footstool
could not keep the floor, but got upon a sofa, and
therefrom proclaimed itself, in high relief of white
and liver-coloured wool, a favourite spaniel coiled up
for repose.

There were books, too, in this room ; books on the
table, books on the chimney-piece, books in an open
press in the corner.   Fielding was there, and Smollett
was there, and Steele and Addison were there, in dispersed volumes ; and there were tales of those who go
down to the sea in ships, for windy nights ; and there
was really a choice of good books for rainy days or fine.
It was so very pleasant to see these things in such a lone-
some by-place—so very agreeable to find these evidences
of a taste, however homely, that went beyond the beautiful cleanliness and trimness of the house—so fanciful to
imagine what a wonder such a room must be to the little
children born in the gloomy village—what grand impres-
sions of it those of them who became wanderers over the
earth would carry away ; and how, at distant ends of
the world, some old voyagers would die, cherishing the

belief that the finest apartment known to men was once in the Hesket-Newmarket Inn, in rare old Cumberland.

Wilkie Collins.

THE RAILWAY HOTEL

WE all know the new hotel near the station, where it is always gusty, going up the lane which is always muddy, where we are sure to arrive at night, and where we make the gas start awfully when we open the front door. We all know the flooring of the passages and staircases that is too new, and the walls that are too new, and the house that is haunted by the ghost of mortar. We all know the doors that have cracked, and the cracked shutters through which we get a glimpse of the disconsolate moon. We all know the new people, who have come to keep the new hotel, and who wish they had never come, and who (inevitable result) wish *we* had never come. We all know how much too scant and smooth and bright the new furniture is, and how it has never settled down, and cannot fit itself into right places, and will get into wrong places. We all know how the gas, being lighted, shows maps of Damp upon the walls. We all know how the ghost of mortar passes into our sandwich, stirs our negus, goes up to bed with us, ascends the pale bedroom chimney, and prevents the smoke from following. We all know how a leg of our chair comes off at breakfast in the morning, and how the dejected waiter attributes the accident to a general greenness pervading the establishment, and informs us, in reply to a local inquiry, that he is thankful to say he is an entire stranger in that part of the country, and is going back to his own connection on Saturday.

We all know, on the other hand, the great station

hotel belonging to the company of proprietors, which has suddenly sprung up in the back outskirts of any place we like to name, and where we look out of our palatial windows, at little back yards and gardens, old summer-houses, fowl-houses, pigeon-traps, and pigsties. We all know this hotel in which we can get anything we want, after its kind, for money ; but where nobody is glad to see us, or sorry to see us, or minds (our bill paid) whether we come or go, or how, or when, or why, or cares about us. We all know this hotel, where we have no indivi-duality, but put ourselves into the general post, as it were, and are sorted and disposed of according to our division. We all know that we can get on very well indeed at such a place, but still not perfectly well ; and this may be, because the place is largely wholesale, and there is a lingering personal retail interest within us that asks to be satisfied.

Charles Dickens.

MINE HOST AND HOSTESS

*H*OME *to my father, who should discerne that I had been drinking, which he did never see or hear of before : so I eat a bit of dinner, and then took horse for London, and with much ado, the ways being very bad, got to Baldwick. There lay, and had a good supper by myself. The landlady being a pretty woman, but I durst not take notice of her, her husband being there.*

Samuel Pepys.

I'll now lead you to a honest ale-house where we shall find a cleanly room, lavender in the windows, and twenty ballads stuck about the wall ; there my hostess, which I may tell you, is both cleanly and handsome, and civil, has dressed many a one for me, and shall now dress it after my fashion, and I warrant it good meat. . . . Come, Hostess, how do you do ? Will you first give me a cup of your best drink, and then dress this chub as you dressed my last, when I and my friend were here about eight or ten days ago.

Izaak Walton.

At Hartley Row the foaming bit we prest,
While the fat landlord welcomed every guest.
Supper was ended, healths the glasses crowned,
Our host extoll'd his wine at every round,
Relates the Justices' late meeting there,
How many bottles drank, and what their cheer ;
What lords had been his guests in days of yore,
And praised their wisdom much, their drinking more.

John Gay.

GREET cheere made oure host us every one,
And to the souper sette he us anon ;
And servèd us with vitaille as he could,
Strong was the wyn, and wel we drynken wolde.
A semely man oure oste was withalle
For to have been a marchal in an halle ;
A large man was he with eyen deep,
A fairere burgeys is ther noon in Chepe :
Bold of his speche, and wys, and wel i-taught,
And of manhoode lakkèd he right naught.
Eke therto he was right a mery man,
And after soper playen he bygan,
And spak of myrthe amonges other thinges,
When that we al hadde made our rekonynges ;
And sayde thus : " Lo, lordynges, trewely
Ye be to me right welcome hertily :
For by my trothe, if that I shal not lye,
I never saw so mery a companye
At one time in this harbour as is now.
Fayn wold I do you merthe, wiste I how.
And of a merthe I am right now bythought,
To do you ese, and it shal coste nought.
Ye go to Caunturbury ; God you speede,
The blisful martir give you al youre meede !
And wel I wot, as ye go by the weye,
Ye shapen you to talken and to pleye ;
For trewely comfórt and merthe is none
To ryde by the weye domb as a stoon ;

And therfore wil I make you some disport,
As I seyde erst, and do you som confórt.
And if you liketh alle by one assent
Now for to standen at my judgement,
And for to werken as I shal you seye,
To morrow, when ye riden by the weye
Now by my fadres soule that is ded,
Save ye be merye, smyteth off myn hed.
Hold up youre hond withoute more speche."
Oure counseil was not longe for to seche ;
Us thoughte it was not worth to say him nay,
And graunted him withoute more delay,
And bad him say his verdite, as him leste.
"Lordynges," quoth he, "now herken for the
    beste ;
But take it not, I pray you, in disdayn ;
This is the poynt, to speken short and playn,
That each of you to shorten this youre weie,
In this viáge, shal telle tales tweye,
To Caunturburi-ward, I mene it so,
And hom-ward he shal tellen other tuo,
Of áventúres that there have bifalle.
And which of you that bereth him best of alle,
That is to seye, that telleth in this case
Tales of best senténce and of soláce,
Shal have a soper at the cost of al
Here in this place sittynge in this halle,
When that we comen ageyn from Canturbery.
And for to make you the more mery,
I wil myselven gladly with you ryde,
Right at myn owen cost, and be youre gyde."

                                Geoffrey Chaucer.

ELYNOUR RUMMYNG, OF LEATHERHEAD

AND this comely dame,
    I understand her name
Is Elynour Rummyng,
At home in her wonnyng ;
And as men say,
She dwelt in Sothray,
In a certain stead
Beside Lederhede.
She is a tonnish gyb ;
The devil and she be syb.

    But to make up my tale,
She breweth nappy ale,
And maketh thereof port sale
To travellers, to tinkers,
To sweaters, to swynkers,
And all good ale drinkers,
That will nothing spare,
But drink till they stare,
And bring themselves bare,
With, Now away the mare,
And let us slay care,
As wise as an hare !
    Come who so will
To Elynour on the hill,
With, Fill the cup, fill,
And sit there by still,
Early and late.
Thither cometh Kate,
Cicely and Sare,
With their legs bare,
And also their feet
Hardly full unsweet ;

With their heels dagged,
Their kirtles all to-jagged,
Their smocks all to-ragged,
With titters and tatters,
Bring dishes and platters,
With all their might running
To Elynour Rummyng,
To have of her tunning.

Such a lewd sort
To Elynour resort
From tide to tide ;
Abide, abide,
And to you shall be told
How her ale is sold,
To Mawte and to Mold.
Instead of coin and money,
Some bring her a coney,
And some a pot with honey,
Some a salt, and some a spoon,
Some their hose, and some their shoon ;
Some run a good trot
With a skellet or a pot ;
Some fill their pot full
Of good Lemster wool ;
An huswife of trust,
When she is athirst,
Such a web can spin,
Her thrift is full thin.
    Some go straight thider,
Be it slaty or slider ;
They hold the high way,
They care not what men say.

Be that as be may ;
Some, loth to be espied,
Start in at the back side,
Over the hedge and pale,
And all for the good ale.

   Then cometh another guest,
She sweared by the rood of rest,
Her lips are so dry,
Without drink she must die ;
Therefore fill it by and by,
And have here a peck of rye.
Anon cometh another,
As dry as the other,
And with her doth bring
Meal, salt, or other thing,
Her harvest girdle, her wedding ring,
To pay for her scot,
As cometh to her lot.
Some bringeth her husband's hood,
Because the ale is good ;
Another brought his cap,
To offer to the ale tap,
With flax and with tow ;
And some brought sour dough,
With Hey and with Ho,
Sit we down a-row,
And drink till we blow,
And pipe tirly tirlow !

   Now in cometh another rabble,
First one with a ladle,
Another with a cradle,
And with a side-saddle ;

And there began a fable
Of clattering and a babel.
Then in came a genet,
And sware by saynt Benet,
I drank not this sennet
A draught to my pay ;
Elynour, I thee pray,
Of thine ale let us assay,
And have here a pilch of gray ;
I wear skins of coney
That causeth I look so donny.
Another then did hie her,
And brought a pottle pitcher,
A tonnel and a bottle,
But she had lost the stoppel ;
She cut off her shoe sole,
And stopped therewith the hole.

    Another sort of sluts
Some brought walnuts,
Some apples, some pears,
Some brought their clipping shears,
Some brought this and that,
Some brought I wot nere what,
Some brought their husband's hat,
Some puddings and links,
Some tripes that stinks.

    But some then sat right sad
That nothing had
There of their own
Neither gelt nor pawn ;
Such were there many
That had not a penny,
But when they should walk,

Were fain with a chalk,
To score on the balk,
Or score on the tail.
God give it ill hail !
For my fingers itch,
I have written too much
Of this mad mumming
Of Elynour Rummyng.

John Skelton.

SORROWS OF MINE HOST

I AM a man now as other men be, and have liv'd in
some shire of England, till all the country was wearie
of mee. I come up to London, and fall to be some
Tapster, Hostler, or Chamberlaine in an Inne. Well,
I get mee a wife, with her a little money ; when we are
married, seeke a house we must, no other occupation
have I but to be an Ale-draper. The Landlord will have
fortie pound fine, and twenty marke a yeare, I and mine
must not lie in the street. He knows by honest courses
I can never paye the Rent. What should I say ? Somewhat must be done, rent must be paid, duties dischargd,
or we undone. To bee short, what must be shall be :
indeede sometimes I have my Landlord's countenance
before a Justice, to cast a cloake over ill-rule, or else hee
might seeke such another tenant to pay his rent so truly.

Quaintly concluded, somewhat yee must bee, and a
bawd ye will bee.

By my troth, sir, why not I as well as my neighbours,
since theres no remedy. You sir, find fault with plays.
Out upon them, they spoile our trade, as you yourselfe
have proved. Besides, they open our crosse-biting, our
conny-catching, our traines, our traps, our gins, our

snares, our subtilties ; for no sooner have we a tricke of deceit, but they make it common, singing jigs and making jests of us, that every boy can point out our houses as they passe by.

Henrie Chettle.

THE DEAD HOST'S WELCOME

'TIS late and cold ; stir up the fire,
   Sit close and draw the table nigher ;
Be merry, and drink wine that's old,
A hearty medicine 'gainst a cold :
Your beds of wanton down the best,
Where you shall tumble to your rest ;
I could wish you wenches too,
But I am dead, and cannot do.
Call for the best the house may ring,
Sack, white, and claret let them bring,
And drink apace, while breath you have ;
You'll find but cold drink in the grave :
Plover, partridge, for your dinner,
And a capon for the sinner,
You shall find ready when you're up,
And your horse shall have his sup :
Welcome, welcome shall fly round,
And I shall smile, though under ground.

John Fletcher.

A DRAW TO CUSTOM

A HANDSOME hostess is the fairer commendation of an inn, above the fair sign or fair lodgings. She is the lodestone that attracts men of iron, gallants and roarers, where they cleave sometimes long, and are not easily got off. Her lips are your welcome, and your

entertainment her company, which is put into the
reckoning too, and is the dearest parcel in it. No
citizen's wife is demurer than she at the first greeting,
nor draws in her mouth with a chaster simper ; but you
may be more familiar without distaste, and she does not
startle at bawdry. She is the confusion of a pottle of sack
more than would have been spent elsewhere, and her
little jugs are accepted to have her kiss excuse them.
She may be an honest woman, but is not believed so in
her parish, and no man is a greater infidel in it than her
husband.

John Earle.

THE MORRICE-DANCER'S HOST

ON Monday morning I daunst to Rockland ere I
rested, and coming to my Inne, where the Hoast
was a very boone companion, I desir'd to see him ; but
in no case he would be spoken with, till he had shifted
himselfe from his working dayes sute. Being armed at
all poyntes, from the cap to the codpeece, his blacke
shooes shining, and made straight with copper buckles of
the best, his garters in the fashion, and every garment
fitting correm-squandam (to use his owne word) ; hee
enters the hall with his bonnet in his hand, and began to
crye out :

O Kemp, deere Master Kemp ; you are even as welcome as as as, and so stammering, he began to study for
a fit comparison, and I thanke him at last he fitted me :
for saith he, thou art even as welcome, as the Queenes
best grey-hound. After this dogged yet well-meaning
salutation, the carrowses were called in ; and my friendly
Hoast of Rockland began with all this : blessing the
houre upon his knees, that any of the Queenes Majesties

well-willers or friends would vouchsafe to come within
his house ; as if never any such had been within his
doores before.

I tooke his good meaning, and gave him great thankes
for his kindness : and having rested mee well, began to
take my course for Hingham, whither my honest Hoast
of Rockland would needs be my guide : but good true
fat-belly he had not followed mee two fieldes, but he
lyes all along, and cryes after me to come backe and
speake with him. I fulfild his request : and coming to
him, dauncer quoth hee if thou daunce a Gods name God
speede thee : I cannot follow thee a foote farther, but
adieu good dauncer, God speed thee if thou daunce a
Gods name.

I having haste of my way, and he being able to keep
no way, there wee parted. Farewell he, he was a kinde
good fellow, a true Trojan : and it ever be my lucke to
meet him at more leasure, Ile make him full amendes
with a cup full of Canarie. But now I am a little better
advis'd, wee must not thus let my madde Hoast passe :
for my friend late mentioned before, that made the odde
rime on my Maide Marian, would needes remember my
Hoast. Such as it is Ile bluntly set down.

> He was a man not over spare,
> In his eyeballs dwelt no care ;
> Anon anon and welcome friend,
> Were the most words he used to spend.
> Save sometimes he would sit and tell
> What wonders once in Bulleyne fell ;
> Closing each period of his tale
> With a full cup of nut-browne Ale.
>   Turvvin and Turneys siege were hot,
> Yet all my Hoast remembers not.

Ketsfield and Musselborough fray
Were battles fought but yesterday.
O twas a goodly matter than
To see your sword and buckler men ;
They would lye here, and here and there,
But I would meete them everywhere :
And now a man is but a pricke,
A boy armed with a poating sticke,
Will dare to challenge Cutting Dicke.
O tis a world the world to see,
But twill not mend for thee nor mee.
By this some guest cryes Ho the house,
A fresh friend hath a fresh carouse,
Still he will drinke, and still be dry,
And quaffe with every company.
Saint Martin send him merry mates
To enter at his hostree gates :
For a blither lad than he
Cannot a Innkeeper be.

Well once againe farewell mine Hoast at Rockland :
after all these farewells I am sure to Hingham I found a
foule way, as before I had done from Thetford to Rockland.

Will Kemp.

HOST OF THE "LIGHT HEART, BARNET"

Enter HOST, *followed by* FERRET.

HOST.   I am not pleased, indeed, you are in the
right ;
Nor is my house pleased, if my sign could speak,
The sign of the Light Heart.   There you may read it ;
So may your master too, if he look on it.

A heart weigh'd with a feather, and outweigh'd too :
A brain-child of my own, and I am proud on't !
And if his worship think, here, to be melancholy,
In spite of me or my wit, he is deceived ;
I will maintain the rebus against all humours,
And all complexions in the body of man,
That is my word, or in the isle of Britain !

    FER.   You have reason, good mine host.

    HOST.   Sir, I have rhyme too.

Whether it be by chance or art,
A heavy purse makes a light heart.
There 'tis exprest : first, by a purse of gold,
A heavy purse,and then two turtles, makes,
A heart with a light stuck in it, a Light Heart.
Old abbot Islip could not invent better,
Or prior Bolton with his bolt and ton.
I am an inn-keeper, and know my grounds,
And study them ; brain o' man ! I study them.
I must have jovial guests to drive my ploughs,
And whistling boys to bring my harvest home,
Or I shall hear no flails thwack. Here, your master
And you have been this fortnight, drawing fleas
Out of my mats, and pounding them in cages
Cut out of cards, and those roped round with pack-
    thread
Drawn through birdlime, a fine subtility !
Or poring through a multiplying-glass,
Upon a captived crab-louse, or a cheese-mite,
To be dissected, as the sports of nature,
With a neat Spanish needle ! speculations
That do become the age, I do confess !
As measuring an ant's eggs with the silk-worm's,
By a phantastic instrument of thread,

Shall give you their just difference to a hair !
Or else recovering of dead flies with crumbs,
Another quaint conclusion in the physics,
Which I have seen you busy at, through the key-hole—
But never had the fate to see a fly

Enter LOVEL.

Alive in your cups, or once heard, *Drink, mine host !*
Or such a cheerful chirping charm come from you.
    LOV.   What's that, what's that ?
    FER.   A buzzing of mine host
About a fly ; a murmur that he has.
    HOST.   Sir, I am telling your Stote here, monsieur
       Ferret,
For that I hear's his name, and dare tell you, sir,
If you have a mind to be melancholy, and musty,
There's Footman's inn at the town's end, the stocks,
Or Carrier's place, at sign of the Broken Wain,
Mansions of state ! take up your harbour there,
There are both flies and fleas, and all variety
Of vermin, for inspection or dissection.
    LOV.   We have set our rest up here, sir, in your
       Heart.
    HOST.   Sir, set your heart at rest, you shall not do it,
Unless you can be jovial.   Brain of man !
Be jovial first, and drink, and dance, and drink.
Your lodging here, and your daily dumps,
Is a mere libel 'gain my house and me ;
And, then, your scandalous commons—
    LOV.   How, mine host !
    HOST.   Sir, they do scandal me upon the road here,
A poor quotidian rack of mutton, roasted
Dry to be grated ! and that driven down

With beer and butter-milk, mingled together.
Or clarified whey instead of claret !
It is against my freehold, my inheritance,
My Magna Charta, *cor lœtificat*,
To drink such balderdash, or bonny-clabber !
Give me good wine, or catholic, or christian,
Wine is the word that glads the heart of man :
And mine's the house of wine : Sack, says my bush,
Be merry, and *drink sherry* ; that's my posie !
For I shall never joy in my light heart,
So long as I conceive a sullen guest,
Or any thing that's earthy.

                                        Ben Jonson.

THE HOSTESS AND THE BULLY

The Windmill Tavern, Fowey

FAWCETT.   In your time have you seen a
sweeter creature ?

ROUGHMAN.   Some week or thereabouts.

FAW.   And in that time she hath almost undone all
the other taverns ; the gallants make no rendezvous
now, but at the Windmill.

ROUGH.   Spite of them, I'll have her.   It shall cost
me the setting on, but I'll have her.

FAW.   Why, do you think she is so easily won ?

ROUGH.   Easily, or not, I'll bid as fair and far as any
man within twenty miles of my head, but I will put her
to the squeak.

FAW.   They say there are knights' sons already come
as suitors to her.

ROUGH.   'Tis like enough, some younger brothers,
and so I intend to make them.

Faw. If these doings hold, she will grow rich in short time.

Rough. There shall be doings that shall make this Windmill my grand seat, my mansion, my palace, and my Constantinople.

(*Enter* Bess Bridges *and* Clem.)

Faw. Here she comes. Observe how modestly she bears herself.

Rough. I must know of what burden this vessel is. I shall not bear with her till she bear with me ; and till then I cannot report her for a woman of good carriage.

Bess. What company is in the Mermaid ?

Clem. There be four sea-captains. I believe they be little better than pirates, they be so flush of their ruddocks.

Bess. No matter ; we will take no note of them. Here they vent many brave commodities by which some gain accrues. They're my good customers, and still return the profit.

Clem. Wot you what, mistress, how the two sailors would have served me that called for the pound and a half of cheese ?

Bess. How was it, Clem ?

Clem. When I brought them a reckoning, they would have had me to have scored it up. They took me for a simple gull, indeed, that would have had me to have taken chalk for cheese.

Bess. Well, go wait upon the captains ; see them want no wine.

Clem. Nor reckoning, neither, take my word, mistress.   (*Exit.*)

ROUGH. She's now at leisure ; I'll to her. Lady, what gentlemen are those above ?

BESS. Sir, they are such as please to be my guests, and they are kindly welcome.

ROUGH. Give me their names.

BESS. You may go search the church-book where they were christened ; there you perhaps may learn them.

ROUGH. Minion, how !

BESS. Pray, hands off !

ROUGH. I tell thee, maid, wife, or whate'er thou beest, no man shall enter here but by my leave. Come, let's be more familiar.

BESS. 'Las, good man !

ROUGH. Why, know'st thou whom thou slightest ? I am Roughman, the only approved gallant of these parts ; a man of whom the roarers stand in awe, and must not be put off.

FAW. What, threat a woman ?

BESS. Sir, if you thus persists to wrong my house, disturb my guests, and nightly domineer to put my friends from patience, I'll complain and right myself before a magistrate.

ROUGH. Go to, wench. I wish thee well. My love can brook no rivals. For this time I am content your captains shall have peace, but must not be used to it.

BESS. Sir, if you come like other free and civil gentlemen you're welcome ; otherwise, my doors are barred you.

Thomas Heywood.

BILKING IN STUART TIMES

THE second " jump " is called Carrying Stones, and
that is performed in this manner : A crew of shark-
ing companions seek out some blind victualling house, or
cook's house, without the bars, whose Host, if it be
possible, is either an ass easy to be ridden, or else a common drunkard. In this Colt's house will they sit
carousing half-cans day and night, and pay royally at
first for what they call, that shoeing-horn of theirs drawing the Host and Hostess on to believe that they shall be
made for ever by these guests ; who to gull the poor
Goose-cap the better, draw all their acquaintance they
can to the house, never either drinking or feeding, but
mine Host must sit at the board's end like a Magnifico in
pomp, with his ale-dropt greasy doublet shining by
candle-light, as if it were an old rusty armour scurvily
scoured. But when these horse-leeches have sucked
their guts full, or rather the pitifully-complaining Host's
guts empty, that he finds by his scores he can trust no
more : then do they at one time or other talk of state
matters, or of Religion, when the Goodman of the
house can scarce stand on his legs under his own roof,
and trip him in some words ; which the next day
(being told of it, and the words justified to his face) he
knows he dares not answer ; with which hook holding
his nose to the grindstone they write their minds in
great round Oes of chalk, behind a door, which Oes
they call stones : the weight of them being such that
look how many shillings they make, so many times the
wretched Hostess cries O, as groaning under the burden.
Now Sir of these Oes, twenty shillings make a load, and
ten pound make a barge full : which when they have

well freighted, these Dunkirks hoist sail and to sea again
they go in another vessel : to find another Braseman,
that is to say into another tippling house to find another
Jade whom they may all saddle and get up upon : if
their last Host follow them with a Bailiff or a Sergeant,
they only hold up a finger, naming a Pursevant and cry
Mum, no more mine Host, you wot what : which words
are of more power to blow him away, than if they fired
him thence with trains of gunpowder. By means of
this jump some victuallers have leaped clean out of
doors and with the fall have been ready to lie in the
streets.

Thomas Dekker.

A SHORT WAY WITH THE PENNILESS

BEFORE TAPWELL'S HOUSE

Enter WELLBORN *in tattered apparel,* TAPWELL *and*
FROTH

WELL. No boose ? nor no tobacco ?

TAP. Not a suck, sir ; nor the remainder of a
single can left by a drunken porter, all night palled
too.

FRO. Not the dropping of the tap for your morning's draught, sir ; 'tis verity, I assure you.

WELL. Verity, you brache ! The devil turned pre-
cisian ! Rogue, what am I ?

TAP. Troth, durst I trust you with a looking-glass
to let you see your trim shape, you would quit me, and
take the name yourself.

WELL. How, dog ?

TAP. Even so, sir. And I must tell you, if you but

advance your Plymouth cloak you shall be soon instructed. There dwells, and within call, if it please your worship, a potent monarch called the constable, that does command a citadel called the stocks.

WELL.   Rascal ! Slave !

FRO.   No rage, sir.

TAP.   At his peril. Do not put yourself in too much heat, there being no water near to quench your thirst ; and sure, for other liquor, as mighty ale, or beer, they are things, I take it, you must no more remember ; not in a dream, sir.

WELL.   Why, thou unthankful villain, dar'st thou talk thus ? Is not thy house, and all thou hast, my gift ?

TAP.   I find it not in chalk, and Timothy Tapwell does keep no other register.

WELL.   Am I not he whose riots fed and clothed thee ? Wert thou not born on my father's land, and proud to be a drudge in his house ?

TAP.   What I was, sir, it skills not ; what you are is apparent ; now for a farewell.

WELL.   Hear me, ungrateful hell-hound. Did not I make purses for you ? Then you licked my boots, and thought your holiday cloak too coarse to clean them. 'Twas I that, when I heard thee swear if ever thou couldst arrive at forty pounds thou wouldst live like an emperor—'twas I that gave it in ready gold. Deny this, wretch !

TAP.   I must, sir ; for, from the tavern to the tap-house, all, on forfeiture of their licenses, stand bound ne'er to remember who their best guests were, if they grow poor like you.

                                        Philip Massinger.

DAME QUICKLY

LONDON : THE BOAR'S HEAD TAVERN IN EAST-
CHEAP.

HOSTESS, DOLL TEARSHEET, FALSTAFF.
Enter FIRST DRAWER.

FIRST DRAW.   Sir, Ancient Pistol's below, and
would speak with you.

DOL.   Hang him, swaggering rascal ! let him not
come hither : it is the foul-mouthed'st rogue in England.

HOST.   If he swagger, let him not come here : no,
by my faith ; I must live among my neighbours ; I'll no
swaggerers : I am in good name and fame with the very
best : shut the door ; there comes no swaggerers here :
I have not lived all this while, to have swaggering now :
shut the door, I pray you.

FAL.   Dost thou hear, hostess ?

HOST.   Pray ye, pacify yourself, Sir John : there
comes no swaggerers here.

FAL.   Dost thou hear ? it is mine ancient.

HOST.   Tilly-fally, Sir John, ne'er tell me : your
ancient swaggerer comes not in my doors. I was before
Master Tisick, the debuty, t'other day ; and, as he said
to me, 'twas no longer ago than than Wednesday last, *I'*
good faith, neighbour Quickly, says he ; Master Dumbe,
our minister, was by then ; *neighbour Quickly*, says he,
receive those that are civil ; for, said he, *you are in an ill*
name : now a' said so, I can tell whereupon ; *for*, says
he, *you are an honest woman, and well thought on ; there-*
fore take heed what guests you receive : receive, says he,
no swaggering companions. There comes none here :

you would bless you to hear what he said : no, I'll no swaggerers.

FAL. He's no swaggerer, hostess ; a tame cheater, i' faith ; you may stroke him as gently as a puppy grey-hound : he'll not swagger with a Barbary hen, if her feathers turn back in any show of resistance. Call him up, drawer. [*Exit* FIRST DRAWER.]

HOST. Cheater, call you him ? I will bar no honest man my house, nor no cheater : but I do not love swaggering, by my troth : I am the worse, when one says swagger : feel, masters, how I shake ; look you, I warrant you.

DOL. So you do, hostess.

HOST. Do I ? yea, in very truth, do I, an 'twere an aspen leaf : I cannot abide swaggerers.

Enter PISTOL, BARDOLPH, *and* PAGE.

PIST. God save you, Sir John !

FAL. Welcome, Ancient Pistol. Here, Pistol, I charge you with a cup of sack : do you discharge upon mine hostess.

PIST. I will discharge upon her, Sir John, with two bullets.

FAL. She is pistol-proof, sir ; you shall hardly offend her.

HOST. Come, I'll drink no proofs nor no bullets : I'll drink no more than will do me good, for no man's pleasure, I.

PIST. Then to you, Mistress Dorothy ; I will charge you.

DOL. Charge me ! I scorn you, scurvy companion. What ! you poor, base, rascally, cheating, lack-linen mate ! Away, you mouldy rogue, away ! I am meat for your master.

G 2

PIST.   I know you, Mistress Dorothy.

DOL.   Away, you cut-purse rascal ! you filthy bung, away ! by this wine, I'll thrust my knife in your mouldy chaps, an you play the saucy cuttle with me. Away, you bottle-ale rascal ! you basket-hilt stale juggler, you ! Since when, I pray you, sir ? God's light, with two points on your shoulder ? much !

PIST.   God let me not live, but I will murder your ruff for this.

FAL.   No more, Pistol ; I would not have you go off here : discharge yourself of our company, Pistol.

HOST.   No, good Captain Pistol ; not here, sweet captain.

William Shakespeare.

THE STUART ALE-WIFE

IF these houses have a boxe-bush, or an old post, it is enough to show their profession. But if they be graced with a sign compleat, it's a sign of good custom : In these houses you shall see the history of Judeth, Susanna, Daniel in the Lyons Den, or Dives and Lazarus painted upon the wall. It may be reckoned a wonder to see, or find the house empty, for either the parson, churchwarden, or clark, or all, are doing some church or court business usually in this place. They thrive best where there are fewest : It is the host's chiefest pride to be speaking of such a gentleman, or such a gallant, that was here, and will be again ere long : Hot weather and thunder, and want of company are the hostess' grief, for then her ale sours : Your drink usually is very young, two days old : her chiefest wealth is seen if she can have one brewing under another : If either the hostess, or her daughter or maid will kiss handsomely at parting, it is a good shoeing-horn or bird-lime to draw the company thither again the sooner. She must be courteous to all, though not by nature, yet by her profession ; for she must entertain all, good and bad ; tag and rag ; cut and long-tail : She suspects tinkers and poor soldiers most, not that they will not drink soundly, but that they will not lustily. She must keep touch with three sorts of men, that is : the maltman, the baker, and the justices' clarkes. She is merry and half-mad upon Shrove Tuesday, May-days, feast-days, and morrice-dances : A good ring of bells in the parish helps her to many a tester ; she prays the parson may not be a puritan : A bag-piper and a puppet-play brings her in birds that are flush ; she defies a wine-tavern as an upstart outlandish fellow, and suspects the wine to be poisoned. Her ale, if new, looks like a misty morning, all think ; well, if her ale be strong, her reckoning right, her house clean, her fire good, her face fair, and the town great or rich ; she shall seldom or never sit without chirping birds to bear her company, and at the next churching or christening, she is sure to be rid of two or three dozen of cakes and ale by gossiping neighbours.

Anon.

AN ENTERPRISING HOST

MY Landlord, although he commonly had the best custom of any house in the town, yet he would practice ways to gain, and bring in more ; among other ways, he used this for one. He would take his horse in an afternoon, and ride out some ten or twelve miles, and so return home again ; but he seldom came home but he brought guests with him, which he would take up by the way, thus.

If he saw a parcel of travellers who he thought to be

good fellows, and fit for his purpose, he would then inquire which way and how far they travelled ; to this they commonly answered directly ; and if they were for our town, then he would join with them ; and soon after, his second question would be to know if they were acquainted at the town, and at what inn they would take up their quarters. If they were strangers, and by that means indifferent of the place where they should lodge, then he told them that the best inn in the town was his house, but not naming it to be his, or that he had any interest in it ; but only that he knew there was a good hostess who had a handsome daughter that would use them well ; and he seldom missed with this bait to win them to agree to go thither with him, and accordingly to bring them home with him. But if they would not agree upon the place, and he saw there was no good to be done, then he would pretend some excuse to stay behind them, and would wait for such company as would at all points be for his turn ; and with them would he enter the house as a stranger ; indeed, he would call the Chamberlain, Hostler and Tapster by their names ; but they, who knew their duties, would in no case show any duty to him. Then would he, as being acquainted in the house, tell his fellow travellers what provisions there was for supper, and would be sure to draw them up to the highest bill of fare he could. If the hostess or her daughter's company were desired, he would be the forwardest to call for them, and only treat and converse with them, as of some small acquaintance ; after supper he would endeavour to draw on the company to drink high, and use all possible means to inflame the reckoning ; and when he saw they were well heated with wine, and the fury of their expenses was over, he would pretend, out of good husbandry, to call for a reckoning before they went to bed, that they might not be mis-reckoned in the morning. To this they would commonly agree, and the sum total of the reckoning being cast up, he would be the first man that would lay down his share, and by his example the rest would follow. Then the reckoning being paid, they went to bed, he retiring with his wife ; and he would lie abed in the morning, and let them march off alone. But if they in the morning did fall to drinking again, taking a hair of the old dog, then would he up and at them again, make one at that sport, and many times put them out of capacity to travel that day, and so keep them there to his profit and their expenses ; he shifting his liquor and in the end shifting himself out of their company, when he had seen his conveniency, leaving them to pay roundly for their folly. If they enquired after him, my hostess would pretend he was a chance guest, as they were ; only she had seen him the last year, or such like ; and thus he would force a trade, and enjoy his pleasure and profit by joining them together.

Richard Head.

A MERRY HOST

THENCE about six o'clock, and with a guide went over the smooth Plain indeed till night ; and then, by a happy mistake, and that looked like an adventure, we were carried out of our way to a town where we would lye, since we could not go as far as we would. And there with great difficulty come about ten at night to a little inn, where we were fain to go into a room where a pedlar was in bed, and made him rise ; and there wife and I lay, and in a truckle-bed Betty Turner and Willett. But good beds, and the master of the house a sober, understanding man, and I had good discourse with him about this country's matters, as wool, and corne, and other things. And he also merry, and made us mighty merry at supper, about manning the new ship, at Bristol, with none but men whose wives do master them ; and it seems it is in reproach to some men of estate that are such hereabouts, that this is become common talk. By and by to bed, glad of this mistake, because, as it seems, had we gone on as we intended, we could not have passed with our coach, and must have lain on the Plain all night. This day from Salisbury I wrote by the post my excuse for not coming home, which I hope will do, for I am resolved to see the Bath, and, it may be, Bristol.

Up, finding our beds good, but lousy ; which made us merry. We set out, the reckoning and servants coming to 9s. 6d. ; my guide thither, 2s. ; coachman, advanced, 10s.

Samuel Pepys.

A SUCCESSFUL VICTUALLER

HIS wife must now be called Madam, his sons, Young Masters, and his daughters, Misses. He now begins to leave off his colours, and to get the print of his apron-strings out of his coat ; that, as he walks along the street it would be a hard matter to guess at his profession.

His own house now is not big enough to hold him ; besides, he begins to have such an aversion to the liquor he sells, that he hates malt-drink as bad as a grocer hates plums or an apothecary physic. Wine is the only cordial that will go down with him, which he purchases with the pence of those poor sots who are guzzling belch at his own ale-house, to maintain him at the tavern. He expects great reverence from all his little neighbours, and will loll against the door-case, and swing his bunch of little keys half a dozen times round his fingers before he will answer a poor neighbour a civil question. Those who were the first instruments in procuring him a trade, are as much out of his memory as a woman's first husband when she's in bed with a second ; especially if they tick sixpence with him, he puts on as pleasing an aspect as the Devil when he looked over Lincoln. If he that has spent fifty pounds in his house, asks to borrow a crown of him, his wife made him swear, not above three days ago, that he would never lend one sixpence again as long as he liv'd, or else he would have don't with all his heart.

There are three sorts of victuallers, all differing very much from each other, according to the several parts of the town wherein they are situated. At Wapping, and that way, they lord it over the people like a Boatswain over a ship's company ; and look as bluff upon their tarpaulin guest as a mate when first made Commander, or a Whitefriars printer over a gang of ballad-singers. In the City he is hail-fellow-well-met with any of his customers on this side a Common Council man ; but to all above he is forced to pay a difference, and bow as low to the Deputy of a Ward as a country inn-keeper does to the Sheriff of a county. And at Charing Cross you may find 'em so very humble and obliging for every twopence they take, that a gentleman foot-soldier or a Lord's footman shall have as many bows and cringes from the master and his family, over the drinking of a pot, as a French dancing-master shall give the mistress of a boarding-school when she gives him half a piece for his day's teaching.

There are scarce any of these sundry sorts of malt-pensioners but what, if you use their houses constantly, shall think you an intail'd customer, and shall use you worse and respect you less than they shall the penurious niggard that spends a penny once in a week and begs a bit of toast into the bargain. Therefore the best method the reader can use to avoid the insolence and ingratitude of these mongrel Christians, is to act pursuant to the advice of an experienc'd toper, which is never to use any one house long, but observe this Maxim : When you find the dog begin to wag his tail upon you, 'tis time for you to seek a new tippling office ; or it's ten to one, if you have been a customer long enough for the spaniel to be acquainted with you, you will find the master grow slighting, and the servants impudent.

Ned Ward.

THE HIGHWAYMAN'S HOST
BONIFACE *and* CHERRY.

CHER. D'ye call, father ?

BON. Ay, child, you must lay by this box for the gentleman ; 'tis full of money.

CHER. Money ! all that money ! why, sure, father, the gentleman comes to be chosen parliament-man. Who is he ?

BON. I don't know what to make of him ; he talks of keeping his horses ready saddled, and of going perhaps at a minute's warning, or of staying perhaps till the best part of this be spent.

CHER. Ay, ten to one, father, he's a highwayman.

BON. A highwayman ! upon my life, girl, you have hit it, and this box is some new-purchased booty. Now, could we find him out, the money were ours.

CHER. He don't belong to our gang.

BON. What horses have they ?

CHER. The master rides upon a black.

BON. A black ! ten to one the man upon the black mare ! And since he don't belong to our fraternity, we may betray him with a safe conscience ; I don't think it lawful to harbour any rogues but my own. Look'ee, child, as the saying is, we must go cunningly to work : proofs we must have. The gentleman's servant loves drink, I'll ply him that way ; and ten to one loves a wench—you must work him t'other way.

CHER. Father, would you have me give my secret for his ?

BON. Consider, child, there's two hundred pound to boot. (Coming ! Coming !) Child, mind your business.   (*Exit.*)

CHER. What a rogue is my father ! My father ! I deny it. My mother was a good, generous, free-hearted woman, and I can't tell how far her good nature might have extended for the good of her children. This landlord of mine, for I think I can call him no more, would betray his guest and debauch his daughter into the bargain—by a footman too !

George Farquhar.

AN EYE TO BUSINESS

JONES now walked downstairs neatly drest, and perhaps the fair Adonis was not a lovelier figure ; and yet he had no charms for my landlady ; for as that good woman did not resemble Venus at all in her person, so neither did she in her taste. Happy had it been for Nanny the chambermaid, if she had seen with the eyes of her mistress, for that poor girl fell so violently in love with Jones in five minutes, that her passion afterwards cost her many a sigh. This Nanny was extremely pretty, and altogether as coy ; for she had refused a drawer, and one or two young farmers in the neighbourhood, but the bright eyes of our hero thawed all her ice in a moment.

When Jones returned to the kitchen, his cloth was not yet laid ; nor indeed was there any occasion it should, his dinner remaining *in statu quo*, as did the fire which was to dress it. This disappointment might have put many a philosophical temper into a passion ; but it had no such effect on Jones. He only gave the landlady a gentle rebuke, saying, " Since it was so difficult to get it heated he would eat the beef cold." But now the good woman, whether moved by compassion, or by shame, or by whatever other motive, I cannot tell, first gave her servants a round scold for disobeying the orders which she had never given, and then bidding the drawer lay a napkin in the Sun, she set about the matter in good earnest, and soon accomplished it.

This Sun, into which Jones was now conducted, was truly named, as *lucus a non lucendo ;* for it was an apartment into which the sun had scarce ever looked. It was indeed the worst room in the house ; and happy was it for Jones that it was so. However, he was now too hungry to find any fault ; but having once satisfied his appetite, he ordered the drawer to carry a bottle of wine into a better room, and expressed some resentment at having been shown into a dungeon.

The drawer having obeyed his commands, he was, after some time, attended by the barber, who would not indeed have suffered him to wait so long for his company had he not been listening in the kitchen to the landlady, who was entertaining a circle that she had gathered round her with the history of poor Jones, part of which she had extracted from his own lips, and the other part was her own ingenious composition ; for she said " he was a poor parish boy, taken into the house of Squire Allworthy, where he was bred up as an apprentice, and now turned out of doors for his misdeeds, particularly for making love to his young mistress, and probably for robbing the house ; for how else should he come by the little money he hath ; and this," said she, " is your gentleman, forsooth ! "— " A servant of Squire Allworthy ! " says the barber ; " what's his name ? "—" Why he told me his name was Jones," says she : " perhaps he goes by a wrong name. Nay, and he told me, too, that the squire had maintained him as his own son, tho' he had quarrelled with him now."—" And if his name be Jones, he told you the truth," said the barber ; " for I have relations who live in that country ; nay, and some people say he is his son."—" Why doth he not go by the name of his father ? " —" I can't tell that," said the barber ; " many people's sons don't go by the name of their father."—" Nay," said the landlady, " if I thought he was a gentleman's son, tho' he was a bye-blow, I should behave to him in another guess manner ; for many of these bye-blows come to be great men, and, as my poor first husband used to say, never affront any customer that's a gentleman."

Henry Fielding.

HOST OF THE BOAR'S HEAD

AGE, care, wisdom, reflection, begone—I give you to the winds ! Let's have t'other bottle : here's to the memory of Shakespeare, Falstaff, and all the merry men of Eastcheap.

Such were the reflections that naturally arose while I sat at the Boar's Head Tavern, still kept at Eastcheap. Here, by a pleasant fire, in the very room where old Sir John Falstaff cracked his jokes, in the very chair which was sometimes honoured by Prince Henry, and sometimes polluted by immoral merry companions, I sat and ruminated on the follies of youth ; wished to be young again ; but was resolved to make the best of life while it lasted ; and now and then compared past and present times together. I considered myself as the only living representative of the old knight, and transported my imagination back to the times when the Prince and he gave life to the revel, and made even debauchery not disgusting. The room also conspired to throw my reflections back into antiquity : the oak floor, the Gothic windows, and the ponderous chimney-piece had long withstood the tooth of time ; the watchman had gone twelve ; my companions had all stolen off : and none now remained with me but the landlord. From him I could have wished to know the history of a tavern that had such a long succession of customers ; I could not help thinking that an account of this kind would be a pleasing contrast of the manners of different ages ; but my landlord could give me no information. He continued to doze and sot, and tell a tedious story, as most other landlords usually do, and though he said nothing, yet was never silent. One good joke followed another good joke ; and the best joke of all was generally begun towards the end of a bottle. I found at last, however, his wine and his conversation operate by degrees. He insensibly began to alter his appearance ; his cravat seemed quilled into a ruff, and his breeches swelled out into a farthingale. I now fancied him changing sexes ; and as my eyes began to close in slumber, I imagined my fat landlord actually converted into as fat a landlady. However, sleep made but few changes in my situation : the tavern, the apartment, and the table continued as before ; nothing suffered mutation but my host, who was fairly altered into a gentlewoman whom I knew to be Dame Quickly, mistress of this tavern in the days of Sir John ; and the liquor we were drinking, which seemed converted into sack and sugar.

Oliver Goldsmith.

MINE HOST CONFESSES

ALL the comforts of life in a tavern are known,
'Tis his home who possesses not one of his own ;
And to him that has rather too much of that one,
'Tis the house of a friend where he's welcome to run ;
The instant you enter my door you're my lord,
With whose taste and whose pleasure I'm proud to
    accord ;
And the louder you call and the longer you stay,
The more I am happy to serve and obey.

To the house of a friend if you're pleased to retire,
You must all things admit, you must all things admire ;
You must pay with observance the price of your treat,
You must eat what is praised, you must praise what you
    eat ;
But here you may come, and no tax we require,
You may loudly condemn what you greatly admire ;
You may growl at our wishes and pains to excel,
And may snarl at the rascals who please you so well.

At your wish we attend, and confess that your speech
On the nation's affairs might the minister teach ;

His views you may blame, and his measures oppose,
There's no tavern-treason—you're under the Rose :
Should rebellions arise in your own little state,
With me you may safely their consequence wait ;
To recruit your lost spirits 'tis prudent to come
And to fly to a friend when the devil's at home.

That I've faults is confess'd ; but it won't be denied,
'Tis my interest the faults of my neighbours to hide ;
If I've sometimes lent Scandal occasion to prate,
I've often conceal'd what she'd love to relate ;
If to Justice's bar some have wander'd from mine,
'Twas because the dull rogues wouldn't stay by their
    wine ;
And for brawls at my house, well the poet explains,
That men drink *shallow draughts,* and so madden their
    brains.

George Crabbe.

THE LEARNED HOST

AS we exerted ourselves more than usual, I found
myself quite spent with fatigue, when we entered a
small village in the twilight. We inquired for a public-
house, and were directed to one of a very sorry appearance. At our entrance, the landlord, who seemed to be
a venerable old man, with long grey hair, rose from a
table placed by a large fire in a very neat paved kitchen,
and, with a cheerful countenance, accosted us in these
words : " *Salvete, pueri, ingredimini.*" I was not a little
pleased to hear our host speak Latin, because I was in
hope of recommending myself to him by my knowledge
in that language ; I therefore answered, without hesitation—" *Dissolve frigus, ligna super foco—large reponens.*"

I had no sooner pronounced these words, than the old gentleman, running toward me, shook me by the hand, crying, " *Fili mi dilectissime ! unde venis ? a superis, ni fallor !* " In short, finding we were both read in the classics, he did not know how to testify his regard enough ; but ordered his daughter, a jolly rosy-cheeked damsel, who was his sole domestic, to bring us a bottle of his *quadrimum*, repeating from Horace at the same time, " *Deprome quadrimum Sabina, O Thaliarche, merum diota.*" This *quadrimum* was excellent ale of his own brewing, of which he told us he had always an amphora four years old for the use of himself and friends. In the course of our conversation, which was interlarded with scraps of Latin, we understood that this facetious person was a schoolmaster, whose income being small, he was fain to keep a glass of good liquor for the entertainment of passengers, by which he made shift to make the two ends of the year meet. " I am this day," said he, " the happiest old fellow in his Majesty's dominions. My wife, rest her soul, is in heaven. My daughter is to be married next week ; but the two chief pleasures of my life are these " (pointing to the bottle and a large edition of Horace that lay on the table). " I am old, 'tis true,— what then ? the more reason I should enjoy the small share of life that remains, as my friend Flaccus advises : *Tu ne quæsieris (scire nefas) quem mihi, quem tibi finem dii dederint. Carpe diem, quam minimum credula postero.*" As he was very inquisitive about our affairs, we made no scruple of acquainting him with our situation, which, when he had learned, he enriched us with advices how to behave in the world, telling us, that he was no stranger to the deceits of mankind. In the meantime, he ordered his daughter to lay a fowl to the fire for supper, for he was resolved this night to regale his friends—*permittens divis cætera*. While our entertainment was preparing, our host recounted the adventures of his own life, which, as they contain nothing remarkable, I forbear to rehearse. When we had fared sumptuously, and drank several bottles of his *quadrimum*, I expressed a desire of going to rest, which was with some difficulty complied with, after he had informed us, that we should overtake the waggon by noon next day ; and that there was room enough in it for half a dozen, for there were only four passengers as yet in that convenience. Before my comrade and I fell asleep, we had some conversation about the good humour of our landlord, which gave Strap such an idea of his benevolence, that he positively believed we should pay nothing for our lodging and entertainment. " Don't you observe," said he, " that he has conceived a particular affection for us ; nay, even treated us at supper with extraordinary fare, which to be sure, we should not of ourselves have called for ? " I was partly of Strap's opinion ; but the experience I had of the world made me suspend my belief till the morning, when, getting up betimes, we breakfasted with our host and his daughter on hasty-pudding and ale, and desired to know what we had to pay. " Biddy will let you know, gentlemen," said he, " for I never mind these matters. Money matters are beneath the concern of one who lives upon the Horatian plan. *Crescentem sequitur cura pecuniam.*" Meanwhile, Biddy having consulted a slate that hung in the corner, told us our reckoning came to 8*s.* 7*d.* " Eight shillings and sevenpence ! " cried Strap ; " 'tis impossible—you must be mistaken, young woman." " Reckon again, child," says her father, very deliberately ; " perhaps you have miscounted." " No, indeed, father,"

she replied, " I know my business better." I could contain my indignation no longer, but said, it was an unconscionable bill, and demanded to know the particulars ;
upon which the old man got up, muttering, " Ay, ay,
let us see the particulars—that's but reasonable." And,
taking pen, ink, and paper, wrote the following items :

		s.	d.
To bread and beer	. .	o	6
To a fowl and sausages	.	2	6
To four bottles *quadrim*	.	2	o
To fire and tobacco	. .	o	7
To lodging	. . .	2	o
To breakfast	. .	1	o
		8	7

As he had not the appearance of a common publican,
and had raised a sort of veneration in me by his demeanour
the preceding night, it was not in my power to upbraid
him as he deserved ; therefore I contented myself with
saying, I was sure he did not learn to be an extortioner
from Horace. He answered, I was but a young man,
and did not know the world, or I would not tax him with
extortion, whose only aim was to live " *contentus parvo,*
and keep off *importuna pauperies.*" My fellow-traveller
could not so easily put up with this imposition ; but
swore he should either take one-third of the money, or
go without. While we were engaged in this dispute, I
perceived the daughter go out, and conjecturing the occasion, immediately paid the exorbitant demand, which was
no sooner done, than Biddy returned with two stout
fellows, who came in on pretence of taking their morning draught ; but in reality to frighten us into compliance.

Tobias Smollett.

THE LADY OF THE "BELL"

MR. JONES and Partridge, having left their last quarters in the manner before described, travelled on to Gloucester without meeting any adventure worth relating.

Being arrived here, they chose for their house of entertainment the sign of the Bell, an excellent house indeed, and which I do most seriously recommend to every reader who shall visit this antient city. The master of it is brother to the great preacher Whitefield; but is absolutely untainted with the pernicious principles of Methodism, or of any other heretical sect. He is indeed a very honest plain man, and, in my opinion, not likely to create any disturbance either in church or state. His wife hath, I believe, had much pretension to beauty, and is still a very fine woman. Her person and deportment might have made a shining figure in the politest assemblies; but though she must be conscious of this and many other perfections, she seems perfectly contented with, and resigned to, that state of life to which she is called; and this resignation is entirely owing to the prudence and wisdom of her temper; for she is at present as free from any Methodistical notions as her husband: I say at present; for she freely confesses that her brother's documents made at first some impression upon her, and that she had put herself to the expense of a long hood, in order to attend the extraordinary emotions of the Spirit; but having found, during an experiment of three weeks, no emotions, she says, worth a farthing, she very wisely laid by her hood, and abandoned the sect. To be concise, she is a very friendly good-natured woman; and so industrious to oblige, that the guests must be of a very morose disposition who are not extremely well satisfied in her house.

Henry Fielding.

MINE HOST'S COMPLIMENT

IN our Return home we met with a very odd Accident ; which I cannot forbear relating, because it shews how desirous all who know Sir Roger are of giving him Marks of their Esteem. When we were arrived upon the Verge of his Estate, we stopped at a little Inn to rest our selves and our Horses. The Man of the House had it seems been formerly a Servant in the Knight's Family ; and to do Honour to his old Master, had some Time since, unknown to Sir Roger, put him up in a Sign-post before the Door ; so that the *Knight's Head* had hung out upon the Road about a Week before he himself knew any thing of the Matter. As soon as Sir Roger was acquainted with it, finding that his Servant's Indiscretion proceeded wholly from Affection and Good-will, he only told him that he had made him too high a Compliment ; and when the Fellow seemed to think that could hardly be, added with a more decisive Look, That it was too great an Honour for any Man under a Duke ; but told him at the same time that it might be altered with a very few Touches, and that he himself would be at the Charge of it. Accordingly they got a Painter by the Knight's Directions to add a pair of Whiskers to the Face, and by a little Aggravation of the Features to change it into the *Saracen's Head*. I should not have known this Story, had not the Inn-keeper upon Sir Roger's alighting told him in my Hearing, That his Honour's Head was brought back last Night with the Alterations that he had ordered to be made in it. Upon this my Friend with his usual Chearfulness related the Particulars above-mentioned, and ordered the Head to be brought into the Room. I could not forbear discovering greater Expressions of Mirth than ordinary upon the Appearance of this monstrous Face, under which, notwithstanding it was made to frown and stare in a most extraordinary Manner, I could still discover a distant Resemblance of my old Friend. Sir Roger, upon seeing me laugh, desired me to tell him truly if I thought it possible for People to know him in that Disguise. I at first kept my usual Silence; but upon the Knight's conjuring me to tell him whether it was not still more like himself than a *Saracen*, I composed my Countenance in the best Manner I could, and replied, *That much might be said on both Sides.*

Joseph Addison.

TRADE SECRETS

"WELL," says Susan, "then I must not believe my own eyes." "No, indeed, must you not always," answered her mistress; "I would not have believed my own eyes against such good gentlefolks. I have not had a better supper ordered this half-year than they ordered last night; and so easy and good-humoured were they, that they found no fault with my Worcestershire perry, which I sold them for champagne; and to be sure it is as well tasted and as wholesome as the best champagne in the kingdom, otherwise I would scorn to give it 'em; and they drank me two bottles. No, no, I will never believe any harm of such sober good sort of people."

Susan being thus silenced, her mistress proceeded to other matters. "And so you tell me," continued she, "that the strange gentleman came post, and there is a footman without with the horses ; why, then, he is certainly some of your great gentlefolks too. Why did not you ask him whether he'd have any supper ? I think he is in the other gentleman's room ; go up and ask whether he called. Perhaps he'll order something when he finds anybody stirring in the house to dress it. Now don't commit any of your usual blunders, by telling him the fire's out, and the fowls alive. And if he should order mutton, don't blab out that we have none. The butcher I know, killed a sheep just before I went to bed, and he never refuses to cut it up warm when I desire it. Go, remember there's all sorts of mutton and fowls ; go, open the door with, Gentlemen, d'ye call ? and if they say nothing, ask what his honour will be pleased to have for supper ? Don't forget his honour. Go ; if you don't mind all these matters better, you'll never come to anything."

Henry Fielding.

THE OFFENDED LANDLORD

BUT I was not equally fortunate in this inn, as in the two former. The kitchen was full of farmers, among whom, I could not distinguish the landlord, whose health I should otherwise immediately have drank. It is true, I heard a country girl, who was also in the kitchen, as often as she drank, say, " your health, gentlemen all ! " But I do not know how it was, I forgot to drink any one's health ; which I afterwards found, was taken much a-miss. The landlord drank twice to my health, sneeringly, as if to reprimand me for my incivility ; and then began to join the rest in ridiculing me ; who almost pointed at me with their fingers. I was thus obliged for a time, to serve the farmers as a laughing stock, till at length one of them compassionately said, " nay, nay, we must do him no harm, for he is a stranger." The landlord, I suppose, to excuse himself, and as if he thought he had perhaps before gone too far, said, " ay, God forbid, we should hurt any stranger," and ceased his ridicule : but when I was going to drink to his health, he slighted and refused my attention, and told me with a sneer, all I had to do was to seat myself in the chimney corner, and not trouble myself about the rest of the world. The landlady seemed to pity me ; and so she led me into another room where I could be alone, saying : " what wicked people ! "

Carl Philip Moritz.

BEAUJEU, OF THE ORDINARY

" A ND tell me now, my dear Malcolm," said Nigel, " where we are bending our course, and whether we shall dine at an apartment of yours ? "

" An apartment of mine—yes, surely," answered Lord Dalgarno, " you shall dine at an apartment of mine, and an apartment of yours, and of twenty gallants besides ; and where the board shall present better cheer, better wine, and better attendance, than if our whole united exhibitions went to maintain it. We are going to the most noted ordinary of London."

" That is, in common language, an inn, or a tavern," said Nigel.

" An inn, or a tavern, my most green and simple friend ! " exclaimed Lord Dalgarno. " No, no—these are places where greasy citizens take pipe and pot, where the knavish pettifoggers of the law spunge on their most unhappy victims—where Templars crack jests as empty as their nuts, and where small gentry imbibe such thin potations, that they get dropsies instead of getting drunk. An ordinary is a late-invented institution, sacred to Bacchus and Momus, where the choicest noble gallants of the time meet with the first and most ethereal wits of the age,—where the wine is the very soul of the choicest grape, refined as the genius of the poet, and ancient and generous as the blood of the nobles. And then the fare is something beyond your ordinary gross terrestrial food ! Sea and land are ransacked to supply it ; and the invention of six ingenious cooks kept eternally upon the rack to make their art hold pace with, and if possible enhance, the exquisite quality of the materials."

" By all which rhapsody," said Lord Glenvarloch, " I can only understand, as I did before, that we are going to a choice tavern, where we shall be handsomely entertained, on paying probably as handsome a reckoning."

" Reckoning ! " exclaimed Lord Dalgarno in the same tone as before, " perish the peasantly phrase ! What profanation ! Monsieur le Chevalier de Beaujeu, pink of Paris and flower of Gascony—he who can tell the age of his wine by the bare smell, who distils his sauces in an alembic by the aid of Lully's philosophy—who carves with such exquisite precision that he gives to noble, knight and squire, the portion of the pheasant which exactly accords with his rank—nay, he who shall divide a becafico into twelve parts with such scrupulous exactness, that of twelve guests not one shall have the advantage of the other in a hair's breadth, or the twentieth part of a drachm, yet you talk of him and of a reckoning in the same breath ! Why, man, he is the well-known and general referee in all matters affecting the mysteries of Passage, Hazard, In and In, Penneeck, and Verquire, and what not—why, Beaujeu is King of the Card-pack, and Duke of the Dice-box—*he* call a reckoning like a green-aproned, red-nosed son of the vulgar spigot ! O, my dearest Nigel, what a word you have spoken, and of what a person ! That you know him not, is your only apology for such blasphemy ; and yet I scarce hold it adequate, for to have been a day in London and not to know Beaujeu, is a crime of its own kind. But you *shall* know him this blessed moment, and shall learn to hold yourself in horror for the enormities you have uttered."

Sir Walter Scott.

A LONDON HOST

" NOW," said Dashall, " we will make the best of our way and just call, by way of taking lunch, among the lads of Newgate Market. There is a house where I have been before, in which we can have some very fine home-brewed ale, et cetera ; and besides, according to the landlord's advertisements, he has opened an academy, and gives instructions in the art of brewing. The College of Physicians is just opposite, and I suppose this wag of a landlord has taken the hint, and opposed his beer to their physic—perhaps you may wish to carry his valuable receipt with you into the country ? "

" I have no inclination to turn brewer," replied Sparkle ; " but I must confess I like the idea of a little genuine beer free from the poisonous ingredients of the public brewer."

" And so do I," said Tallyho.

" Come along, then," said Tom, " the Bell, in Warwick Lane, is the shop, where you may be served to a
shaving."

In passing along Warwick Lane, Bob observed he
thought his friend was leading him through a not very
agreeable neighbourhood.

" This place is filled with slaughter-houses, and is to
be sure a great nuisance to the City ; yet such places are
necessary ; therefore bear up a few minutes, and you
will have comfortable house-room and agreeable refreshment."

Entering the Bell, they were met by the landlord of
the house, a round-faced, good-natured, real John-Bull-
looking man, who, knowing his customer, Dashall,
immediately ushered them into the coffee-room, where
being supplied with stout and mutton chops in high
perfection, they enjoyed themselves with their regale.
This done they had an opportunity of looking about
them.

In one corner sat two or three tip-top salesmen of the
market, conversing on the price of meat, while devouring
a succession of rump-steaks with most voracious appetite.
In another was a hungry author bargaining with a book-
seller of Paternoster Row for the sale of a manuscript,
by which he expected to realise a dinner. Bob liked the
stout ; ordered a replenish, and asked the landlord to
partake.

" With all my heart, gentlemen. Good health. Real
malt and hops, gentlemen—nothing else—all brewed
under my own eye. Good ordinary at two. Excellent
fare. Good treatment ; comfortable beds. Happy to
see you at all times at the Bell ! "

Pierce Egan.

A MAN OF PARTS

I FOUND the master of the house a very kind and civil person. Before being an inn-keeper he had been in some other line of business ; but on the death of the former proprietor of the inn had married his widow, who was still alive, but, being somewhat infirm, lived in a retired part of the house. I have said that he was kind and civil ; he was, however, not one of those people who suffer themselves to be made fools of by anybody ; he knew his customers, and had a calm, clear eye, which would look through a man without seeming to do so. The accommodation of his house was of the very best description ; his wines were good, his viands equally so, and his charges not immoderate ; though he very properly took care of himself. He was no vulgar inn-keeper, had a host of friends, and deserved them all. During the time I lived with him, he was presented by a large assemblage of his friends and customers with a dinner at his own house, which was very costly, and at which the best of wines were sported, and after the dinner with a piece of plate estimated at fifty guineas. He received the plate, made a neat speech of thanks, and when the bill was called for, made another neat speech, in which he refused to receive one farthing for the entertainment, ordering in at the same time two dozen more of the best champagne, and sitting down amidst uproarious applause, and cries of " You shall be no loser by it ! " Nothing very wonderful in such conduct, some people will say ; I don't say there is, nor have I any intention to endeavour to persuade the reader that the landlord was a Carlo Boromeo ; he merely gave a *quid pro quo ;* but it is not every person who will give you a *quid pro quo.* Had he

been a vulgar publican, he would have sent in a swinging
bill after receiving the plate ; but then no vulgar publican
would have been presented with plate ; perhaps not, but
many a vulgar public character has been presented with
plate, whose admirers never received a *quid pro quo*,
except in the shape of a swinging bill.

George Borrow.

WAGSTAFF, OF LITTLE BRITAIN

THIS, indeed (the Half Moon) has been a temple of
Bacchus and Momus from time immemorial.   It
has always been in the family of the Wagstaffs, so that its
history is tolerably preserved by the present landlord.   It
was much frequented by the gallants and cavalieros of
the reign of Elizabeth, and was looked into now and
then by the wits of Charles the Second's day.   But what
Wagstaff principally prides himself upon is, that Henry
the Eighth, in one of his nocturnal rambles, broke the
head of one of his ancestors with his famous walking-
staff.   This, however, is considered as rather a dubious
and vain-glorious boast of the landlord.

The club which now holds its weekly sessions here
goes by the name of " The Roaring Lads of Little
Britain."   They abound in old catches, glees, and choice
stories, that are traditional in the place, and not to be met
with in any other part of the metropolis.   There is a
mad-cap undertaker who is inimitable at a merry song ;
but the life of the club, and indeed the prime wit of Little
Britain, is bully Wagstaff himself.   His ancestors were
all wags before him, and he has inherited with the inn a
large stock of songs and jokes, which go with it from
generation to generation as heir-looms.   He is a dapper
little fellow, with bandy legs and pot belly, a red face,

with a moist merry eye, and a little shock of gray hair behind. At the opening of every club-night he is called in to sing his " Confession of Faith," which is the famous old drinking trowl from Gammer Gurton's Needle. He sings it, to be sure, with many variations, as he received it from his father's lips ; for it has been a standing favourite at the Half Moon and Bunch of Grapes ever since it was written ; nay, he affirms that his predecessors have often had the honour of singing it before the nobility and gentry at Christmas mummeries, when Little Britain was in all its glory.   *Washington Irving.*

A TREACHEROUS HOST

MY brother went to an inn, after his long, long journey to Liverpool, foot-sore (for he had walked through four days, and, from ignorance of the world, combined with excessive shyness—oh ! how shy do people become from pride !—had not profited by those well-known incidents upon English high-roads—return post-chaises, stage-coaches, led horses, or waggons) foot-sore, and eager for sleep. Sleep, supper, breakfast in the morning—all these he had, so far as his slender finances reached ; and for these he paid the treacherous landlord : who then proposed to him that they should take a walk out together, by way of looking at the public buildings and the docks. It seems that the man had noticed my brother's beauty, some circumstances about his dress inconsistent with his mode of travelling, and also his style of conversation. Accordingly, he wiled him along from street to street, until they reached the Town Hall. " Here seems to be a fine building," said this Jesuitical guide, as if it had been some new Pompeii—some Luxor or Palmyra that he had unexpectedly lit upon amongst the undiscovered parts of Liverpool—" here seems to be a fine building ; shall we go in and ask leave to look at it ? " My brother, thinking less of the spectacle than the spectator, whom, in a wilderness of man, naturally he wished to make his friend, consented readily. In they went ; and, by the merest accident, Mr. Mayor and the town-council were then sitting. To them the insidious landlord communicated privately an account of his suspicions. He himself conducted my brother, under pretence of discovering the best station for picturesque purposes, to the particular box for prisoners at the bar.

Thomas de Quincey.

GENTLEMAN GEORGE, OF FINCHLEY

OUR wanderers now leaving the haystack, struck across part of Finchley Common ; for the abode of the worthy publican was felicitously situated, and the scene in which his guests celebrated their festivities was close by that on which they often performed their exploits.

As they proceeded, Paul questioned his friend touching the name and character of " mine host " ; and the all-knowing Augustus Tomlinson answered him, Quaker-like, by a question,—

" Have you never heard of Gentleman George ? "

" What ! the noted head of a flash public-house in the country ? To be sure I have, often ; my poor nurse, Dame Lobkins, used to say he was the best-spoken man in the trade ! "

" Ay, so he is still. In his youth George was a very handsome fellow, but a little too fond of his lass and his bottle to please his father, a very staid old gentleman, who walked about on Sundays in a bob-wig and a gold-headed cane, and was a much better farmer on week-

days than he was head of a public-house. George used to
be a remarkably smart-dressed fellow, and so he is to this
day. He has a great deal of wit, is a very good whist-
player, has a capital cellar, and is so fond of seeing his
friends drunk that he bought some time ago a large
pewter measure in which six men can stand upright.
The girls, or rather the old women, to which last he used
to be much more civil of the two, always liked him ;
they say, nothing is so fine as his fine speeches, and they
give him the title of ' *Gentleman* George.' He is a nice,
kind-hearted man in many things. Pray Heaven we
shall have no cause to miss him when he departs. But,
to tell you the truth, he takes more than his share of our
common purse."

" What, is he avaricious ? "

" Quite the reverse ; but he's so cursedly fond of
building, he invests all *his* money (and wants us to invest
all *ours*) in houses ; and there's one confounded dog of a
bricklayer, who runs him up terrible bills,—a fellow
called ' Cunning Nat,' who is equally adroit in spoiling
ground and improving *ground rent*."

" What do you mean ? "

" Ah ! thereby hangs a tale. But we are near the
place now ; you will see a curious set."

As Tomlinson said this, the pair approached a house
standing alone, and seemingly without any other abode
in the vicinity. It was of curious and grotesque shape,
painted white with a Gothic chimney, a Chinese sign-
post (on which was depicted a gentleman fishing, with
the words " The Jolly Angler " written beneath), and
a porch that would have been Grecian, if it had not been
Dutch. It stood in a little field, with a hedge behind it,
and the common in front ! Augustus stopped at the

door, and while he paused, bursts of laughter rang cheerily within.

"Ah, the merry boys ! " he muttered : " I long to be with them ! " and then with his clenched fist he knocked four times at the door. There was a sudden silence which lasted about a minute, and was broken by a voice within, asking who was there. Tomlinson answered by some cabalistic word ; the door was opened, and a little boy presented himself.

"Well, my lad," said Augustus, "and how is your master ?—Stout and hearty, if I may judge by his voice."

"Ay, Master Tommy, ay, he's boosing away at a fine rate in the back-parlour, with Mr. Pepper and fighting Attie, and half-a-score more of them. He'll be woundy glad to see you, I'll be bound."

"Show this gentleman into the bar," rejoined Augustus, "while I go and pay my respects to honest Geordie ! "

The boy made a sort of a bow, and leading our hero into the bar, consigned him to the care of Sal, a buxom barmaid, who reflected credit on the taste of the landlord, and who received Paul with marked distinction and a gill of brandy.

Paul had not long to play the amiable, before Tomlinson rejoined him with the information that Gentleman George would be most happy to see him in the back-parlour, and that he would there find an old friend in the person of Mr. Pepper.

"What ! is he here ? " cried Paul. "The sorry knave ! to let me be caged in his stead ! "

"Gently, gently, no misapplication of terms," said Augustus ; "that was not knavery, that was *prudence*, the greatest of all virtues and the rarest. But come along, and Pepper shall *explain* to-morrow."

Threading a gallery or passage, Augustus preceded our hero, opened a door, and introduced him into a long low apartment, where sat, round a table spread with pipes and liquor, some ten or a dozen men, while at the top of the table, in an arm-chair, presided Gentleman George. That dignitary was a portly and comely gentleman, with a knowing look, and a Welsh wig, worn, as the *Morning Chronicle* says of his Majesty's hat, " in a *dégagé* manner, on one side." Being afflicted with the gout, his left foot reclined on a stool ; and the attitude developed, despite of a lamb's-wool stocking, the remains of an exceedingly good leg.

Lord Lytton.

AT THE SARACEN'S HEAD

AFTER waiting some time, in hopes that a pair of horses that had gone southward would return in time for her use, she at length, feeling ashamed of her own pusillanimity, resolved to prosecute her journey in her usual manner.

" It was all plain road," she was assured, " except a high mountain, called Gunnerby Hill, about three miles from Grantham, which was her stage for the night."

" I'm glad to hear there's a hill," replied Jeanie, " for baith my sight and my very feet are weary o' sic tracts o' level ground—it looks a' the way between this and York as if a' the land had been trenched and levelled, whilk is very wearisome to my Scotch een. When I lost sight of a muckle blue hill they ca' Ingleboro', I thought I hadna a friend left in this strange land."

" As for the matter of that, young woman," said mine host, " and you be so fond o' hill, I carena an thou couldst carry Gunnerby away with thee in thy lap, for it's a murder to post-horses. But here's to thy journey, and mayst thou win well through it, for thou is a bold and a canny lass."

So saying, he took a powerful pull at a solemn tankard of home-brewed ale.

" I hope there is nae bad company on the road, sir ? " said Jeanie.

"Why, when it's clean without them I'll thatch Groby pool wi' pancakes. But there arena sae mony now ; and since they hae lost Jim the Rat, they hold together no better than the men of Marsham when they lost their common. Take a drop ere thou goest," he concluded, offering her the tankard ; " thou wilt get naething at night save Grantham gruel, nine grots and a gallon of water."

Jeanie courteously declined the tankard, and inquired what was her " lawing " ?

" Thy lawing ? Heaven help thee, wench ! What ca'st thou that ? "

" It is—I was wanting to ken what was to pay," replied Jeanie.

" Pay ? Lord help thee !—why nought, woman— we hae drawn no liquor but a gill o' beer, and the Saracen's Head can spare a mouthful o' meat to a stranger like o' thee, that cannot speak Christian language. So here's to thee once more. The same again, quoth Mark of Bellgrave," and he took another profound pull at the tankard.

The travellers who have visited Newark more lately, will not fail to remember the remarkably civil and gentlemanly manners of the person who now keeps the principal inn there, and may find some amusement in

contrasting them with those of his more rough predecessor. But we believe it will be found that the polish
has worn off none of the real worth of the metal.

Sir Walter Scott.

A WEST COUNTRY HOST

THE innkeeper was a friend of his ; for, in the first
place, they had lived within three doors of each other
all their lives ; and next, Jack was quite pleasant company
enough, besides being a learned man and an Oxford
scholar, to be asked in now and then to the innkeeper's
private parlour, when there were no gentlemen there, to
crack his little joke and tell his little story, sip the leavings
of the guests' sack, and sometimes help the host to eat
the leavings of their supper. And it was, perhaps, with
some such hope that Jack trotted off round the corner to
the Ship that very afternoon ; for that faithful little nose
of his, as it sniffed out of a back window of the school,
had given him warning of Sabean gales, and scents of
Paradise, from the inn kitchen below ; so he went round,
and asked for his pot of small ale (his only luxury), and
stood at the bar to drink it ; and looked inward with his
little twinkling right eye and sniffed inward with his little
curling right nostril, and beheld, in the kitchen beyond,
salad in stacks and faggots : salad of lettuce, salad of
cress and endive, salad of boiled coleworts, salad of pickled
coleworts, salad of angelica, salad of scurvywort, and
seven salads more ; for potatoes were not as yet, and
salads were during eight months of the year the only
vegetable. And on the dresser, and before the fire, whole
hecatombs of fragrant victims, which needed neither
frankincense nor myrrh ; Clovelly herrings and Tor-
ridge salmon, Exmoor mutton and Stow venison, stubble

geese and woodcocks, curlew and snipe, hams of Hampshire, chitterlings of Taunton, and botargos of Cadiz, such as Pantagruel himself might have devoured. And Jack eyed them, as a ragged boy eyes the cakes in a pastrycook's window ; and thought of the scraps from the commoner's dinner, which were his wages for cleaning out the hall ; and meditated deeply on the unequal distribution of human bliss.

"Ah, Mr. Brimblecombe ! " said the host, bustling out with knife and apron to cool himself in the passage. "Here are doings ! Nine gentlemen to supper ! "

"Nine ! Are they going to eat all that ? "

"Well, I can't say—that Mr. Amyas is as good as three to his trencher ; but still there's crumbs, Mr. Brimblecombe, crumbs ; and Waste not, want not, is my doctrine ; so you and I may have a somewhat to stay our stomachs, about an eight o'clock."

"Eight ? " said Jack, looking wistfully at the clock. "It's but four now. Well, it's kind of you, and perhaps I'll look in."

"Just you step in now, and look to this venison. There's a breast ! you may lay your two fingers into the say there, and not get to the bottom of the fat. That's Sir Richard's sending. He's all for them Leighs, and no wonder, they'm brave lads, surely ; and there's a saddle-o'-mutton ! I rode twenty miles for mun yesterday, I did, over beyond Barnstaple ; and five year old, Mr. John, it is, if ever five years was ; and not a tooth to mun's head, for I looked to that ; and smelt all the way home like any apple ; and if it don't ate so soft as ever was scald cream, never you call me Thomas Burman."

"Humph ! " said Jack. "And that's their dinner. Well, some are born with a silver spoon in their mouth."

"Some be born with roast beef in their mouths, and plum-pudding in their pocket to take away the taste o' mun ; and that's better than empty spunes, eh ? "

"For them that get it," said Jack. "But for them that don't——" and with a sigh he returned to his small ale, and then lingered in and out of the inn, watching the dinner as it went into the best room, where the guests were assembled.

Charles Kingsley.

A LORDLY BILL

HERE we were interrupted by the entrance of the landlord. "O, Mr. Wallace, you are the very person I wished to see, let me have my bill if you please."

"It's not of the least consequence, sir," replied he ; "but if you wish it, I have posted down to yesterday," and the landlord left the room.

"You were both of one mind, at all events," said Timothy, laughing, "for he had the bill in his hand, and concealed it the moment you asked for it."

In about ten minutes the landlord reappeared, and presenting the bill upon a salver, made his bow and retired. I looked it over ; it amounted to £104, which, for little more than three weeks, was pretty well. Timothy shrugged up his shoulders, while I ran over the items. "I do not see that there is anything to complain of, Tim," observed I, when I came to the bottom of it ; "but I do see that living here, with the major keeping me an open house, will never do. Let us see how much money we have left."

Tim brought the dressing-case in which our cash was deposited, and we found, that after paying the waiters, and a few small bills not yet liquidated, our whole stock was reduced to fifty shillings.

" Merciful Heaven ! what an escape ! " cried Timothy ; " if it had not been for this new supply, what should we have done ? "

" Very badly, Timothy ; but the money is well spent, after all. I have now entrance into the first circles. I can do without Major Carbonnell ; at all events, I shall quit this hotel, and take furnished apartments, and live at the clubs. I know how to put him off."

I laid the money on the salver, and desired Timothy to ring for the landlord, when who should come up but the major and Harcourt. " Why, Newland, what are you going to do with that money ? " said the major.

" I am paying my bill, major."

" Paying your bill, indeed ; let us see—£104. Oh, this is a confounded imposition. You mustn't pay this." At this moment the landlord entered. " Mr. Wallace," said the major, " my friend Mr. Newland was about, as you may see, to pay you the whole of your demand ; but allow me to observe, that being my very particular friend, and the Piazza having been particularly recommended by me, I do think that your charges are somewhat exorbitant. I shall certainly advise Mr. Newland to leave the house to-morrow, if you are not more reasonable."

" Allow me to observe, major, that my reason for sending for my bill, was to pay it before I went into the country, which I must do to-morrow, for a few days."

" Then I shall certainly recommend Mr. Newland not to come here when he returns, Mr. Wallace ; for I hold myself, to a certain degree, after the many dinners we have ordered here, and of which I have partaken, as

I may say, *particeps criminis*, or in other words, as having been a party to this extortion. Indeed, Mr. Wallace, some reduction must be made, or you will greatly hurt the credit of your house."

Mr. Wallace declared, that really he had made nothing but the usual charges, that he would look over the bill again, and see what he could do.

" My dear Newland," said the major, " I have ordered your dinners, allow me to settle your bill. Now, Mr. Wallace, suppose we take off *one-third* ? "

"One-*third*, Major Carbonnell ! I should be a loser."

" I am not exactly of your opinion ; but let me see— now take your choice. Take off £20, or you lose my patronage, and that of all my friends. Yes or no ? "

The landlord, with some expostulation, at last consented : he receipted the bill, and leaving £20 of the money on the salver, made his bow, and retired.

" Rather fortunate that I slipped in, my dear Newland ; now there are £20 saved. By-the-by, I'm short of cash. You've no objection to let me have this ? I shall never pay you, you know."

" I do know you *never* will pay me, major ; nevertheless, as I should have paid it to the landlord had you not interfered, I will lend it to you."

Frederick Marryat.

MR. CREED, OF THE WHITE HART

HE besought Green to step on to the White Hart and see about accommodation. Accordingly Green ran his fingers through the bushy sides of his yellow wig, jerked up his gills, and with a *negligé* air strutted up to that inn, which, as all frequenters of Margate know,

stands near the landing place, and commands a fine view
of the harbour. Mr. Creed, the landlord, was airing
himself at the door, or, as Shakespeare has it, taking his
ease at his inn, and knowing Green of old to be a most
unprofitable customer, he did not trouble to move his
position further than just to draw up one leg so as not
wholly to obstruct the passage, and looked at him as
much as to say, " I prefer your room to your company."
" Quite full here, sir," said he, anticipating Green's
question. " Full, indeed ? " replied Jemmy, pulling up
his gills, " that's werry awkward. Mr. Jorrocks has
come down with myself and a friend, and we want
accommodation." " Mr. Jorrocks, indeed ! " replied
Mr. Creed, altering his tone and his manner ; " I'm
sure I shall be delighted to receive Mr. Jorrocks. He's
one of the oldest customers I have—and one of the best
—none of your glass-of-water-and-toothpick gentlemen
—real, downright black-strap man, likes it hot and strong
from the wood—always pays like a gentleman—never
fights about threepences, like some people I know,"
looking at Jemmy. " Pray, what rooms may you
require ? " " Vy, there's myself, Mr. Jorrocks, and Mr.
Jorrocks' other friend—three in all, and we shall want
three good hairy bedrooms." " Well, I don't know,"
replied Mr. Creed laughing, " about their hairiness, but
I can rub them with bear's grease for you." Jemmy
pulled up his gills and was about to reply, when Mr.
Jorrocks' appearance interrupted the dialogue. Mr.
Creed advanced to receive him, blowing up his porters
for not having been down to carry up the hamper, which
he took himself and bore to the coffee-room, amid pro-
testations of his delight at seeing his worthy visitor.

R. S. Surtees.

A HANDSOME HOSTESS

WATCHETT town was not to be seen, on account of a little foreland, a mile or more upon my course, and standing to the right of me. There was room enough below the cliffs (which are nothing there to yours, John) for horse and man to get along, although the tide was running high with a northerly gale to back it. But close at hand and in the corner, drawn above the yellow sands and long eye-brows of rackweed, as snug a little house blinked on me as ever I saw, or wished to see.

You know that I am not luxurious, neither in any way given to the common lusts of the flesh, John. My father never allowed his hair to grow a fourth part of an inch in length, and he was a thoroughly godly man ; and I try to follow in his footsteps, whenever I think about it. Nevertheless I do assure you that my view of that little house and the way the lights were twinkling, so different from the cold and darkness of the rolling sea, moved the ancient Adam in me, if he could be found to move. I love not a house with too many windows : being out of house and doors some three-quarters of my time, when I get inside a house I like to feel the difference. Air and light are good for people who have any lack of them ; and if a man once talks about them, 'tis enough to prove his need of them. But, as you well know, John Ridd, the horse who has been at work all day, with the sunshine on his eyes, sleeps better in dark stables, and needs no moon to help him.

Seeing therefore that this same inn had four windows, and no more, I thought to myself how snug it was, and

how beautifully I could sleep there.   And so I made the
old horse draw hand, which he was only too glad to do,
and we clomb above the spring-tide mark, and over a
little piece of turf, and struck the door of the hostelry.
Some one came and peeped at me through the lattice
overhead, which was full of bulls' eyes ; and then the
bolt was drawn back, and a woman met me very courteously.   A dark and foreign-looking woman, very hot
of blood, I doubt, but not altogether a bad one.   And she
waited for me to speak first, which an Englishwoman
would not have done.

" Can I rest here for the night ? " I asked, with a lift
of my hat to her ; for she was no provincial dame, who
would stare at me for the courtesy : " my horse is weary
from the sloughs, and myself but little better : beside
that, we both are famished."

" Yes, sir, you can rest and welcome.   But of food,
I fear, there is but little, unless of the common order.
Our fishers would have drawn the nets, but the waves
were violent.   However, we have—what you call it ?
I never can remember, it is so hard to say—the flesh of
the hog salted."

" Bacon ! " said I ; " what can be better ?   And half-
dozen of eggs with it, and a quart of fresh-drawn ale.
You make me rage with hunger, madam.   Is it cruelty,
or hospitality ? "

" Ah, good ! " she replied, with a merry smile, full of
southern sunshine : " you are not of the men round
here ; you can think, and you can laugh ! "

" And most of all, I can eat, good madam.   In that
way I shall astonish you ; even more than by my
intellect."

She laughed aloud, and swung her shoulders, as your

natives cannot do ; and then she called a little maid to lead my horse to stable. However, I preferred to see that matter done myself, and told her to send the little maid for the frying-pan and the egg-box.

Whether it were my natural wit and elegance of manner ; or whether it were my London freedom and knowledge of the world ; or (which is perhaps the most probable, because the least pleasing supposition) my ready and permanent appetite, and appreciation of garlic—I leave you to decide, John : but perhaps all three combined to recommend me to the graces of my charming hostess. When I say " charming " I mean of course by manners and by intelligence, and most of all by cooking ; for as regards external charms (most fleeting and fallacious) hers had ceased to cause distress, for I cannot say how many years. She said that it was the climate—for even upon that subject she requested my opinion—and I answered, " if there be a change, let madam blame the seasons."

However, not to dwell too much upon our little pleasantries (for I always get on with these foreign women better than with your Molls and Pegs), I became, not inquisitive, but reasonably desirous to know, by what strange hap or hazard, a clever and a handsome woman, as she must have been some day, a woman moreover with great contempt for the rustic minds around her, could have settled here in this lonely inn, with only the waves for company, and a boorish husband who slaved all day in turning a potter's wheel at Watchett. And what was the meaning of the emblem set above her doorway, a very unattractive cat sitting in a ruined tree ?

R. D. Blackmore.

THE COMPASSIONATE HOST

I SET out from Heytesbury this morning about six
o'clock. Last night, before I went to bed, I found that
there were some men and boys in the house, who had
come all the way from Bradford, about twelve miles, in
order to get nuts. These people were men and boys that
had been employed in the cloth factories at Bradford and
about Bradford. I had some talk with some of these
nutters, and I am quite convinced, not that the cloth
making is at an end, but that it never will be again what
it has been. Before last Christmas these manufacturers
had full work, at one shilling and threepence a yard at
broadcloth weaving. They have now a quarter work,
and one shilling a yard ! One and threepence a yard for
this weaving has been given at all times within the
memory of man ! Nothing can show more clearly than
this, and in a stronger light, the great change which has
taken place in the remuneration of labour. There was a
turn-out last winter, when the price was reduced to a
shilling a yard ; but it was put an end to in the usual
way ; the constable's staff, the bayonet, the gaol. These
poor nutters were extremely ragged. I saved my supper,
and I fasted instead of breakfasting. That was three
shillings, which I had saved, and I added five to them,
with a resolution to save them afterwards, in order to
give these chaps a breakfast for once in their lives. There
were eight of them, six men and two boys ; and I gave
them two quartern loaves, two pounds of cheese, and
eight pints of strong beer. The fellows were very
thankful, but the conduct of the landlord and landlady
pleased me exceedingly. When I came to pay my bill,
they had said nothing about my bed, which had been a

very good one ; and, when I asked, why they had not put the bed into the bill, they said they would not charge anything for the bed, since I had been so good to the poor men. Yes, said I, but I must not throw the expense upon you. I had no supper, and I have had no breakfast, and, therefore, I am not called upon to pay for them, but I have had the bed. It ended by my paying for the bed, and coming off, leaving the nutters at their breakfast, and very much delighted with the landlord and his wife ; and I must here observe that I have pretty generally found a good deal of compassion for the poor people to prevail amongst publicans and their wives.

William Cobbett.

THE TRICKSTER

WHEN we reached the inn, we seized our luggage, in the hope of procuring dry garments. Alas ! when I went upstairs, mine might have been the carpet-bag of a merman : it was wet to the inmost core. Soaked to the skin, it was our interest to proceed without delay. We waited on the landlord, and desired a conveyance. The landlord informed us that the only vehicle which he possessed was a phaeton, at present in hire till the evening, and advised us, now that it was Saturday, to remain in his establishment till Monday, when he could send us on comfortably. To wait till Monday, however, would never do. We told the man our story, how for two days we had been the sport of fortune, tossed hither and thither ; but he—feeling he had us in his power—would render no assistance. We wandered out towards the rocks to hold a consultation, and had almost resolved to leave our things where they were, and start on foot, when a son of the innkeeper's joined us. He—whether cognisant of his parent's statement I cannot say—admitted that there were a horse and gig in the stable ; that he knew Mr. M'Ian's place, and offered to drive us to a little fishing village within three miles of it, where our things could be left and a cart sent to bring them up in the evening. The charge was—never mind what !— but we closed with it at once. We entered the inn while our friend went round to the stable to bring the machine to the door ; met the landlord on the stairs, sent an indignant broadside into him, which he received with the utmost coolness. The imperturbable man ! He swallowed our shot like a sandbank, and was nothing the worse.

Alexander Smith.

A YORKSHIRE CHARACTER

THE Donnithorne Arms stood at the entrance of the village, and a small farmyard and stackyard which flanked it, indicating that there was a pretty take of land attached to the inn, gave the traveller a promise of good feed for himself and his horse, which might well console him for the ignorance in which the weather-beaten sign left him as to the heraldic bearings of that ancient family, the Donnithornes. Mr. Casson, the landlord, had been for some time standing at the door with his hands in his pockets, balancing himself on his heels and toes, and looking towards a piece of unenclosed ground with a maple in the middle of it, which he knew to be the destination of certain grave-looking men and women whom he had observed passing at intervals.

Mr. Casson's person was by no means of that common type which can be allowed to pass without description. On a front view it appeared to consist principally of two spheres, bearing about the same relation to each other as the earth and the moon : that is to say, the lower sphere might be said, at a rough guess, to be thirteen times larger than the upper, which naturally performed the function of a mere satellite and tributary. But here the resemblance ceased, for Mr. Casson's head was not at all a melancholy-looking satellite, nor was it a "spotty globe," as Milton has irreverently called the moon ; on the contrary, no head and face could look more sleek and healthy, and its expression, which was chiefly confined to a pair of round and ruddy cheeks, the slight knot and interruptions forming the nose and eyes being scarcely worth mention, was one of jolly contentment, only tempered by that sense of personal dignity which usually made itself felt in his attitude and bearing. This sense of dignity could hardly be considered excessive in a man who had been butler to "the family" for fifteen years, and who, in his present high position, was necessarily very much in contact with his inferiors. How to reconcile his dignity with the satisfaction of his curiosity by walking towards the Green, was the problem that Mr. Casson had been revolving in his mind for the last five minutes ; but when he had partly solved it by taking his hands out of his pockets, and thrusting them into the armholes of his waistcoat, by throwing his head on one side, and providing himself with an air of contemptuous indifference to whatever might fall under his notice, his thoughts were diverted by the approach of the horseman whom we lately saw pausing to have another look at our friend Adam, and who now pulled up at the door of the Donnithorne Arms.

George Eliot.

A CITY HOSTESS

THE house which he frequented was hardly more like a London gin-palace than was that other house in the city which Mr. McRuen honoured with his custom. It was one of those small tranquil shrines of Bacchus in which the god is worshipped perhaps with as constant a devotion, though with less noisy demonstrations of zeal than in his larger and more public temples. None absolutely of the lower orders were encouraged to come thither for oblivion. It had about it nothing inviting to the general eye. No gas illuminations proclaimed its midnight grandeur. No huge folding doors, one set here and another there, gave ingress and egress to a wretched crowd of poverty-stricken midnight revellers. No re-iterated assertions in gaudy letters, each a foot long, as to the peculiar merits of the old tom or Hodge's cream of the valley, seduced the thirsty traveller. The panelling over the window bore the simple announcement, in modest letters of the name of the landlady, Mrs. Davis ; and the same name appeared with equal modesty on the one gas lamp opposite the door.

Mrs. Davis was a widow, and her customers were chiefly people who knew her and frequented her house regularly. Lawyers' clerks, who were either unmarried, or whose married homes were perhaps not so comfort-able as the widow's front parlour ; tradesmen, not of the best sort, glad to get away from the noise of their chil-dren ; young men who had begun the cares of life in ambiguous positions, just on the confines of respectability, and who, finding themselves too weak in flesh to cling on to the round of the ladder above them, were sinking from year to year to lower steps, and depths even below the

level of Mrs. Davis's public-house. To these might be
added some few of a somewhat higher rank in life,
though perhaps of a lower rank of respectability ; young
men who, like Charley Tudor and his comrades, liked
their ease and self-indulgence, and were too indifferent
as to the class of companions against whom they might
rub their shoulders while seeking it.

The " Cat and Whistle," for such was the name of
Mrs. Davis's establishment, had been a house of call for
the young men of the Internal Navigation long before
Charley's time. What first gave rise to the connection
it is not now easy to say ; but Charley had found it, and
had fostered it into a close alliance, which greatly ex-
ceeded any amount of intimacy which existed previously
to his day.   *Anthony Trollope.*

THE HOTEL-KEEPER

MINE Host, whether of the Garter or Star, was
formerly a mighty pleasant fellow, who drank and
jested with his customers, making them pay for his jokes
and potations. In the present day, when the diffusion
of classes renders their fusion more difficult (so that
human beings are stuck up in rows in the world, like
plants in the horticultural gardens, classed and labelled,
stiff as the sticks that intercept them), you pay for the
wine and pastime of your host, but without participating
in the entertainment.

Mine Host of the Hotel is a well-bred gentleman,
whom its inmates never behold from the day when he
inaugurates them in their apartments, with as many bows
as would place an unpopular candidate at the head of the
poll, to that on which, with similar ceremonial, he pre-
sents them their bill—as though a highwayman were to

make three glissades and a coupè, preparatory to his
" Your money or your life ! "

With all their penalties on purse and comfort, however, the London Hotels afford a satisfactory relief from
the cares of temporary housekeeping. The happy
wretch relieved from an East India voyage, the *un*happy
one subpœnæd for a Chancery suit, sees in the gas-lamps
blazing over the door of a fashionable hotel, a beacon of
hope. The courteous welcome of the cringing host and
bowing waiters appears auspicious. Everything comes
with a call. In one's own domicile, a ring of the bell is
an injury inflicted on one or more members of the establishment, who have nothing to gain by answering the
summons. But in an hotel, every ring secures expendi-
ture, varying from twelve-pence to a guinea. Coals, a
sandwich, nay, even a candle to seal a letter, becomes an
item to swell the amount of the narrow folios arrayed
against the peace and purse of the lodger. Satisfy your
conscience, therefore, oh ye who sojourn in hotels, that,
give as much trouble as ye may, none but yourselves are
the worse for it. A hotel-keeper knows how to value a
perpetual ringer of bells.

The nearest approach, by the way, to the ancient
hostel and host of former times, exists, or till the invention of railroads, *did* exist, in certain crack stages of the
old North Road ; inns of good dimension and repute,
where the mail-coach supped or dined, and the great
northern families stopped to sleep ; where portly sir-
loins, huge rounds of beef, hams of inviting complexion,
fowls, supportable even after those of dainty London,
spitch-cocked eels, and compotes of wine-sours, were
evermore forthcoming on demand.

What home-brewed—what home-baked—what cream

cheese—what snow-white linen—what airy chambers—
and what a jolly-faced old gentleman, and comely old
gentlewoman, to bid you welcome. It was a pleasure to
arrive—a pain to depart. The very Boots seemed to
receive his gratuity reluctantly. The waiters *really*
wished you a safe and pleasant journey. The chambermaid, after keeping you in hot water during your stay,
gave you a warm farewell. There was a barn-yard
homeliness of good cheer about the place, how different
from the flashy gaudiness of a station-house albergo !
One experienced a feeling of cordial goodwill towards
the broad-faced old gentleman in velveteens and a buff
waistcoat who, bowing on his doorstep, officiated in such
a spot as—the Hotel-keeper.

Mrs. Gore.

ARRIVAL AND DEPARTURE

HE often said that if he were to choose a place to die in, it should be an inn ; it looking like a pilgrim's going home.

> *Gilbert Burnet (of Archbishop Leighton, who died at the Bell, Warwick Lane).*

Now swelling clouds roll'd on ; the rainy load
Steam'd down our hats, and smok'd along the road ;
When (O blest sight !) a friendly sign we spy'd,
Our spurs are slackened from the horse's side ;
For sure a civil host the house commands,
Upon whose sign this courteous motto stands—
"This is the ancient hand, and eke the pen ;
Here is for horses hay, and meat for men."

> *John Gay.*

"But what do I mean by keeping you broiling in the sun with your horse's bridle in your hand, and you on my own ground ? Do you know where you are ? Why, that great house is my inn, that is, it's my master's, the best fellow in ——. Come along, you and your horse both will find a welcome at my inn."

> *George Borrow.*

BYFEL that, in that seson on a day,
In Southwerk at the Tabbard as I lay,
Redy to wenden on my pilgrimáge
To Canturbury with ful devout coráge,
At night was come into that hostelrie
Wel nyne and twenty in a companye,
Of sondry folk, by áventúre i-fall*e*,
In felowshipe, and pilgryms were they all*e*,
That toward Canturbury wolden ryd*e*.
The chambres and the stables weren wyd*e*,
And wel we weren lodgèd at the best*e*.
And shortly, when the sonn*e* was to rest*e*,
So hadde I spoken with them everyone,
That I was of their felowshipe anon,
And mad*e* covenant erly to aryse,
To take oure weye where I shal you devyse.
But nonetheles, whiles I have tyme and space,
Or that I ferther in this tal*e* pace,
Me thinketh it according to resoún,
To tell*e* you alle the condicioún
Of eche of them, so as it semèd me,
And who they weren, and of what degree.

Geoffrey Chaucer.

ADVICE TO TRAVELLERS

I HAVE heard some Germans complain of the English inns, by the high way, as well for dearness, as for
that they had only roasted meats : But these Germans,
landing at Gravesend, perhaps were injured by those
knaves that flock thither only to deceive strangers, and
use Englishmen no better, and after went from thence to

London, and were there entertained by some ordinary hosts of strangers, returning home little acquainted with English customs. But if these strangers had known the English tongue, or had had an honest guide in their journeys, and had known to live at Rome after the Roman fashion, which they seldom do (using rather Dutch inns and companions), surely they should have found that the world affords not such inns as England hath, either for good and cheap entertainment after the guests' own pleasure, or for humble attendance on passengers, yea, even in very poor villages, where if Curculio of Plautus should see the thatched houses, he would fall into a fainting of his spirits, but if he should smell the variety of meats, his starveling look would be much cheered. For as soon as a passenger comes to an inn, the servants run to him, and one takes his horse and walks him till he be cold, then rubs him, and gives him meat, yet I must say that they are not much to be trusted in this last point, without the eye of the master or his servant to oversee them. Another servant gives the passenger his private chamber, and kindles his fire, the third pulls off his boots, and makes them clean. Then the Host or Hostess visits him, and if he will eat with the Host, or at a common table with others, his meal will cost him six pence, or in some places but four pence (yet this course is less honourable, and not used by Gentlemen) ; but if he will eat in his chamber, he commands what meat he will, according to his appetite, and as much as he thinks fit for him and his company ; yea, the kitchen is open to him, to command the meat to be drest as he best likes ; and when he sits at table, the Host or Hostess will accompany him, or if they have many guests, will at least visit him, taking it for curtesie to be

bid sit down. While he eats, if he have company especially, he shall be offered musick, which he may freely
take or refuse, and if he be solitary, the musicians will
give him the good day with musick in the morning. It
is the custom and no way disgraceful to set up part of
supper for his breakfast. In the evening or in the morning after breakfast (for the common sort use not to dine,
but ride from breakfast to supper time, yet coming early
to the inn for the better resting of their horses) he shall
have a reckoning in writing, and if it seem unreasonable,
the Host will satisfy him, either for the due price, or by
abating part, especially if the servant deceive him any
way, which one of experience will soon find. Having
formerly spoken of ordinary expenses by the high way,
I will now only add that a gentleman and his man shall
spend as much as if he were accompanied with another
gentleman and his man, and if gentlemen will in such
sort join together, to eat at one table, the expenses
will be much diminished. Lastly, a man cannot more
freely command at home in his own house, than he
may do in his inn, and at parting if he give some few
pence to the Chamberlain and Ostler, they wish him a
happy journey.

Fynes Moryson.

THE CARRIERS SET OUT

Rochester. An Inn Yard

Enter a Carrier *with a lantern in his hand.*

First Car. Heigh-ho ! an it be not four by the day,
I'll be hanged : Charles' wain is over the new
chimney, and yet our horse not packed. What, ostler !

Ost. (*Within.*) Anon, anon.

FIRST CAR.   I prithee, Tom, beat Cut's saddle, put a few flocks in the point ; poor jade, is wrung in the withers out of all cess.

Enter another CARRIER.

SEC. CAR.   Peas and beans are as dank here as a dog, and that is the next way to give poor jades the bots : this house is turned upside down since Robin Ostler died.

FIRST CAR.   Poor fellow, never joyed since the price of oats rose ; it was the death of him.

SEC. CAR.   I think this be the most villanous house in all London road for fleas : I am stung like a tench.

FIRST CAR.   Like a tench ! by the mass, there is ne'er a king christen could be better bit than I have been since the first cock.

SEC. CAR.   Why, they will allow us ne'er a jordan, and then we leak in your chimney ; and your chamber-lie breeds fleas like a loach.

FIRST CAR.   What, ostler !   Come away and be hanged !   Come away.

SEC. CAR.   I have a gammon of bacon and two razes of ginger, to be delivered as far as Charing-cross.

FIRST CAR.   God's body ! the turkeys in my pannier are quite starved.   What, ostler !   A plague on thee ! Hast thou never an eye in thy head ?   Canst not hear ? An 'twere not as good deed as drink, to break the pate on thee, I am a very villain.   Come, and be hanged !   Hast no faith in thee ?

Enter GADSHILL.

GADS.   Good morrow, carriers.   What's o'clock ?

FIRST CAR.   I think it be two o'clock.

GADS.   I prithee, lend me thy lantern, to see my gelding in the stable.

First Car. Nay, by God, soft ; I know a trick worth two of that, i' faith.

Gads. I pray thee, lend me thine.

Sec. Car. Ay, when ? Canst tell ? Lend me thy lantern, quoth he ? Marry, I'll see thee hanged first.

Gads. Sirrah, carrier, what time do you mean to come to London ?

Sec. Car. Time enough to go to bed with a candle, I warrant thee. Come, neighbour Mugs, we'll call up the gentlemen ; they will along with company, for they have great charge.

(Exeunt Carriers.)

Gads. What, ho ! chamberlain !

Cham. (*Within.*) At hand, quoth pick-purse.

Gads. That's even as fair as—at hand, quoth the chamberlain ; for thou variest no more from picking of purses than giving direction doth from labouring ; thou layest the plot how.

Enter Chamberlain.

Cham. Good morrow, Master Gadshill. It holds current that I told you yesternight : there's a franklin in the wild of Kent hath brought three hundred marks with him in gold : I heard him tell it to one of his company last night at supper ; a kind of auditor ; one that hath abundance of charge too, God knows what. They are up already, and call for eggs and butter : they will away presently.

Gads. Sirrah, if they meet not with Saint Nicholas' clerks, I'll give thee this neck.

Cham. No, I'll none of it : I pray thee, keep that for the hangman ; for I know thou worshippest Saint Nicholas as truly as a man of falsehood may.

GADS. What talkest thou to me of the hangman ?
If I hang, I'll make a fat pair of gallows ; for if I hang,
old Sir John hangs with me, and thou knowest he is no
starveling. Tut ! there are other Trojans that thou
dreamest not of, the which for sport sake are content to
do the profession some grace ; that would, if matters
should be looked into, for their own credit sake, make all
whole. I am joined with no foot landrakers, no long-
staff sixpenny strikers, none of these mad mustachio
purple-hued malt-worms ; but with nobility and tran-
quillity, burgomasters and great oneyers, such as can
hold in, such as will strike sooner than speak, and speak
sooner than drink, and drink sooner than pray : and yet,
'zounds, I lie ; for they pray continually to their saint,
the commonwealth ; or rather, not pray to her, but prey
on her, for they ride up and down on her and make her
their boots.

CHAM. What, the commonwealth their boots ? Will
she hold out water in foul way ?

GADS. She will, she will ; justice hath liquored her.
We steal as in a castle, cock-sure ; we have the receipt
of fern-seed, we walk invisible.

CHAM. Nay, by my faith, I think you are more be-
holding to the night than to fern-seed for your walking
invisible.

GADS. Give me thy hand : thou shalt have a share in
our purchase, as I am a true man.

CHAM. Nay, rather let me have it, as you are a false
thief.

GADS. Go to ; " homo " is a common name to all
men. Bid the ostler bring my gelding out of the stable.
Farewell, you muddy knave.

William Shakespeare.

A JOYOUS MEETING

LOOK, yonder comes mine hostess, to call us to supper. How now ? Is my brother Peter come ?

Yes, and a friend with him ; they are both glad to hear that you are in these parts, and long to see you, and long to be at supper, for they be very hungry.

Well met, brother Peter ; I heard you and a friend would lodge here to-night, and that hath made me bring my friend to lodge here too. My friend is one that would fain be a brother of the angle. . . . But pray, brother Peter, who is your companion ?

Brother Piscator, my friend is an honest countryman, and his name is Coridon, and he is a downright witty companion, that met me here purposely to be pleasant and eat a trout, and I have not yet wetted my line since we met together ; but I hope to fit him with a trout for his breakfast, for I'll be early up.

Nay, brother, you shall not stay so long : for, look you, here is a trout will fill six reasonable bellies. Come, hostess, dress it presently, and get us what other meat the house will afford, and give us some of your best barley-wine, the good liquor that our honest forefathers did use to drink of ; the drink which preserved their health, and made them live so long, and do so many good deeds.

Izaak Walton.

THE FAVOURED GUEST

HOST.   My guest, my guest, be jovial, I beseech thee.
I have fresh golden guests, guests of the game,
Three coachful ! lords ! and ladies ! new come in ;

And I will cry them to thee, and thee to them,
So I can spring a smile but in this brow,
That, like the rugged Roman alderman,
Old master Gross, surnam'd 'Aγέλαστος,
Was never seen to laugh, but at an ass.

Re-enter FERRET.

FER.   Sir, here's the lady Frampul.

LOV.   How !

FER.   And her train.

Lord Beaufort, and lord Latimer, the colonel
Tipto, with mistress Prue, the chambermaid,
Trundle, the coachman—

LOV.   Stop—discharge the house,
And get my horses ready ; bid the groom
Bring them to the back gate.   (*Exit* FERRET.)

HOST.   What mean you, sir ?

LOV.   To take fair leave, mine host.

HOST.   I hope, my guest,
Though I have talk'd somewhat above my share,
At large, and been in the altitudes, the extravagants,
Neither my self nor any of mine have given you
The cause to quit my house thus on the sudden.

LOV.   No, I affirm it on my faith.   Excuse me
From such a rudeness ; I was now beginning
To taste and love you : and am heartily sorry,
Any occasion should be so compelling,
To urge my abrupt departure thus.   But—
Necessity's a tyrant, and commands it.

HOST.   She shall command me first to fire my
        bush ;
Then break up house : or, if that will not serve,
To break with all the world ; turn country bankrupt
In mine own town, upon the market-day,

And be protested for my butter and eggs,
To the last bodge of oats, and bottle of hay.
Ere you shall leave me I will break my Heart ;
Coach and coach-horses, lords and ladies pack :
All my fresh guests shall stink.   I'll pull my sign
    down,
Convert mine inn to an alms-house, or a spittle
For lazars, or switch-sellers ; turn it to
An academy of rogues ; or give it away
For a free-school to breed up beggars in,
And send them to the canting universities,
Before you leave me !

Ben Jonson.

MOLL FLANDERS DECAMPS

I MADE off with this little booty to Ipswich, and from
thence to Harwich, where I went into an inn, as if I
had newly arrived from Holland, not doubting but I
should make some purchase among the foreigners that
came on shore there ; but I found them generally empty
of things of value, except what was in their portmanteaus
and Dutch hampers, which were always guarded by footmen ; however, I fairly got one of their portmanteaus
one evening out of the chamber where the gentleman
lay, the footman being fast asleep on the bed, and I
suppose very drunk.

The room in which I lodged lay next to the Dutchman's, and having dragged the heavy thing with much
ado out of the chamber into mine, I went out into the
street to see if I could find any possibility of carrying it
off.   I walked about a great while, but could see no
probability either of getting out the thing, or of conveying
away the goods that were in it, the town being so small,

and I a perfect stranger in it ; so I was returning with a resolution to carry it back again, and leave it where I found it. Just at that very moment I heard a man make a noise to some people to make haste, for the boat was going to put off and the tide would be spent. I called the fellow : " What boat is it, friend," said I, " that you belong to ? " " The Ipswich wherry, madam," says he. " When do you go off ? " says I. " This moment, madam," says he ; " do you want to go thither ? " " Yes," said I, " if you can stay till I fetch my things." " Where are your things, madam ? " says he. " At such an inn," said I. " Well, I'll go with you, madam," says he, very civilly, " and bring them for you." " Come away, then," says I, and takes him with me.

The people of the inn were in a great hurry, the packet-boat from Holland being just come in, and two coaches just come also with passengers from London for another packet-boat that was going off for Holland, which coaches were to go back next day with the passengers that were just landed. In this hurry it was that I came to the bar, and paid my reckoning, telling my landlady I had gotten my passage by sea in a wherry. My landlady was very courteous, took my money for the reckoning, but was called away, all the house being in a hurry. So I left her, took the fellow up in my chamber, gave him the trunk, or portmanteau, for it was like a trunk, and wrapped it about with an old apron, and he went directly to his boat with it, and I after him, nobody asking us the least question about it. As for the drunken Dutch footman, he was still asleep, and his master with other foreign gentlemen at supper, and very merry below ; so I went clean off with it to Ipswich.

Daniel Defoe.

LIEUTENANT LISMAHAGO AT THE DOOR

A TALL, meager figure, answering, with his horse, the description of Don Quixote mounted on Rozinante, appeared in the twilight at the inn door, while my aunt and Liddy stood at the window in the dining-room. He wore a coat, the cloth of which had once been scarlet, trimmed with Brandenburgs, now totally deprived of their metal, and he had holster cases and housing of the same stuff and same antiquity. Perceiving ladies at the window above, he endeavoured to dismount with the most graceful air he could assume ; but the hostler neglected to hold the stirrup, when he wheeled off his right foot, and stood with his whole weight on the other, the girth unfortunately gave way, the saddle turned, down came the cavalier to the ground, and his hat and periwig falling off, displayed a headpiece of various colors, patched and plastered in a woeful condition. The ladies, at the window above, shrieked with affright, on the supposition that the stranger had received some notable damage in his fall ; but the greatest injury he had sustained, arose from the dishonour of his descent, aggravated by the disgrace of exposing the condition of his cranium ; for certain plebeians that were about the door, laughed aloud, in the belief that the captain had got either a scald head, or a broken head, both equally opprobrious.

He forthwith leaped up in a fury, and snatching one of his pistols, threatened to put the hostler to death, when another squall from the women checked his resentment. He then bowed to the window, while he kissed the butt-end of his pistol, which he replaced, adjusted his wig in great confusion, and led his horse into the stable. By this time I had come to the door, and could not help gazing at the strange figure that presented itself to my view. He would have measured about six feet in height, had he stood upright ; but he stooped very much, was very narrow in the shoulders, and very thick in the calves of the legs, which were cased in black spatter-dashes. As for his thighs, they were long and slender, like those of a grasshopper ; his face was at least half a yard in length, brown and shrivelled, with projecting cheek-bones, little grey eyes of a greenish hue, a large hook nose, a pointed chin, a mouth from ear to ear, very ill furnished with teeth, and a high, narrow forehead, well furrowed with wrinkles. His horse was exactly in the style of its rider ; a resurrection of dry bones, which (as we afterwards learned) he valued exceedingly, as the only present he had ever received in his life.

Tobias Smollett.

ARRIVAL OF THE BEAUX
An Inn at Lichfield.
Enter Boniface, *running.*

BON. Chamberlain ! Maid ! Cherry ! daughter Cherry ! All asleep ? All dead ?

Enter Cherry, *running.*

CHER. Here ! Here ! Why d'ye bawl so, father ? D'ye think we have no ears ?

BON. You deserve to have none, you young minx ! The company of the Warrington coach has stood in the hall this hour, and nobody to show them to their chambers.

CHER. And let 'em wait, father ; there's neither red-coat in the coach, nor footman behind it.

Bon. But they threaten to go to another inn to-night.

Cher. That they dare not, for fear the coachman should overturn them to-morrow. Coming ! Coming ! Here's the London coach arrived.

(Exit.)

Enter Aimwell *in riding habit,* Archer *as Footman, carrying a portmantle.*

Bon. This way, this way, gentlemen !

Aim. *(To* Archer.) Set down the things ; go to the stable, and see my horses well rubbed.

Ar. I shall, sir. *(Exit.)*

Aim. You're my landlord, I suppose ?

Bon. Yes, sir ; I'm old Will Boniface, pretty well known upon this road, as the saying is.

Aim. O Mr. Boniface, your servant !

Bon. O sir ! What will your honour please to drink, as the saying is ?

Aim. I have heard your town of Lichfield much famed for ale ; I think I'll taste that.

Bon. Sir, I have now in my cellar ten tun of the best ale in Staffordshire ; 'tis smooth as oil, sweet as milk, clear as amber, and strong as brandy ; and will be just fourteen year old the fifth day of next March, old style.

Aim. You're very exact, I find, in the age of your ale.

Bon. As punctual, sir, as I am in the age of my children. I'll show you such ale ! Here, tapster, broach number 1706, as the saying is. Sir, you shall taste my Anno Domini. I have lived in Lichfield, man and boy, above fifty-eight years, and, I believe, have not consumed eight-and-fifty ounces of meat.

2

AIM. At a meal, you mean, if one may guess your sense by your bulk.

BON. Not in my life, sir. I have fed purely upon ale. I have eat my ale, drank my ale, and I always sleep upon ale. . . . Now, sir, you shall see ! Your worship's health. Ha ! delicious, delicious ! Fancy it burgundy, only fancy it, and 'tis worth ten shillings a quart.

AIM. 'Tis confounded strong.

BON. Strong ! It must be so, or how should we be strong that drink it ?

AIM. And have you lived so long upon this ale, landlord ?

BON. Eight-and-fifty years, upon my credit, sir ; but it killed my wife, poor woman, as the saying is.

AIM. How came that to pass ?

BON. I don't know how, sir ; she would not let the ale take its natural course, sir ; she was for qualifying it every now and then with a dram, as the saying is ; and an honest gentleman that came this way from Ireland made her a present of a dozen bottles of usquebaugh— but the poor woman was never well after. But, howe'er, I was obliged to the gentleman, you know. . . . What will your worship please to have for supper ?

AIM. What have you got ?

BON. Sir, we have a delicate piece of beef in the pot, and a pig at the fire.

AIM. Good supper-meat, I must confess. I can't eat beef, landlord.

BON. Please to bespeak something else ; I have everything in the house.

AIM. Have you any veal ?

BON. Veal, sir ! We had a delicate loin of veal on Wednesday last.

AIM.   Have you got any fish or wildfowl ?

BON.   As for fish, truly, sir, we are an inland town and indifferently provided with fish, that's the truth on't ; and then for wildfowl—we have a delicate couple of rabbits.

AIM.   Get me the rabbits fricasseed.

BON.   Fricasseed ! Lard, sir, they'll eat much better smothered with onions.

AIM.   Well, landlord, what you please.

George Farquhar.

THE MAN OF FEELING IN TROUBLE

HARLEY stood in the attitude of hesitation ; which she, interpreting to her advantage, repeated her request, and endeavoured to force a leer of invitation into her countenance. He took her arm, and they walked on to one of those obsequious taverns in the neighbourhood, where the dearness of the wine is a discharge in full for the character of the house. From what impulse he did this we do not mean to enquire ; as it has ever been against our nature to search for motives where bad ones are to be found. They entered, and a waiter showed them a room, and placed a bottle of claret on the table.

Harley filled the lady's glass : which she had no sooner tasted, than dropping it on the floor, and eagerly catching his arm, her eye grew fixed, her lip assumed a clayey whiteness, and she fell back lifeless in her chair.

Harley started from his seat, and, catching her in his arms, supported her from falling to the ground, looking wildly at the door, as if he wanted to run for assistance, but durst not leave the miserable creature. It was not till some minutes after that it occurred to him to ring the bell, which at last, however, he thought of, and rung with repeated violence even after the waiter appeared. Luckily the waiter had his senses somewhat more about him ; and snatching up a bottle of water, which stood on a buffet at the end of the room, he sprinkled it over the hands and face of the dying figure before him. She began to revive, and, with the assistance of some hartshorn drops, which Harley now for the first time drew from his pocket, was able to desire the waiter to bring her a crust of bread, of which she swallowed some mouthfuls with the appearance of the keenest hunger. The waiter withdrew : when turning to Harley, sobbing at the same time, and shedding tears, " I am sorry, sir," said she, " that I should have given you so much trouble ; but you will pity me when I tell you that till now I have not tasted a morsel these two days past."—He fixed his eyes on hers—every circumstance but the last was forgotten ; and he took her hand with as much respect as if she had been a duchess. It was ever the privilege of misfortune to be revered by him. " Two days ! " said he ; " and I have fared sumptuously every day ! " He was reaching to the bell ; she understood his meaning and prevented him. " I beg, sir," said she, " that you would give yourself no more trouble about a wretch who does not wish to live ; but at present I could not eat a bit." He rung and ordered a chair. She burst into tears : " Your generosity, sir, is abused ; to bestow it on me is to take it from the virtuous." " No more of that," answered Harley ; " there is virtue in these tears ; let the fruit of them be virtue."—Here the waiter entered, and told them the chair was at the door ; the lady informed Harley of her lodgings, and he promised to wait on her at ten next morning.

He led her to the chair, and returned to clear with the waiter, without ever once reflecting that he had no money in his pocket. He was ashamed to make an excuse ; yet an excuse must be made ; he was beginning to frame one, when the waiter cut him short by telling him that he could not run scores ; but that, if he would leave his watch, or any other pledge, it would be as safe as if it lay in his pocket. Harley jumped at the proposal, and pulling out his watch, delivered it into his hands immediately, and having, for once, had the precaution to take a note of the lodging he intended to visit next morning, sallied forth with a blush of triumph on his face, without taking notice of the sneer of the waiter, who, twirling the watch in his hand, made him a profound bow at the door, and whispered to a girl, who stood in the passage, something, in which the word CULLY was honoured with a particular emphasis.

Henry Mackenzie.

SOPHIA WESTERN REACHES UPTON

AND now arrived another post-boy at the gate ; upon which Susan, being ordered out, returned, introducing two young women in riding habits, one of which was so very richly laced, that Partridge and the post-boy instantly started from their chairs, and my landlady fell to her courtsies, and her ladyships, with great eagerness.

The lady in the rich habit said, with a smile of great condescension, " If you will give me leave, madam, I will warm myself a few minutes at your kitchen fire, for it is really very cold ; but I must insist on disturbing no one from his seat." This was spoken on account of Partridge, who had retreated to the other end of the room, struck with the utmost awe and astonishment at the splendour of the lady's dress. Indeed, she had a much better title to respect than this ; for she was one of the most beautiful creatures in the world.

The lady earnestly desired Partridge to return to his seat ; but could not prevail. She then pulled off her gloves, and displayed to the fire two hands, which had every property of snow in them, except that of melting. Her companion, who was indeed her maid, likewise pulled off her gloves, and discovered what bore an exact resemblance, in cold and colour, to a piece of frozen beef.

" I wish, madam," quoth the latter, " your ladyship would not think of going any farther to-night. I am terribly afraid your ladyship will not be able to bear the fatigue."

" Why sure," cries the landlady, " her lady-ship's honour can never intend it. O, bless me ! farther to-night, indeed ! let me beseech your ladyship not to think on't——But, to be sure, your ladyship can't. What will your honour be pleased to have for supper ? I have mutton of all kinds, and some nice chicken."

" I think, madam," said the lady, " it would be rather breakfast than supper ; but I can't eat anything ; and if I stay, shall only lie down for an hour or two. However, if you please, madam, you may get me a little sack whey, made very small and thin."

" Yes, madam," cries the mistress of the house, " I have some excellent white wine."—" You have no sack, then ? " says the lady. " Yes, an't please your honour, I have ; I may challenge the country for that—but let me beg your ladyship to eat something."

" Upon my word, I can't eat a morsel," answered the lady ; " and I shall be much obliged to you if you will please to get my apartment ready as soon as possible ; for I am resolved to be on horseback again in three hours."

" Why, Susan," cries the landlady, " is there a fire lit yet in the Wild-goose ? I am sorry, madam, all my best rooms are full. Several people of the first quality are now in bed. Here's a great young squire, and many other great gentlefolks of quality." Susan answered, " That the Irish gentlemen were got into the Wild-goose."

" Was ever anything like it ? " says the mistress ; " why the devil would you not keep some of the best rooms for the quality, when you know scarce a day passes without some calling here ? If they be gentlemen, I am certain, when they know it is for her ladyship, they will get up again."

" Not upon my account," says the lady ; " I will have no person disturbed for me. If you have a room that is commonly decent, it will serve me very well, though it be never so plain. I beg, madam, you will not give yourself so much trouble on my account." " O, madam ! " cries the other, " I have several very good rooms for that matter, but none good enough for your honour's ladyship. However, as you are so condescending to take up with the best I have, do, Susan, get a fire in the Rose this minute. Will your ladyship be pleased to go up now, or stay till the fire is lighted ? " " I think I have sufficiently warmed myself," answered the lady ; " so, if you please, I will go now ; I am afraid I have kept people, and particularly that gentleman (meaning Partridge), too long in the cold already. Indeed, I cannot bear to think of keeping any person from the fire this dreadful weather."—She then departed with her maid, the landlady marching with two lighted candles before her.

Henry Fielding.

A GERMAN FOOT-TRAVELLER

I WAS now again in Windsor ; and found myself not far from the castle, opposite to a very capital inn, where I saw many officers and several persons of consequence going in and out. And here, at this inn, contrary to all expectation, I was received by the landlord, with great civility, and even kindness ; very contrary to the haughty and insolent airs, which the upstart at the other, and his jackanapes of a waiter, there thought fit to give themselves.

However, it seemed to be my fate to be still a scandal, and an eye-sore to all the waiters. The maid, by the order of her master, shewed me a room where I might adjust my dress a little ; but I could hear her mutter and grumble, as she went along with me. Having put myself a little to rights, I went down into the coffee-room, which is immediately at the entrance of the house, and told the landlord, that I thought I wished to have yet one more walk. On this, he obligingly directed me to stroll down a pleasant field behind his house, at the foot of which, he said, I should find the Thames, and a good bathing place.

On my return, the waiters (who from my appearance, too probably expected but a trifling reward for their attentions to me) received me gruffly, and as if they were sorry to see me again. This was not all : I had the additional mortification to be again roughly accosted by the cross maid, who had before shewn me to the bed-chamber ; and who, dropping a kind of half courtesy, with a suppressed laugh, sneeringly told me, I might look out for another lodging, as I could not sleep there, since the room she had by mistake shewn me, was already engaged. It can hardly be necessary to tell you, that I loudly protested against this sudden change. At length the landlord came and I appealed to him : and he with great courtesy, immediately desired another room to be shewn me ; in which, however, there were two beds ; so that I was obliged to admit a companion. Thus was I very near being a second time turned out of an inn.

Directly under my room, was the tap-room : from which I could plainly hear too much of the conversation of some low people, who were drinking and singing songs, in which, as far as I could understand them, there were many passages at least as vulgar and nonsensical as ours.

This company, I guessed, consisted chiefly of soldiers, and low fellows. I was hardly well lulled to sleep by this hurly-burly, when my chum came stumbling into the room and against my bed. At length, though not without some difficulty, he found his own bed ; into which he threw himself just as he was, without staying to pull off either cloaths or boots.

As I was going away, the waiter who had served me with so very ill a grace, placed himself on the stairs and said, " Pray remember the waiter ! " I gave him three half-pence : on which he saluted me with the heartiest *G—d d—m you*, sir ! I had ever heard. At the door stood the cross maid, who also accosted me with—" Pray remember the chamber-maid ! " Yes, yes, said I, I shall long remember your most ill-mannered behaviour and shameful incivility ; and so I gave her nothing. I hope she was stung and nettled at my reproof : however she strove to stifle her anger by a contemptuous, loud horse laugh. Thus, as I left Windsor, I was literally followed by abuse and curses.

Carl Philip Moritz.

CAPTAIN CROWE ARRIVES

THE knight Sir Launcelot and the novice Crowe, retreated with equal order and expedition to the distance of half a league from the field of battle, where the former, halting, proposed to make a lodgment in a very decent house of entertainment, distinguished by the sign of St. George of Cappadocia encountering the dragon, an achievement in which temporal and spiritual chivalry were happily reconciled. Two such figures alighting at the inn gate did not pass through the yard unnoticed and unadmired by the guests and attendants, some of whom fairly took to their heels, on the supposition that these outlandish creatures were the avant-couriers or heralds of a French invasion. The fears and doubts, however, of those who ventured to stay were soon dispelled, when our hero accosted them in the English tongue, and with the most courteous demeanour desired to be shown into an apartment.

Had Captain Crowe been spokesman, perhaps their suspicions would not have so quickly subsided, for he was, in reality, a very extraordinary novice, not only in chivalry, but also in his external appearance, and particularly in those dialects of the English language which are used by the terrestrial animals of this kingdom. He desired the hostler to take his horse in tow, and bring him to his moorings in a safe riding.   He ordered the waiter, who showed them into a parlour, to bear a hand, ship his oars, mind his helm, and bring alongside a short allowance of brandy or grog, that he might cant a slug into his bread-room, for there was such a heaving and pitching, that he believed he should shift his ballast. The fellow understood no part of this address but the word brandy, at mention of which he disappeared. . . . Our knight detached one of the postboys to the field of action for intelligence concerning Mr. Clarke and squire Timothy, and, in the interim, desired to know the particulars of Crowe's adventures since he parted from him at the White Hart.

A connected relation, in plain English, was what he had little reason to expect from the novice, who, nevertheless, exerted his faculties to the utmost for his satisfaction.   He gave him to understand that in steering his course to Birmingham, where he thought of fitting himself with tackle, he had fallen in, by accident, at a public-house, with a itinerant tinker, in the very act of mending a kettle ; that, seeing him do his business like an able workman, he had applied to him for advice, and the tinker, after having considered the subject, had undertaken to make him such a suit of armour as neither sword nor lance should penetrate ; that they adjourned to the next town, where the leather coat, the plates of tinned iron, the lance and the broadsword were purchased, together with a copper saucepan, which the artist was now at work upon in converting it to a shield ; but the captain, being impatient to begin his career of chivalry, had accommodated himself with a pot-lid, and taken to the highway.

Tobias Smollett.

NOW COMES THE RECKONING

BEHOLD him then, renew'd by rest,
His chin well shav'd, his peruke dress'd,
Conning with solemn air the news,
His welcome breakfast to amuse ;
And when the well-fed meal was o'er,
Grizzle was order'd to the door ;
Betty was also told to say
The mighty sum there was to pay ;
Betty, obedient to his will,
Her curtsey makes, and brings the bill.
Down the long page he cast his eye,
Then shook his head and heav'd a sigh.
" What ! am I doom'd, where'er I go,
In all I meet to find a foe ?
Where'er I wander to be cheated,
To be bamboozled and ill-treated ! "
Thus, as he read each item o'er,
The hostess op'd the parlour door ;
When Syntax rose in solemn state,
And thus began the fierce debate.

SYNTAX.

" Good woman ; here, your bill retake,
And prithee, some abatement make ;
I could not such demands afford,
Were I a Bishop or a Lord ;
The paper fills me with affright ;
I surely do not read it right ;
For at the bottom here I see
The enormous total—one pound three ! "

HOSTESS.

" The charges all are fairly made ;
If you will eat, I must be paid.

My bills have never found reproaches
From Lords and Ladies in their coaches.
This house, that's call'd the Royal Crown,
Is the first inn throughout the town ;
The best of gentry, every day,
Become my guests, and freely pay.
I gave you all my choicest cheer,
The best of meat, the best of beer ;
And then you snor'd yourself to rest
In the best bed—I say the best.
You've had such tea as few can boast,
With a whole loaf turn'd into toast."

SYNTAX.

" And for your beef and beer and tea,
You kindly charge me—one pound three."

HOSTESS.

" Think you, besides, there's nought to pay
For all your horse's corn and hay ?
And ointments too, to cure the ail
Of her cropp'd ears and mangled tail ? "

SYNTAX.

" I wish the wight would bring the shears
Which dock'd that tail and cropp'd those ears,
And just exert the self-same skill
To crop and dock your monstrous bill !
But I'm in haste to get away,
Though one pound three I will not pay ;
So if you'll take one half th'amount,
We'll quickly settle the account.
There is your money, do you see ?
And let us part in charity."

HOSTESS.

" Well, as a charitable deed,

I'll e'en consent, so mount your steed,
And on your journey straight proceed."

The Doctor smil'd, the bill was paid,
The hostess left him to the maid ;
When Betty stood in humble guise,
With expectation in her eyes,
That he was surely so good-hearted,
To give her something ere they parted.

William Combe.

JOSEPH ANDREWS HELD TO RANSOM

THE sun had now been risen some hours, when
Joseph, finding his leg surprisingly recovered, proposed to walk forwards ; but when they were all ready to
set out, an accident a little retarded them. This was no
other than the reckoning, which amounted to seven
shillings ; no great sum if we consider the immense
quantity of ale which Mr. Adams poured in. Indeed,
they had no objection to the reasonableness of the bill, but
many to the probability of paying it ; for the fellow who
had taken poor Fanny's purse had unluckily forgot to
return it. So that the account stood thus :

	£	s.	d.
Mr. Adams and company, Dr. . .	0	7	0
In Mr. Adams's pocket . .	0	0	$6\frac{1}{2}$
In Mr. Joseph's . . .	0	0	0
In Mrs. Fanny's . . .	0	0	0
Balance . . .	0	6	$5\frac{1}{2}$

They stood silent some few minutes, staring at each other,
when Adams whipt out on his toes, and asked the hostess,
" If there was no clergyman in that parish ? " She

answered, " There was."—" Is he wealthy ? " replied
he ; to which she likewise answered in the affirmative.
Adams then snapping his fingers returned overjoyed to
his companions, crying out, " Heureka, Heureka " ;
which not being understood, he told them in plain English, " They need give themselves no trouble, for he had
a brother in the parish who would defray the reckoning,
and that he would just step to his house and fetch the
money, and return to them instantly."

When he came back to the inn he found Joseph and
Fanny sitting together. They were so far from thinking
his absence long, as he had feared they would, that they
never once missed or thought of him. Indeed, I have
been often assured by both, that they spent these hours in
a most delightful conversation ; but, as I never could
prevail on either to relate it, so I cannot communicate it
to the reader.

Adams acquainted the lovers with the ill success of his
enterprise. They were all greatly confounded, none
being able to propose any method of departing, till Joseph
at last advised calling in the hostess, and desiring her to
trust them ; which Fanny said she despaired of her
doing, as she was one of the sourest-faced women she had
ever beheld.

But she was agreeably disappointed ; for the hostess
was no sooner asked the question than she readily agreed ;
and, with a curtsy and smile, wished them a good journey.
However, lest Fanny's skill in physiognomy should be
called in question, we will venture to assign one reason
which might probably incline her to this confidence and
good-humour. When Adams said he was going to visit
his brother, he had unwittingly imposed on Joseph and
Fanny, who both believed he had meant his natural

brother, and not his brother in divinity, and had so informed the hostess, on her inquiry after him. Now Mr. Trulliber had, by his professions of piety, by his gravity, austerity, reserve, and the opinion of his great wealth, so great an authority in his parish, that they all lived in the utmost fear and apprehension of him. It was therefore no wonder that the hostess, who knew it was in his option whether she should ever sell another mug of drink, did not dare to affront his supposed brother by denying him credit.

They were now just on their departure when Adams recollected he had left his great-coat and hat at Mr. Trulliber's. As he was not desirous of renewing his visit, the hostess herself, having no servant at home, offered to fetch them.

This was an unfortunate expedient ; for the hostess was soon undeceived in the opinion she had entertained of Adams, whom Trulliber abused in the grossest terms, especially when he heard he had had the assurance to pretend to be his near relation.

At her return, therefore, she entirely changed her note. She said, " Folks might be ashamed of travelling about, and pretending to be what they were not. That taxes were high, and for her part she was obliged to pay for what she had ; she could not therefore possibly, nor would she, trust anybody ; no, not her own father. That money was never scarcer, and she wanted to make up a sum. That she expected, therefore, they should pay their reckoning before they left the house."

Adams was now greatly perplexed ; but, as he knew that he could easily have borrowed such a sum in his own parish, and as he knew he would have lent it himself to any mortal in distress, so he took fresh courage, and sallied out all round the parish, but to no purpose ; he returned as pennyless as he went, groaning and lamenting that it was possible, in a country professing Christianity, for a wretch to starve in the midst of his fellow-creatures who abounded.

Whilst he was gone, the hostess, who stayed as a sort of guard with Joseph and Fanny, entertained them with the goodness of parson Trulliber. And, indeed, he had not only a very good character as to other qualities in the neighbourhood, but was reputed a man of great charity ; for, though he never gave a farthing, he had always that word in his mouth.

Adams was no sooner returned the second time than the storm grew exceedingly high, the hostess declaring, among other things, that, if they offered to stir without paying her, she would soon overtake them with a warrant.

There chanced (for Adams had not cunning enough to contrive it) to be at that time in the alehouse a fellow who had been formerly a drummer in an Irish regiment, and now travelled the country as a pedlar. This man, having attentively listened to the discourse of the hostess, at last took Adams aside, and asked him what the sum was for which they were detained. As soon as he was informed, he sighed, and said, " He was sorry it was so much ; for that he had no more than six shillings and sixpence in his pocket, which he would lend them with all his heart." Adams gave a caper, and cried out, " It would do ; for that he had sixpence himself." And thus these poor people, who could not engage the compassion of riches and piety, were at length delivered out of their distress by the charity of a poor pedlar.

Henry Fielding.

M 2

BORROW TAKES THE ROAD

I THEN proceeded to the stable, told the horse we were bound on an expedition, and giving him a feed of corn, left him to discuss it, and returned to the bar-room to have a little farewell chat with the landlord, and at the same time to drink with him a farewell glass of ale. Whilst we were talking and drinking, the niece came and joined us : she was a decent, sensible young woman, who appeared to take a great interest in her uncle, whom she regarded with a singular mixture of pride and dis-approbation—pride for the renown which he had acquired by his feats of old, and disapprobation for his late impru-dences. She said that she hoped that his misfortunes would be a warning to him to turn more to his God than he had hitherto done, and to give up cock-fighting and other low-life practices. To which the landlord replied, that with respect to cock-fighting he intended to give it up entirely, being determined no longer to risk his capital upon birds, and with respect to his religious duties, he should attend the church of which he was churchwarden at least once a quarter, adding, however, that he did not intend to become either canter or driveller, neither of which characters would befit a publican surrounded by such customers as he was, and that to the last day of his life he hoped to be able to make use of his fists. After a stay of about two hours I settled accounts, and having bridled and saddled my horse, and strapped on my valise, I mounted, shook hands with the landlord and his niece, and departed, notwithstanding that they both entreated me to tarry until the evening, it being then the heat of the day.

George Borrow.

THE PLEASURES OF ARRIVAL

I GRANT there is one subject on which it is pleasant
to talk on a journey, and that is, what one shall have
for supper when we get to our inn at night. The open
air improves this sort of conversation or friendly alterca-
tion, by setting a keener edge on appetite. Every mile
of the road heightens the flavour of the viands we expect
at the end of it. How fine it is to enter some old town,
walled and turreted, just at approach of nightfall, or to
come to some straggling village, with the lights streaming
through the surrounding gloom ; and then, after inquiring for the best entertainment that the place affords,
to " take one's ease at one's inn " ! These eventful
moments in our lives' history are too precious, too full of
solid heartfelt happiness to be frittered and dribbled away
in imperfect sympathy. I would have them all to myself,
and drain them to the last drop ; they will do to talk of
or to write about afterwards. What a delicate speculation
it is, after drinking whole goblets of tea—the cups that
cheer, but not inebriate—and letting the fumes ascend
into the brain, to sit considering what we shall have for
supper—eggs and a rasher, a rabbit smothered in onions,
or an excellent veal cutlet ! Sancho, in such a situation,
once fixed on cow-heel ; and his choice, though he
could not help it, is not to be disparaged. Then, in the
intervals of pictured scenery and Shandean contemplation, to catch the preparation and the stir in the kitchen
(getting ready for the gentleman in the parlour). *Procul,
O procul este profani !* These hours are sacred to silence
and to musing, to be treasured up in the memory, and to
feed the source of smiling thoughts hereafter. I would
not waste them in idle talk ; or if I must have the inte-

grity of fancy broken in upon, I would rather it were by a
stranger than a friend.   A stranger takes his hue and
character from the time and place ;   he is a part of the
furniture and costume of an inn.   If he is a Quaker, or
from the West Riding of Yorkshire, so much the better.
I do not even try to sympathise with him, and he breaks
no squares.   (How I love to see the camps of the gypsies,
and to sigh my soul into that sort of life.   If I express
this feeling to another, he may qualify and spoil it with
some objection.)   I associate nothing with my travelling
companion but present objects and passing events.   In
his ignorance of me and my affairs, I in a manner forget
myself.   But a friend reminds one of other things, rips
up old grievances, and destroys the abstraction of the
scene.   He comes in ungraciously between us and our
imaginary character.   Something is dropped in the course
of conversation that gives a hint of your profession and
pursuits ;   or from having someone with you that knows
the less sublime portions of your history, it seems that
other people do.   You are no longer a citizen of the
world ;   but your " unhoused free condition is put into
circumspection and confine."   The incognito of an inn
is one of its striking privileges—" lord of one's self, un-
cumbered with a name."   Oh ! it is great to shake off
the trammels of the world and of public opinion—to lose
our importunate, tormenting, everlasting personal identity in the elements of nature, and become the creature
of the moment, clear of all ties—to hold to the universe
only by a dish of sweetbreads, and to owe nothing but
the score of the evening—and no longer seeking for
applause and meeting with contempt, to be known by no
other title than *the Gentleman in the parlour !*   One may
take one's choice of all characters in this romantic state

of uncertainty as to one's real pretensions, and become indefinitely respectable and negatively right-worshipped. We baffle prejudice and disappoint conjecture ; and from being so to others, begin to be objects of curiosity and wonder even to ourselves. We are no more those hackneyed common-places that we appear in the world ; an inn restores us to the level of nature, and quits scores with society ! I have certainly spent some enviable hours at inns—sometimes when I have been left entirely to myself, and have tried to solve some metaphysical problem, as once at Witham Common, where I found out the proof that likeness is not a case of the association of ideas—at other times, when there have been pictures in the room, as at St. Neot's (I think it was), where I first met with Gribelin's engravings of the Cartoons, into which I entered at once, and at a little inn on the borders of Wales, where there happened to be hanging some of Westall's drawings, which I compared trium-phantly (for a theory that I had, not for the admired artist) with the figure of a girl who had ferried me over the Severn, standing up in a boat between me and the twilight—at other times I might mention luxuriating in books, with a peculiar interest in this way, as I remember sitting up half the night to read " Paul and Virginia," which I picked up at an inn at Bridgwater, after being drenched in the rain all day ; and at the same place I got through two volumes of Madame D'Arblay's " Camilla." It was on the 10th of April, 1798, that I sat down to a volume of the " New Eloise," at the inn at Llangollen, over a bottle of sherry and a cold chicken.

William Hazlitt.

A SUNDAY ARRIVAL

THERE was, in the days of which I write, an old-fashioned custom on the English road, which I suspect is now obsolete, or practised only by the vulgar. Journeys of length being made on horseback, and, of course, by brief stages, it was usual always to make a halt on the Sunday in some town where the traveller might attend divine service, and his horse have the benefit of the day of rest, the institution of which is as humane to our brute labourers as profitable to ourselves. A counterpart to this decent practice, and a remnant of old English hospitality, was, that the landlord of a principal inn laid aside his character of publican on the seventh day, and invited the guests who chanced to be within his walls to take a part of his family beef and pudding. This invitation was usually complied with by all whose distinguished rank did not induce them to think compliance a derogation ; and the proposal of a bottle of wine after dinner, to drink the landlord's health was the only recompense ever offered or accepted.

I was born a citizen of the world, and my inclination led me into all scenes where my knowledge of mankind could be enlarged ; I had, besides, no pretensions to sequester myself on the score of superior dignity, and therefore seldom failed to accept of the Sunday's hospitality of mine host, whether of the Garter, Lion, or Bear. The honest publican, dilated into additional consequence by a sense of his own importance, while presiding among the guests on whom it was his ordinary duty to attend, was in himself an entertaining spectacle ; and around his genial orbit, other planets of inferior consequence performed their revolutions. The wits and humorists, the distinguished worthies of the town or village, the apothe-cary, the attorney, even the curate himself, did not dis-dain to partake of this hebdomadal festivity. The guests assembled from different quarters, and following different professions, formed, in language, manners and senti-ments, a curious contrast to each other, not indifferent to those who desired to possess a knowledge of mankind in its varieties.

It was on such a day, and such an occasion, that my timorous acquaintance and I were about to grace the board of the ruddy-faced host of the Black Bear, in the town of Darlington, and bishopric of Durham, when our landlord informed us, with a sort of apologetic tone, that there was a Scotch gentleman to dine with us.

" A gentleman ?—what sort of a gentleman ? " said my companion, somewhat hastily, his mind, I suppose, running on gentlemen of the pad, as they were then termed.

" Why, a Scotch sort of a gentleman, as I said before," returned mine host ; " they are all gentle, ye mun know, though they ha' narra shirt to back ; but this is a decentish hallion—a canny North Briton as e'er cross'd Berwick bridge—I trow he's a dealer in cattle."

" Let us have his company, by all means," answered my companion ; and then, turning to me, he gave vent to the tenor of his own reflections. " I respect the Scotch, sir ; I love and honour the nation for their sense of morality. Men talk of their filth and their poverty : but commend me to sterling honesty, though clad in rags, as the poet saith. I have been credibly assured, sir, by men on whom I can depend, that there was never known such a thing in Scotland as a highway robbery."

"That's because they have nothing to lose," said mine host, with the chuckle of a self-applauding wit.

"No, no, landlord," answered a strong deep voice behind him, "it's e'en because your English gaugers and supervisors, that you have sent down benorth the Tweed, have taen up the trade of thievery over the heads of the native professors."

"Well said, Mr. Campbell!" answered the landlord; "I did nat think thoud'st been sae near us, mon. But thou kens I'm an outspoken Yorkshire tyke—And how go markets in the south?"

"Even in the ordinar," replied Mr. Campbell; "wise folks buy and sell, and fools are bought and sold."

"But wise men and fools both eat their dinner," answered our jolly entertainer; "and here a comes— as prime a buttock of beef as e'er hungry mon stuck fork in."

So saying, he eagerly whetted his knife, assumed his seat of empire at the head of the board, and loaded the plates of his sundry guests with his good cheer.

Sir Walter Scott.

RECEPTION AT THE SHREWSBURY LION

MY plan had been, to walk over the border into England, as far as Shrewsbury (distant from Oswestry, I think, about eighteen miles), and there to ascend any of the heavy stages which would convey me cheaply to Birmingham—the grand focus to which all the routes of England in its main central area converge. Any such plan moved on the assumption that rain would be falling steadily and heavily—a reasonable assumption at the close of November. But, in the possible event of

fair weather lasting over four or five days, what should
prevent me from traversing the whole distance on foot ?
It is true, that the aristocratic scowl of the landlord
might be looked for as a customary salutation at the
close of each day's journey ; but, unless at solitary post-
ing-houses, this criminal fact of having advanced by base
pedestrian methods, known only to patriarchs of older
days and to modern ' *tramps* ' (so they are called in solemn
acts of Parliament), is easily expiated and cleansed, by
distributing your dust, should you fortunately have any
to show, amongst the streets that you have invaded as a
stranger.   Happily the scandal of pedestrianism is in one
respect more hopefully situated than that of scrofula or
leprosy ; it is not in any case written in your face. The
man who is guilty of pedestrianism, on entering any town
whatever, by the simple artifice of diving into the crowds
of those untainted by that guilt, will emerge, for all prac-
tical purposes, washed and re-baptised. The landlord,
indeed, of any one inn knows that you did not reach *him*
on horseback, or in a carriage ; but you may have been
visiting for weeks at the house of some distinguished
citizen, whom it might be dangerous to offend ; and
you may even be favourably known at some other inn.
Else, as a general imputation, undoubtedly pedestrianism,
in the estimate of English landlords, carries with it the
most awful shadow and shibboleth of the pariah. . . .

It was not late, but it was at least two hours after
nightfall, when I reached Shrewsbury. Was I not liable
to the suspicion of pedestrianism ? Certainly I was : but,
even if my criminality had been more unequivocally
attested than it could be under the circumstances, still
there is a *locus penitentiæ* in such a case. Surely a man
may repent of *any* crime ; and therefore of pedestrianism.

I might have erred ; and a court of *pié poudré* (dusty
foot) might have found the evidence of my crime on my
shoes. Yet secretly I might be forming good resolutions
to do so no more. Certainly it looked like this, when I
announced myself as a passenger booked for that night's
mail. This character at once installed me as rightfully
a guest of the inn, however profligate a life I might have
previously led as a pedestrian. Accordingly I was
received with special courtesy ; and it so happened that
I was received with something even like pomp. Four
wax-lights carried before me by obedient mutes, these
were but ordinary honours, meant (as old experience had
instructed me) for the first engineering step towards
affecting a lodgment upon the stranger's purse. In fact,
the wax-lights are used by innkeepers, both abroad and
at home, to " try the range of their guns." If the
stranger submits quietly, as a good anti-pedestrian ought
surely to do, and fires no counter gun by way of protest,
then he is recognised at once as passively within range,
and amenable to orders. I have always looked upon this
fine of five or seven shillings (for wax that you do not
absolutely need) as a sort of inaugural honorarium
entrance-money, what in jails used to be known as
smart money, proclaiming me to be a man *comme il faut ;*
and no toll in this world of tolls do I pay so cheerfully.

Thomas de Quincey.

TOM SMART ON MARLBORO' DOWNS

TOM cast a hasty glance at the upper part of the
house as he threw the reins to the hostler, and stuck
the whip in the box. It was a strange old place, built of
a kind of shingle, inlaid, as it were, with cross-beams,
with gabled-topped windows projecting completely over

the pathway, and a low door with a dark porch, and a
couple of steep steps leading down into the house, instead
of the modern fashion of half a dozen shallow ones leading up to it.   It was a comfortable-looking place though,
for there was a strong cheerful light in the bar-window,
which shed a bright ray across the road, and even lighted
up the hedge on the other side ; and there was a red
flickering light in the opposite window, one moment
but faintly discernible, and the next gleaming strongly
through the drawn curtains, which intimated that a
rousing fire was blazing within.   Marking these little
evidences with the eye of an experienced traveller, Tom
dismounted with as much agility as his half-frozen limbs
would permit, and entered the house.

In less than five minutes' time, Tom was ensconced in
the room opposite the bar—the very room where he had
imagined the fire blazing—before a substantial matter-
of-fact roaring fire, composed of something short of a
bushel of coals, and wood enough to make half a dozen
decent gooseberry bushes, piled half way up the chimney,
and roaring and crackling with a sound that of itself
would have warmed the heart of any reasonable man.
This was comfortable, but this was not all, for a smartly-
dressed girl, with a bright eye and a neat ankle, was laying
a very clean white cloth on the table ; and as Tom sat
with his slippered feet on the fender, and his back to the
open door, he saw a charming prospect of the bar reflected
in the glass over the chimney-piece, with delightful rows
of green bottles and gold labels, together with jars of
pickles and preserves, and cheeses and boiled hams, and
rounds of beef, arranged on shelves in the most tempting and delicious array.   Well, this was comfortable too ;
but even this was not all—for in the bar, seated at tea at

the nicest possible little table, drawn close up before the brightest possible little fire, was a buxom widow of somewhere about eight and forty or thereabouts, with a face as comfortable as the bar, who was evidently the landlady of the house, and the supreme ruler over all these agreeable possessions.

Charles Dickens.

THE OLD-TIME "COMMERCIAL"

YOUR commercial man is often a fellow of infinite jest, a travelling vocabulary of provincial knowledge and a faithful narrator of the passing events of the time. The moment he enters a new place he expects the landlord to be ready, cap in hand, to welcome him ; he first sees his horse into a stall, and lectures the ostler upon the art of rubbing him down—orders boots to bring in his travelling bag or his driving box, and bids the waiter send the chambermaid to show him his bedroom—grumbles that it is too high up, has no chimney in the apartment, or is situate over the kitchen or the taproom—swears a tremendous oath that he will order his baggage to be taken to the next house, and frightens the poor girl into giving him one of the best bed-apartments, usually reserved for the coffee-room company. Returning below he abuses the waiter for not giving him his letters, that have been awaiting his arrival, before he went upstairs—directs boots to be ready to make the circuit of the town with him after dinner, carrying his pattern-books, perhaps half a hundredweight of Birmingham wares, brass articles, or patterns of coffin furniture ; and having thus succeeded in putting the whole house into confusion, only to let them know that the Brummagem gentleman has arrived on his annual visit, with a new stock of everything in the brass line, he places himself down at a side table to answer to his principals for being some days later on his march than they had concluded—remits a good sum in bills and acceptances, and adds thereunto a sheet of orders that will suffice to keep the firm in good temper for a week to come. . . . It is at his inn alone that his independence breaks forth, and here he often assumes as much consequence as if he was the head of the firm he represents and always carried about him a plum at least in his breeches pocket. This is a general character, and one, too, formed upon no slight knowledge of commercial men ; but with all this the man of the world will admire them and seek their company : first, that his accommodations are generally better, and the charges not subject to the caprice of the landlord ; and, secondly, for the sake of society ; for what on earth can be more horrible than to be shut up in a lone room, a stranger in a provincial town, to eat, drink, and pass the cheerless hour a prey to solitude and ennui ?

The privilege of finding fault with the dinner—which, by the by, was excellent—is always conceded to the ancients of the fraternity of traders ; these gentlemen who, having been half a century upon the road, remember all the previous proprietors of the hotel to the fifteenth or twentieth generation removed, make a point of enumerating their gracious qualities upon such occasions, to keep the living host and representative up to the mark, as they phrase it.

Edward Westmacott.

THE "WASH AND BRUSH-UP"

ONE point of refinement, as regards the comfort of travellers, remains to be mentioned, in which the improvement began a good deal earlier, perhaps by ten years, than in the construction of the roads. Luxurious as was the system of English travelling at all periods, after the general establishment of post-chaises, it must be granted that, in the circumstance of cleanliness, there was far from being that attention, or that provision for the traveller's comfort, which might have been anticipated from the general habits of the country. I, at all periods of my life a great traveller, was witness to the first steps and the whole struggle of this revolution. Maréchal Saxe professed always to look under his bed, applying his caution chiefly to the attempts of robbers. Now, if at the greatest inns of England, you had, in the days I speak of, adopted this maréchal's policy of reconnoitring, what would you have seen? Beyond a doubt, you would have seen what, upon all principles of seniority, was entitled to your veneration, viz., a dense accumulation of dust far older than yourself. A foreign author made some experiments upon the deposition of dust, and the rate of its accumulation, in a room left wholly undisturbed. If I recollect, a century would produce a stratum about half an inch in depth. Upon this principle, I conjecture that much dust which I have seen in inns, during the first four or five years of the present century, must have belonged to the reign of George II. It was, however, upon travellers by coaches that the full oppression of the old vicious system operated. . . . Post-chaise travellers could, of course, have what they liked, and generally they asked for a bedroom. It is of coach travellers that I speak. Well do I remember the astonishment of some waiters, the indignation of others, the sympathetic uproars which spread to the bar, the kitchen, and even to the stables, at the first opening of our extravagant demands. But gradually we made our way. Like Scaliger, at first we got but one basin amongst us, and that one was brought into the breakfast-room ; but scarcely had two years revolved before we began to see four, and all appurtenances, arranged duly in correspondence to the number of inside passengers by the mail ; and as outside travelling was continually gaining ground amongst the wealthier classes, more comprehensive arrangements were often made. Dust from the reign of George II. became scarcer ; gradually it came to bear an antiquarian value : basins lost their grim appearance, and looked as clean as in gentlemen's houses. And at length the whole system was so thoroughly ventilated and purified, that all good inns, nay, generally speaking, even second-rate inns, at this day reflect the best features, as to cleanliness and neatness, of well-managed private establishments.

Thomas de Quincey.

ONE KIND OF COACH DINNER

TWO other coaches are dining, while some few passengers, whose hour is not yet come, sit patiently on the roof, or pace up and down the street with short and hurried turns, anxious to see the horses brought out that are to forward them on their journey. And what a commotion this new arrival creates ! From the arched doorway of the inn issue two chambermaids, one in curls, the other in a cap ; boots, with both curls and a cap, and a ladder in his hand ; a knock-kneed waiter, with a dirty duster, to count noses ; while the neat landlady, in a spruce black silk gown and clean white apron, stands smirking, smiling, and rubbing her hands down her sides, inveighing the passengers into the house, where she will turn them over to the waiters to take their chance the instant she gets them in. . . . The table, which was covered with a thrice-used cloth, was set out with lumps of bread, knives, and two and three-pronged forks laid alternately. Altogether it was anything but inviting, but coach passengers are very complacent ; and on the Dover road it matters little if they are not. Coats No. 1, No. 2 and No. 3 are taken off in succession, for some people wear top-coats to keep out the heat ; hats are hid in corners, and fur caps thrust into the pockets of their owners. Inside passengers eye outside ones with suspi-cion. . . . " Come, waiter, bring dinner ! " roared Mr. Jorrocks at the top of his voice ; and presently the two dishes of pork, a couple of ducks, and a lump of half-raw, sadly-mangled cold roast beef, with waxy potatoes and overgrown cabbages, were scattered along the table. . . .

" Now, hark'e, waiter, there's the guard blowing his horn, and we have scarcely had a bite apiece," cries Mr. Jorrocks, as that functionary sounded his instrument most energetically in the passage ; " blow me tight if I stir before the half-hour's up, so he may blow till he's black in the face." " Take some cheese, sir ? " inquires the waiter. " No, surely not, some more pork and then some tarts." " Sorry, sir, we have no tarts we can recommend. Cheese is partiklar good."

Having exhausted his wind the guard squeezed through the door, and with an extremely red face assured the company that " time was h'up," and the coach quite ready. Then out came the purses, brown, green and blue, with the usual inquiry, " What's dinner, waiter ? " Two-and-six dinner, beer, three—two-and-nine yours," replied the knock-kneed caitiff to the first inquirer, push-ing a blue and white plate under his nose ; " yours is three-and-six, ma'm—two glasses of brandy and water, four shillings, if you please, sir." " Now, gentlemen and ladies, pray, come, time's h'up, carn't wait—must go ! "

roars the guard, as the passengers shuffle themselves into
their coats, cloaks and cravats, and Joe " Boots " runs up
the passage with the ladder for the lady.

R. S. Surtees.

ANOTHER KIND

" THE coach stops here half an hour, gentlemen ;
dinner quite ready."

'Tis a delightful sound. And what a dinner ! What
a profusion of substantial delicacies ! What mighty and
iris-tinted rounds of beef ! What vast and marble-
veined ribs ! What gelatinous veal-pies ! What
colossal hams ! Those are evidently prize cheese !
And how invigorating is the perfume of those various
and variegated pickles ! Then the bustle emulating the
plenty ; the ringing of bells, the clash of thoroughfare,
the summoning of ubiquitous waiters, and the all-per-
vading feeling of omnipotence from the guests, who
order what they please to the landlord, who can produce
and execute everything they can desire. 'Tis a wondrous
sight !

Benjamin Disraeli.

EARLY MORNING AT THE INN

IT was early on a fine May morning when a young
man of gentleman-like appearance alighted from one of
the Northern mails at the front of the old Fallow Deer
Inn, at Newark—a comfortable-looking public-house,
as all know who have travelled that road, which faces the
sweet south, and overlooks one of those rich pastoral
landscapes, such as are to be found nowhere but in England. A rudely-clad, merry-faced hostler issued from an
opposite stable, whistling the tune of " We'll all be
married when plums come in," and, shouldering the

N 2

heavy portmanteau, walked into the house. The guard touched his hat in acknowledgment of the handsome fee he had received from the young traveller, swung himself once more into his seat, blew his horn to warn a sluggish waggoner to alter the course of his team, and the coach with all its muffled and thoughtful passengers was soon lost to the eye.

" How long will the coach be before it arrives ? " inquired the young man.

The hostler pulled up one side of his waistcoat, straddled out his legs, and, laying hold of a faded red ribbon to which was appended a brass seal and key, dragged forth a little old-fashioned watch, and said " About three hours, sir. My watch goes very reg'lar. I set it by the coachman's chronometer."

" How say you—can I be accommodated ? "

" With breakfast ? Oh, yes, sir. Though ours isn't what's called a tip-top inn, you'll find everything as clean and comfortable as if it was, and a good deal more so than some I know." So saying he led the way into the house.

Notwithstanding the hostler's boast about cleanliness and comfort, the room into which the traveller was conducted presented an appearance the very reverse of that promised. This the guide, who had doubtless forgotten himself for a moment, detected at a glance, and he made off under cover of his favourite tune, though not before he received a volley of abuse from the servant girl who was black-leading the gate. The tables bore visible signs of the overnight business—the marks of ale-jugs, half-burnt splints, broken pipes and the ashes of tobacco, with scraps of paper in which were left the remnants of unsmoked pennyworths. The floor was strewn with sand which had received its share of the homely libations, while the chairs stood at all angles ; added to which the apartment smelt strongly of tobacco-smoke that, however pleasant it might have been on the previous evening, sent up such an odour as even a lover of the soothing weed would fain have avoided. . . .

The kitchen or tap-room into which the stranger now entered was very unlike such places as go under the same denomination in crowded cities. The slabbed floor was dry and white, having been well scoured with freestone, and looked, in a country phrase, " as if you could have eaten your dinner off it." The tables had also the same clean appearance ; the long settle was bright and free from dust ; and in a large old-fashioned fireplace hung the huge kettle, singing its quiet tune even at that early hour, while a good-looking damsel, niece to mine host, was already setting out the breakfast-table.

The hams and flitches which hung around told that this was a land of plenty, while a goodly array of brass, copper and block-tin utensils, plated spurs, bits and stirrup irons, with a number of other et ceteras, told that Betty the servant-maid must have had a good deal of scrubbing and rubbing to have kept them all in such good order.

At one end of the settle sat the landlord, his foot cased in a large listing shoe, and resting on a stool, telling at once a tale of good eating, good drinking, and—the gout. He was still a fine, tall, hearty old fellow, with a twinkle of good humour in his eye, and a glow of health in his countenance, which was mottled with hundreds of small red lines, telling of the number of bottles of brandy he had drunk in his lifetime. He had been a horse-soldier and guard of the mail ; had fought at more than one battle in the field and encountered highwaymen on the road ; and now seventy, hale and sound (excepting an occasional twinge of the gout), had for the last twenty years of his life settled down staidly and (sometimes) soberly into the character of mine host of the Fallow Deer.

He made an attempt to rise as the young traveller entered, caught his gouty foot against the table leg, swore a huge round oath and bade him good-morning in the same breath ; then, smoothing down the wry face the accident had called up, resumed his conversation with a man who sat on the long settle, and who, although at so early an hour, had already made a deep inroad into a quart jug of ale.   *Thomas Miller.*

THE GREAT ARISTODEMUS

AFTER that time, Melchior, Timothy, and I again set off for the town of ——, and stopping at a superior inn in another part of the town, dressed as travellers, that is, people who go about the country for orders from the manufacturers, ordered our beds and supper in the coffee-room. The conversation was soon turned upon the wonderful powers of Nattée, the gipsy. "Nonsense," said Melchior, "she knows nothing. I have heard of her. But there *is* a man coming this way (should he happen to pass through this town) who will surprise and frighten you. No one knows who he is. He is named the Great Aristodemus. He knows the past, the present, and the future. He never looks at people's hands—he only looks you in the face, and *woe be to them who tell him a lie*. . . ." At this information many expressed their doubts, and many others vaunted the powers of the gipsy. Melchior replied, "that all he knew was, that for the sum of two guineas paid down, he had told him of a legacy left him of six hundred pounds, which otherwise he would never have known of or received." All the town of —— being quite alive for fortune-telling, this new report gained wind, and after a week's sojourn, Melchior thought that the attempt should be made.

We accordingly packed up and departed to another market-town. Timothy, dressed in a sombre suit of black, very much like an undertaker, was provided with a horse, with the following directions : to proceed leisurely until he was within half a mile of the town of ——, and then to gallop in as fast as he could, stop at the best inn in the place, and order apartments for the Great Aristodemus, who might be expected in half an hour. Everything in this world depends upon appearances, that is, when you intend to gull it ; and as every one in the town had heard of the Great Aristodemus, so every one was anxious to know something about him, and Timothy was pestered with all manner of questions : but he declared that he was only his courier, and could only tell what other people said ; but then what other people said, by Timothy's account, was very marvellous indeed. Timothy had hardly time to secure the best rooms in the hotel, when Melchior, dressed in a long flowing silk gown, with a wig of long white hair, a square cap, and two or three gold chains hanging from his neck, certainly most admirably disguised, and attended by me in the dress of a German student, a wig of long brown locks hanging down my shoulders, made our appearance in a postchaise and four, and drove up to the door of the inn, at a pace which shook every house in the street, and occasioned every window to be tenanted with one or more heads to ascertain the cause of this unusual occurrence, for it was not a very great town, although once of importance ; but the manufactures had been removed, and it was occupied by those who had become independent by their own exertions, or by those of their forefathers.

The door of the chaise was opened by the obsequious Timothy, who pushed away the ostlers and waiters, as if unworthy to approach his master, and the Great Aristodemus made his appearance. As he ascended the steps of the door, his passage was for a moment barred by one whose profession Melchior well knew. " Stand aside, exciseman ! " said he, in a commanding voice. " No one crosses my path with impunity." Astonished at hearing his profession thus mentioned, the exciseman, who was the greatest bully in the town, slipped on one side with consternation, and all those present lifted up their eyes and hands with astonishment. The Great Aristodemus gained his room, and shut his door ; and I went out to pay for the chaise and order supper, while Timothy and the porters were busy with our luggage, which was very considerable.

" My master will not see anyone," said I to the landlord : " he quits this town to-morrow, if the letters arrive which he expects by the post ; therefore, pray get rid of this crowd, and let him be quiet, for he is very tired, having travelled one hundred and fifty miles since the dawn of day."

When Tim and I had performed this duty, we joined Melchior in his room, leaving the news to be circulated. " This promises well," observed Melchior ; " up to the present we have expended much time and money ; now we must see if we cannot recover it tenfold. Japhet, you must take an opportunity of going out again after supper, and make inquiries of the landlord what poor people they have in the town, as I am very generous, and like to relieve them ; you may observe, that all the money offered to me for practising my art, I give away to the poor, having no occasion for it." This I did, and we then sat down to supper, and having unpacked our baggage, went to bed, after locking the door of the room, and taking out the key.   *Frederick Marryat.*

A COACH BREAKFAST

AND here comes breakfast.

"Twenty minutes here, gentlemen," says the coachman, as they pull up at half-past seven at the inn-door.

Have not we endured nobly this morning, and is not this a worthy reward for much endurance ? There is the low dark wainscoted room hung with sporting prints ; the hat-stand, with a whip or two standing up in it, belonging to bagmen, who are still snug in bed, by the door ; the blazing fire, with the quaint old glass over the mantelpiece, in which is stuck a large card with the list of the meets for the week of the county hounds. The table covered with the whitest of cloths and of china, and bearing a pigeon-pie, ham, round of cold boiled beef cut from a mammoth ox, and the great loaf of household bread on a wooden trencher. And here comes in the stout head waiter, puffing under a tray of hot viands ; kidneys and a steak, transparent rashers and poached eggs, buttered toast and muffins, coffee and tea, all smoking hot. The table can never hold it all ; the cold meats are removed to the sideboard, they were only put on for show, and to give us an appetite. And now fall on, gentlemen all. It is a well-known sporting house, and the breakfasts are famous. Two or three men in pink, on their way to the meet, drop in, and are very jovial and sharp-set, as indeed we all are.

" Tea or coffee, sir ? " says head waiter, coming round to Tom.

" Coffee, please," says Tom with his mouth full of muffin and kidney ; coffee is a treat to him, tea is not.

Our coachman, I perceive, who breakfasts with us, is a cold-beef man. He also eschews hot potations, and addicts himself to a tankard of ale, which is brought him by the barmaid. Sportsman looks on approvingly, and orders a ditto for himself.

Tom has eaten kidney and pigeon-pie, and imbibed coffee, till his little skin is as tight as a drum ; and then has the further pleasure of paying head waiter out of his own purse, in a dignified manner, and walks out before the inn-door to see the horses put to. This is done leisurely and in a highly finished manner by the ostlers, as if they enjoyed the not being hurried. Coachman comes out with his way-bill, and puffing a fat cigar which the sportsman has given him. Guard emerges from the tap, where he prefers breakfasting, licking round a tough-looking doubtful cheroot, which you might tie round your finger, and three whiffs of which would knock any one else out of time.

The pinks stand about the inn-door lighting cigars and waiting to see us start, while their hacks are led up and down the market-place on which the inn looks. They all know our sportsman, and we feel a reflected credit when we see him chatting and laughing with them.

Thomas Hughes.

AN EARLY DEPARTURE

WE had slept in a room, the access to which was only through another sleeping-room, which was also occupied ; and, as I had got up about two o'clock at Andover, we went to bed, at Lyndhurst, about half-past seven o'clock. I was, of course, awake by three or four ; I had eaten little over night ; so that here lay I, not liking (even after day-light began to glimmer) to go through a chamber, where, by possibility, there might be a lady actually in bed ; here lay I, my bones aching with lying in bed, my stomach growling for victuals, imprisoned by my modesty. But at last I grew impatient ; for, modesty here or modesty there, I was not to be penned up and starved ; so, after having shaved and dressed and got ready to go down, I thrusted George out a little before me into the other room ; and through we pushed, previously resolving, of course, not to look towards the bed that was there. But, as the devil would have it, just as I was about the middle of the room, I, like Lot's wife, turned my head ! All that I shall say is, first, that the consequences that befell her did not befall me, and second, that I advise those who are likely to be hungry in the morning, not to sleep in inner rooms ; or, if they do, to take some bread and cheese in their pockets.

Having got safe downstairs, I lost no time in inquiry after the means of obtaining a breakfast to make up for the bad fare of the previous day ; and finding my landlady rather tardy in the work, and not, seemingly, having a proper notion of the affair, I went myself and, having found a butcher's shop, bought a loin of small, fat, wether mutton, which I saw cut out of the sheep and cut into chops. These were brought to the inn ; George and I ate about two pound out of the five pound, and, while I was writing a letter, and making up my packet, to be ready to send from Southampton, George went out and found a poor woman to come and take away the rest of the loin of mutton ; for our fastings of the day before enabled us to do this ; and though we had about forty miles to go to get to this place, I had resolved that we would go without any more purchase of victuals and drink this day also. Some poet has said that that which is given in charity gives a blessing on both sides ; to the giver as well as the receiver. But I really think that if, in general, the food and drink given came out of food and drink *deducted* from the usual quantity swallowed by the giver, the blessing would be still greater, and much more certain.

William Cobbett.

HETTY SORREL TURNS BACK

THE good landlady was amazed when she saw Hetty come downstairs soon after herself, neatly dressed, and looking resolutely self-possessed. Hetty told her she was quite well this morning : she had only been very tired and overcome with her journey, for she had come a long way to ask about her brother, who had run away, and they thought he was gone for a soldier, and Captain Donnithorne might know, for he had been very kind to her brother once. It was a lame story, and the landlady looked doubtfully at Hetty as she told it ; but there was a resolute air of self-reliance about her this morning, so different from the helpless prostration of yesterday, that the landlady hardly knew how to make a remark that might seem like prying into other people's affairs. She only invited her to sit down to breakfast with them, and in the course of it Hetty brought out her ear-rings and locket, and asked the landlord if he could help her to get money for them : her journey, she said, had cost her much more than she expected, and now she had no money to get back to her friends, which she wanted to do at once.

It was not the first time the landlady had seen the ornaments, for she had examined the contents of Hetty's pocket yesterday, and she and her husband had discussed the fact of a country girl having these beautiful things, with a stronger conviction than ever that Hetty had been miserably deluded by the fine young officer.

" Well," said the landlord, when Hetty had spread the precious trifles before him, " we might take 'em to the jeweller's shop, for there's one not far off ; but Lord bless you, they wouldn't give you a quarter o' what the things are worth. And you wouldn't like to part with 'em ? " he added, looking at her inquiringly.

" Oh, I don't mind," said Hetty, hastily, " so as I can get money to go back."

" And they might think the things were stolen, as you wanted to sell 'em," he went on ; " for it isn't usual for a young woman like you to have fine jewellery like that."

The blood rushed to Hetty's face with anger. " I belong to respectable folks," she said ; " I'm not a thief."

" No, that you aren't, I'll be bound," said the land-lady ; " and you'd no call to say that," looking indig-nantly at her husband. " The things were gev to her : that's plain enough to be seen."

" I didn't mean as I thought so," said the husband, apologetically, " but I said it was what the jeweller might think, and so he wouldn't be offering much money for 'em."

"Well," said the wife, "suppose you were to advance some money on the things yourself, and then if she liked to redeem them when she got home, she could. But if we heard nothing from her after two months, we might do as we liked with 'em."

The landlord took up the ornaments and pushed out his lips in a meditative manner. He wished Hetty well, doubtless; but pray, how many of your well-wishers would decline to make a little gain out of you? Your landlady is sincerely affected at parting with you, respects you highly, and will really rejoice if any one else is generous to you; but at the same time she hands you a bill by which she gains as high a percentage as possible.

"How much money do you want to get home with, young woman?" said the well-wisher, at length.

"Three guineas," answered Hetty, fixing on the sum she set out with, for want of any other standard, and afraid of asking too much.

"Well, I've no objections to advance you three guineas," said the landlord; "and if you like to send it me back and get the jewellery again, you can, you know : the Green Man isn't going to run away."

"Oh, yes, I'll be very glad if you'll give me that," said Hetty, relieved at the thought that she would not have to go to the jeweller's, and be stared at and questioned.

"But if you want the things again, you'll write before long," said the landlady, "because when two months are up, we shall make up our minds as you don't want 'em."

"Yes," said Hetty, indifferently.

The husband and wife were equally content with this arrangement. The husband thought, if the ornaments were not redeemed, he could make a good thing of it by taking them to London and selling them : the wife thought she would coax the good man into letting her keep them. And they were accommodating Hetty, poor thing :—a pretty, respectable-looking young woman, apparently in a sad case. They declined to take anything for her food and bed : she was quite welcome. And at eleven o'clock Hetty said good-bye to them, mounting the coach that was to take her twenty miles back along the way she had come.

George Eliot.

AN HISTORIC ARRIVAL

IN the main street of Ipswich, on the left-hand side of the way, a short distance after you have passed through the open space fronting the Town Hall, stands an inn known far and wide by the appellation of The Great White Horse, rendered the more conspicuous by a stone statue of some rampacious animal with flowing mane and tail, distantly resembling an insane cart-horse, which is elevated above the principal door. The Great White Horse is famous in the neighbourhood, in the same degree as a prize ox, or county paper-chronicled turnip, or unwieldy pig—for its enormous size. Never were such labyrinths of uncarpeted passages, such clusters of mouldy, ill-lighted rooms, such huge numbers of small dens for eating or sleeping in, beneath any one roof, as are collected together between the four walls of The Great White Horse at Ipswich.

It was at the door of this overgrown tavern that the London coach stopped, at the same hour every evening ; and it was from this same London coach, that Mr. Pickwick, Sam Weller, and Mr. Peter Magnus dismounted, on the particular evening to which this chapter of our history bears reference.

" Do you stop here, sir ? " inquired Mr. Peter Magnus

when the striped bag, and the red bag, and the brown-paper parcel, and the leather hat-box, had all been deposited in the passage. "Do you stop here, sir?"

"I do," said Mr. Pickwick.

"Dear me," said Mr. Magnus, "I never knew anything like these extraordinary coincidences. Why, I stop here too. I hope we dine together."

"With pleasure," replied Mr. Pickwick. "I am not quite certain whether I have any friends here or not, though. Is there any gentleman of the name of Tupman here, waiter?"

A corpulent man, with a fortnight's napkin under his arm, and coeval stockings on his legs, slowly desisted from his occupation of staring down the street, on this question being put to him by Mr. Pickwick; and, after minutely inspecting that gentleman's appearance, from the crown of his hat to the lowest button of his gaiters, replied emphatically:

"No."

"Nor any gentleman of the name of Snodgrass?" inquired Mr. Pickwick.

"No!"

"Nor Winkle?"

"No."

"My friends have not arrived to-day, sir," said Mr. Pickwick. "We will dine alone, then. Show us a private room, waiter."

On this request being preferred, the corpulent man condescended to order the boots to bring in the gentlemen's luggage; and preceding them down a long dark passage, ushered them into a large badly-furnished apartment, with a dirty grate, in which a small fire was making a wretched attempt to be cheerful, but was fast sinking beneath the dispiriting influence of the place. After the lapse of an hour, a bit of fish and a steak were served up to the travellers, and when the dinner was cleared away, Mr. Pickwick and Mr. Peter Magnus drew their chairs up to the fire, and having ordered a bottle of the worst possible port wine, at the highest possible price, for the good of the house, drank brandy and water for their own.

Charles Dickens.

CHAMBERMAID, OSTLER, DRAWER

"SIR, *if you be ill at ease, go and take your rest, your chambre is ready. Jone, make a good fier in his chambre, and let him lacke nothing.*"

"*My shee friende, is my bed made ? Is it good ?*"

"*Yea, sir, it is a good feder bed, the scheetes be very cleane.*"

"*Pull off my hosen and warme my bed.*"

"*Take your rest in God's name, God give you goode night and goode rest.*"

(*Dialogue with Chambermaid : Manual for the Use of Travellers,* 1589.)

. . . . . .

FALSTAFF. *Mine host of the Garter !*

HOST. *What says my bully-rook ? speak scholarly and wisely.*

FAL. *Truly, mine host, I must turn away some of my followers.*

HOST. *Discard, bully Hercules ; cashier : let them wag ; trot, trot.*

FAL. *I sit at ten pounds a week.*

HOST. *Thou 'rt an Emperor, Cæsar, Keisar, and Pheezar. I will entertain Bardolph ; he shall draw, he shall tap : said I well, bully Hector ?*

FAL. *Do so, good mine host.*

HOST. *I have spoke ; let him follow. Let me see thee froth and lime : I am at a word ; follow.*

FAL. *Bardolph, follow him. A tapster is a good trade : an old cloak makes a new jerkin ; a withered serving-man a fresh tapster. Go ; adieu.*

BARD. *It is a life that I have desired : I will thrive.*

William Shakespeare.

ON a night *Scogin* and his chamber-fellow, and two
or three of the Bishops servants being merrily disposed, consult how they might have good cheere and pay
no money, and every one invented a way as they thought
best. At last *Scogin* said, I have invented a cleanly shift.
At the signe of the Crowne against Peter's Church, is a
new Tapster, which ere this hath not seene any of us,
and he is also purblind, so that if he see us hereafter, he
cannot know us. Therefore wee will goe thither and
make good cheere, and when we have a reckoning, we
will contend who shall pay all ; then will I say to avoid
the contention, that the Tapster shall be blinded, and we
will run round about him, and whosoever he catcheth
first, let him pay for all, and so we may escape away.
Every man liked *Scogin's* device best, so in conclusion
they came thither, and had good cheere, for they spared
no cost : so that in the end their reckoning drew to ten
Shillings. Then as *Scogin* had devised afore, they did.
The Tapster was blinded, so they ran round about him,
and first *Scogin* got out, and then another, so that at last
they got all away, and left the Tapster groping in every
place about the house for him that should pay the shot.
The master of the house being in a chamber next to the
place where they were, and hearing the stamping that
they made, came in to see what they did, whom the
Tapster caught in his armes, saying, Sir, you must pay
the reckoning. Marry, said his Master, so I thinke I
must indeed, for here is no body else to pay it. Then the
Tapster and his Master sought and enquired for *Scogin*
and the rest, but they could neither find them, nor heare
newes of them.

Scogin's Jest Book.

197

ENGAGING A MAID

AFTER the carrier had set up his horse, and despatched his lading, he remembered his oath, and
therefore bethought him how he might place these three
maids ; with that he called to mind that the mistress at
The Eagle, in Westminster, had spoken divers times to
him for a servant ; he with his carriage passed over the
fields to her house, where he found her sitting and drinking with a Spanish knight, called Sir James of Castile,
doctor Skelton, and Will Sommers ; told her how he
had brought up to London three Lancashire lasses, and
seeing she was oft desirous to have a maid, now she should
take her choice which of them she would have. Marry,
quoth she (being a very merry and a pleasant woman),
carrier, thou comest in good time ; for not only I want
a maid, but here be three gentlemen that shall give me
their opinions which of them I shall have. With that
the maids were bidden come in, and she entreated them
to give their verdict. Straight as soon as they saw Long
Meg, they began to smile ; and doctor Skelton, in his
mad, merry vein, blessing himself, began thus :

> *Domine, domine, unde hoc,*
> What is she in the grey cassock ?
> Methinks she is of a large length,
> Of a tall pitch and a good strength,
> With strong arms and stiff bones ;
> This is a wench for the nones ;
> Her looks are bonny and blithe,
> She seems neither lither nor lithe,
> But young of age,
> And of merry visage,

Neither beastly nor bowsie,
Sleep nor drowsy,
But fair fac'd and of a good size ;
Therefore, hostess, if you be wise,
Once be ruled by me,
Take this wench to thee ;
For this is plain,
She'll do more work than these twain ;
I tell thee, hostess, I do not mock,
Take her in the grey cassock.

What is your opinion, quoth the hostess to Sir James of Castile. Question with her, quoth he, what she can do, and then I'll give you my opinion ; and yet first, hostess, ask Will Sommers' opinion. Will smiled, and swore that his hostess should not have her, but King Harry should buy her. Why so, Will ? quoth Doctor Skelton. Because, quoth Will Sommers, that she shall be kept for breed ; for if the king would marry her to Long Sanders of the court, they would bring forth none but soldiers. Well, the hostess demanded what her name was. Margaret, forsooth, quoth she. And what work can you do ? Faith, little, mistress, quoth she, but handy labour, as to wash and wring, to make clean a house, to brew, bake, or any such drudgery ; for my needle, to that I have been little used. Thou art, quoth the hostess, a good lusty wench, and therefore I like thee the better. I have here a great charge, for I keep a victualling house, and divers times there come in swaggering fellows that, when they have eat and drank, will not pay what they call for ; yet, if thou take the charge of my drink, I must be answered out of your wages. Content, mistress, quoth she ; for while I serve you, if any stale cutter comes in, and thinks to pay the shot with swearing, hey, gogs wounds, let me alone ! I'll not only (if his clothes be worth it) make him pay ere he pass, but lend him as many bats as his crag will carry, and then throw him out of doors. At this they all smiled. Nay, mistress, quoth the carrier, 'tis true, for my poor pilch here is able with a pair of blue shoulders to swear as much ; and with that he told them how she had used him at her coming to London. I cannot think, quoth Sir James of Castile, that she is so strong. Try her, quoth Skelton, for I have heard that Spaniards are of wonderful strength. Sir James in a bravery would needs make experience, and therefore asked the maid if she durst change a box on the ear with him. I, sir, quoth she, that I dare, if my mistress will give me leave. Yes, Meg, quoth she ; do thy best. And with that it was a question who should stand first. Marry, that I will, sir, quoth she ; and so stood to abide Sir James his blow ; who, forcing himself with all his might, gave her such a box that she could scarcely stand, yet she stirred no more than a post. Then Sir James, he stood, and the hostess willed her not spare her strength. No, quoth Skelton ; and if she fell him down, I'll give her a pair of new hose and shoon. Mistress, quoth Meg (and with that she struck up her sleeve), here is a foul fist, and it hath passed much drudgery, but, trust me, I think it will give a good blow ; and with that she wrought at him so strongly, that down fell Sir James at her feet. By my faith, quoth Will Sommers, she strikes a blow like an ox, for she hath struck down an ass. At this they all laughed. Sir James was ashamed, and Meg was entertained into service.

Adventures of Long Meg of Westminster.

FRANCIS AND THE PRINCE

THE BOAR'S HEAD TAVERN IN EASTCHEAP.

Enter the PRINCE *and* POINS.

PRINCE.   Ned, prithee, come out of that fat room, and lend me thy hand to laugh a little.

POINS.   Where hast been, Hal ?

PRINCE.   With three or four loggerheads amongst three or four-score hogsheads. I have sounded the very base-string of humility. Sirrah, I am sworn brother to a leash of drawers ; and can call them all by their christen names, as Tom, Dick, and Francis. They take it already upon their salvation, that though I be but Prince of Wales, yet I am the king of courtesy : and tell me flatly I am no proud Jack, like Falstaff, but a Corinthian, a lad of mettle, a good boy, by the Lord, so they call me, and when I am king of England, I shall command all the good lads in Eastcheap. They call drinking deep, dyeing scarlet ; and when you breathe in your watering, they cry " hem ! " and bid you play it off. To conclude, I am so good a proficient in one quarter of an hour, that I can drink with any tinker in his own language during my life. I tell thee, Ned, thou hast lost much honour, that thou wert not with me in this action. But, sweet Ned, —to sweeten which name of Ned, I give thee this penny-worth of sugar, clapped even now into my hand by an under-skinker, one that never spake other English in his life than " Eight shillings and sixpence," and " You are welcome," with this shrill addition, " Anon, anon, sir ! Score a pint of bastard in the Half-moon," or so. But, Ned, to drive away the time till Falstaff come, I prithee, do thou stand in some by-room, while I question my puny drawer to what end he gave me the sugar ; and do thou never leave calling " Francis," that his tale to me may be nothing but " Anon." Step inside, and I'll show thee a precedent.

POINS. Francis !

PRINCE. Thou art perfect.

POINS. Francis ! (*Exit* POINS.)

Enter FRANCIS.

FRAN. Anon, anon, sir. Look down into the Pomgarnet, Ralph.

PRINCE. Come hither, Francis.

FRAN. My lord ?

PRINCE. How long hast thou to serve, Francis.

FRAN. Forsooth, five years, and as much as to——

POINS. (*Within.*) Francis !

FRAN. Anon, anon, sir.

PRINCE. Five year ! by'r lady, a long lease for the clinking of pewter. But, Francis, darest thou be so valiant as to play the coward with thy indenture and show it a fair pair of heels and run from it ?

FRAN. O Lord, sir, I'll be sworn upon all the books in England, I could find in my heart.

POINS. (*Within.*) Francis !

FRAN. Anon, sir.

PRINCE. How old art thou, Francis ?

FRAN. Let me see—about Michaelmas next I shall be——

POINS. (*Within.*) Francis !

FRAN. Anon, sir. Pray stay a little, my lord.

PRINCE. Nay, but hark you, Francis : for the sugar thou gavest me, 'twas a pennyworth, was't not ?

FRAN. O Lord, I would it had been two !

PRINCE. I will give thee for it a thousand pound : ask me when thou wilt, and thou shalt have it.

Poins. (*Within.*) Francis !

Fran. Anon, anon.

Prince. Anon, Francis ? No, Francis ; but to-morrow, Francis ; or Francis, o' Thursday ; or indeed, Francis, when thou wilt. But Francis !

Fran. My lord ?

Prince. Wilt thou rob this leathern jerkin, crystal-button, not-pated, agate-ring, puke-stocking, caddis-garter, smooth-tongue, Spanish-pouch,——

Fran. O lord, sir, who do you mean ?

Prince. Why then, your brown bastard is your only drink ; for look you, Francis, your white canvas doublet will sully : in Barbary, sir, it cannot come to so much.

Fran. What, sir ?

Poins. (*Within.*) Francis !

Prince. Away, you rogue ! dost thou not hear them call ?

> (*Here they both call him ; the drawer stands*
> *amazed, not knowing which way to go.*)
>   *Enter* Vintner.

Vint. What, standest thou still, and hearest such a calling ? Look to the guests within. (*Exit* Francis.) My lord, old Sir John, with half-a-dozen more, are at the door : shall I let them in ?

Prince. Let them alone awhile, and then open the door. (*Exit* Vintner.) Poins !

>   *Re-enter* Poins.

Poins. Anon, anon, sir.

Prince. Sirrah, Falstaff and the rest of the thieves are at the door : shall we be merry ?

Poins. As merry as crickets, my lad. But hark ye ; what cunning match have you made with this jest of the drawer ? come, what's the issue ?

PRINCE.   I am now of all humours that have showed themselves humours since the old days of goodman Adam to the pupil age of this present twelve o'clock at midnight.

(*Re-enter* FRANCIS.)

What's o'clock, Francis ?

FRAN.   Anon, anon, sir.

William Shakespeare.

THE STUART GALLANT IN THE TAVERN

HAVING therefore thrust yourself into a case most in fashion (how coarse soever the stuff be, 'tis no matter so it hold fashion) your office is (if you mean to do your judgment right) to enquire out those Taverns which are best custom'd, whose masters are oftenest drunk (for that confirms their taste, and that they choose wholesome wines), and such as stand farthest from the counters ; where, landing yourself and your followers, your first complement shall be to grow most inwardly acquainted with the drawers, to learn their names, as Jack, and Will, and Tom, to drive into their inclinations, as whether this fellow useth to the Fencing School, this to the Dauncing School ; whether that young conjurer (in Hogsheads) at midnight keeps a Gelding now and then to visit his Cockatrice, or whether he love dogs, or be addicted to any other eminent and citizen-like quality : and protest yourself to be extremely in love, and that you spend much money in a year, upon any one of those exercises which you perceive is followed by them. The use which you shall make of this familiarity is this : If you want money five or six days together, you may still pay the reckoning with this most Gentlemanlike language, Boy, fetch me money from the bar, and keep yourself most providently from a hungry melancholy in your chamber. Besides, you shall be sure (if there be but one fawcet that can betray neat wine to the bar) to have that arraigned before you, sooner than a better and worthier person. . . . At your departure forth the house, to kiss mine hostess over the bar, or to accept of the courtesy of the cellar when 'tis offered you by the drawers, or to bid any of the vintners good-night, is as commendable as for a barber after trimming to lave your face with sweet water.

Thomas Dekker.

GEORGE, OF THE MITRE

A Room at the Mitre.

(Enter CARLO.*)*

CAR.   Halloa !   Where be these shot-sharks ?
        (Enter DRAWER.*)*

DRAW.   By and by—you're welcome, good Master Buffone.

CAR.   Where's George ?   Call me George hither, quickly.

DRAW.   What wine please you have, sir ?   I'll draw you that's neat, Master Buffone.

CAR.   Away, neophite, do as I bid thee, bring my dear George to me :—Mass, here he comes.

(Enter GEORGE.*)*

GEO.   Welcome, Master Carlo.

CAR.   What ! is supper ready, George ?

GEO.   Ay, sir, almost ;   will you have the cloth laid, Master Carol ?

CAR.   O, what else ?   Are none of the gallants come yet ?

GEO.   None yet, sir.

CAR.   Stay, take me with you, George ; let me have a good fat loin of pork laid to the fire presently.

GEO.   It shall, sir.

CAR.   And withal, hear you ? Draw me the biggest shaft you have, out of the butt you wot of : away, you know my meaning, George, quick.

GEO.   Done, sir.   (*Exit.*)
        (*Re-enter* GEORGE *with a large jug of wine.*)
Here, Master Carlo.

CAR.   Is't right, boy ?

GEO.   Ay, sir, I assure you 'tis right.

CAR.   Well said, my dear George, depart ;—Come, my small gimlet, you in the false scabbard—away. (*Puts forth the drawers and shuts the door.*) So. Now to you, Sir Burgomaster, let's taste of your bounty. (*Drinks.*) Ay, marry, sir, here's purity ; O, George—I could bite off his nose for this now ; sweet rogue, he has drawn nectar, the very soul of the grape ! I'll wash my temples with some on't presently, and drink some half a score draughts ; 'twill heat the brain, kindle my imagination, I shall talk nothing but crackers and fireworks to-night.

                                            Ben Jonson.

THE FAIR SERVING-MAID

A ROOM IN THE CASTLE TAVERN.

(SPENCER, GOODLACK, *and* BESS BRIDGES.)

SPEN.   See, she's come.

BESS.   Sweet Master Spencer, y'are a stranger grown. Where have you been these three days ?

SPEN.   The last night I sat up late at game. Here, take this bag, and lay't up till I call for't.

BESS.   Sir, I shall.

SPEN.   Bring me some wine.

BESS.   I know your taste, and I shall please your
palate.   (*Exit.*)

GOOD.   Troth, 'tis a pretty soul !

SPEN.   To thee I will unbosom all my thoughts ;
were her low birth but equal with her beauty, here would
I fix my thoughts.

GOOD.   You are not mad, sir ?   You say you love
her.

SPEN.   Never question that.

GOOD.   Then put her to 't ;   win Opportunity, she's
the best bawd.   If, as you say, she loves you, she can deny
you nothing.

SPEN.   I have proved her, unto the utmost test ;
examined her even to a modest force.   But all in vain.
She'll laugh, confer, keep company, discourse, and something more—kiss ;   but beyond that compass she no way
can be drawn.

GOOD.   'Tis a virtue but seldom found in taverns.
                (*Re-enter* BESS, *with wine.*)

BESS.   'Tis of the best Graves wine, sir.

SPEN.   Gramercy, girl, come sit.

BESS.   Pray pardon, sir, I dare not.

SPEN.   I'll ha't so.

BESS.   My fellows love me not ;   and will complain
of such a saucy boldness.

SPEN.   Pox on your fellows.   I'll try whether their
pottle-pots or heads be harder, if I do but hear them
grumble.   Sit ;   now, Bess, drink to me.

BESS.   To your good voyage.
                    (*Enter* DRAWER.)

DRAW.   Did you call, sir ?

SPEN.   Yes, sir, to have your absence.   Captain, this
health.

GOOD.   Let it come, sir.

DRAW.   Must you be set, and we wait, with a——

SPEN.   What say you, sir?

DRAW.   Anon, anon.   I come there.   (*Exit.*)

SPEN.   What will you venture, Bess, to sea with me?

BESS.   What I love best, my heart; for I could wish I had been born to equal you in fortune, or you so low, to have been ranked with me.   I could have then presumed boldly to say I love none but my Spencer.

(*Re-enter* DRAWER.)

DRAW.   Bess, you must fill some wine into the Portcullis; the gentlemen there will drink none but of your drawing.

SPEN.   She shall not rise, sir.   Go, let your master snick-up.

DRAW.   And that should be cousin-german to the hick-up.

(*Enter* SECOND DRAWER.)

2ND DRAW.   Bess, you must needs come.   The gentlemen fling pots, pottles, drawers and all down stairs. The whole house is in an uproar.

BESS.   Pray pardon, sir; I must be gone.

2ND DRAW.   The gentlemen swear if she come not up to them, they will come down to her.

SPEN.   If they come in peace like civil gentlemen, they may be welcome.   If otherwise, let them usurp their pleasures.   We stand prepared for both.

Thomas Heywood.

A GROAT'S WORTH OF WIT

*G*EORGE PEELE was making merry with three or foure of his friends in Pye Corner; where the Tapster of the house was much given to Poetrie: for he had ingrossed The Knight of the Sunne, Venus and Adonis, and other Pamphlets which the Stripling had collected together ; and knowing *George* to be a Poet, he tooke great delight in his company, and out of his bounty would bestow a brace of Cannes on him. *George* observing the humour of the Tapster, meant presently to worke upon him. What will you say, quoth *George* to his friends, if, out of this spirit of the Cellar, I fetch a good Angell, that shall bid us all to supper. We would gladly see that, quoth his friends. Content your selfe, quoth *George*. The Tapster ascends with his two Cannes, delivers one to Master *Peele*, and the other to his friends : gives them kind welcome : but *George*, in stead of giving him thankes, bids him not to trouble him : and beginnes in these termes : I protest, Gentlemen, I wonder you will urge me so much ; I sweare I have it not about me. What is the matter ? quoth the Tapster. Hath any one angered you ? No, faith, quoth *George*, Ile tell thee, it is this : There is a friend of ours in Newgate, for nothing but onely the command of the Justices, and he being now to be released, sends to me to bring him an Angell ; now the man I love dearely well ; and if hee want tenne Angells he shall have them ; for I know him sure ; but heere's the misery, either I must goe home, or I must be forced to pawne this ; and pluckes an old Harry-groat out of his pocket. The Tapster lookes upon it : Why, and it please you, Sir, quoth he, this is but a groat. No, Sir, quoth *George*, I know it is but a groat : but this groat will I not lose for forty pound : for this groat had I of my mother, as a testimony of a Lease of a House I am to possesse after her decease ; and if I should lose this groat, I were in a faire case : and either I must pawne this groat, or there the fellow must lye still. Quoth the

Tapster, If it please you, I will lend you an Angell on it, and I will assure you it shall bee safe. Wilt thou ? quoth *George ;* as thou art an honest man, locke it up in thy Chest, and let me have it whensoever I call for it. As I am an honest man, you shall, quoth the Tapster. *George* delivered him his groat ; the Tapster gave him ten shillings : to the Taverne goe they with the money and there merrily spend it. It fell out, some time after, the Tapster, having many of these lurches, fell to decay, and indeede was turned out of service, having no more coine in the world than this groat, and in this misery, hee met *George,* as poore as himselfe. O, Sir, quoth the Tapster, you are happily met ; I have your groat safe, though since I saw you last, I have bid great extremitie ; and I protest, save that groat, I have not any one penny in the world ; therefore I pray you, Sir, helpe me to my money, and take your pawne. Not for the World, quoth George : thou saist thou hast but that Groat in the world : my bargaine was, that thou shouldst keepe that groat, untill I did demand it of thee : I ask thee none. I will doe thee farre more good ; because thou art an honest fellow, keepe thou that groat still, till I call for it : and so doing, the proudest Jacke in England cannot justifie that thou are not worth a groat ; otherwise, they might : and so, honest Michael, farewell. So George leaves the poore Tapster picking of his fingers, his head full of proclamations what he might doe : at last sighing, hee ends with this Proverbe

> For the price of a Barrel of Beere
> I have bought a groats worth of wit,
> Is not that deare ?

Old Chap Book.

CLEM, OF THE CASTLE, PLYMOUTH

ROUGHMAN.   Where be these drawers—rascals, I should say—that will give no attendance ?

(Enter CLEM.*)*

CLEM.   Anon, anon, sir : please you see a room ? What—you here again ! Now we shall have such roaring !

ROUGH.   You, sirrah, call your mistress.

CLEM.   Yes, sir, I know it is my duty to call her mistress.

ROUGH.   See an the slave will stir.

CLEM.   Yes, I do stir.

ROUGH.   Shall we have humours, sauce-box ? You have ears ; I'll teach you prick-song.

CLEM.   But you have now a wrong sow by the ear. I will call her.

ROUGH.   Do, sir, you had best.

CLEM.   If you were twenty Roughmans, if you lug me by the ears again, I'll draw.

ROUGH.   Ha ! what will you draw ?

CLEM.   The best wine in the house for your worship ; and I would call her, but I can assure you that she is either not stirring, or else not in case.

ROUGH.   How not in case ?

CLEM.   I think she hath not her smock on ; for I think I saw it lie at her bed's head.

ROUGH.   What ! drawers grow capricious ?

CLEM.   Help ! Help !

(Enter BESS BRIDGES.*)*

BESS.   What uproar's this ? Shall we be never rid from these disturbances ?

ROUGH.   Why, how now, Bess ? Is this your house-wifery ? When you are mine, I'll have you rise as early as the lark. Look to the bar yourself ; these lazy rascals will bring your state behindhand.

CLEM. You lie, sir.

ROUGH. How ! Lie !

CLEM. Yes, sir, at the Raven in the High Street. I was at your lodging this morning for a pottle-pot.

ROUGH. You will about your business ; must you here stand gaping and idle ?

BESS. You wrong me, sir, and tyrannise too much over my servants. I will have no man touch them but myself.

CLEM. If I do not put ratsbane into his wine, instead of sugar, say I am no true baker. (*Exit.*)

(*Enter* KITCHEN-MAID.)

MAID. I pray, forsooth, what shall I reckon for the jowl of ling in the Portcullis ?

ROUGH. A pox upon your jowls, you kitchen-stuff ! Go, scour your skillets, pots, and dripping-pans, and interrupt not us.

MAID. The devil take your ox-heels, you foul cod's head ! Must you be kicking ?

ROUGH. Minion—dare you scold ?

MAID. Yes, sir ; and lay my ladle over your coxcomb !

Thomas Heywood.

THE INN-YARD "PRIG"

I HAD dressed myself up in a very mean habit, for as I had several shapes to appear in, I was now in an ordinary stuff gown, a blue apron, and a straw hat ; and I placed myself at the door of the Three Cups Inn in St. John's Street. There were several carriers used the inn, and the stage-coaches for Barnet, for Totteridge, and other towns that way stood always in the street in the evening, when they prepared to set out, so that I was ready for anything that offered. The meaning was this : people came frequently with bundles and small parcels to those inns, and call for such carriers or coaches as they want, to carry them into the country ; and there generally attends women, porters' wives or daughters, ready to take in such things for the people that employ them.

It happened very oddly that I was standing at the inn-gate, and a woman that stood there before, and which was the porter's wife belonging to the Barnet stage-coach, having observed me, asked if I waited for any of the coaches. I told her yes, I waited for my mistress, that was coming to go to Barnet. She asked me who was my mistress, and I told her any madam's name that came next me ; but it seemed I happened upon a name a family of which name lived at Hadley, near Barnet. I said no more to her, or she to me, a good while ; but by-and-by, somebody calling her at a door a little way off, she desired me that if anybody called for the Barnet coach, I would step and call her at the house, which it seems was an ale-house. I said " Yes," very readily, and away she went.

She was no sooner gone but comes a wench and a child, puffing and sweating, and asks for the Barnet coach. I answered presently, " Here." " Do you belong to the Barnet coach ? " says she. " Yes, sweetheart," said I ; " what do you want ? " " I want room for two passengers," says she. " Where are they, sweetheart ? " said I. " Here's this girl ; pray let her go into the coach," says she, " and I'll go and fetch my mistress." " Make haste, then, sweetheart," says I, " for we may be full else." The maid had a great bundle under her arm, so she put the child into the coach, and I said,

" You had best put your bundle into the coach too."
" No," said she ; " I am afraid somebody should slip it
away from the child." "Give it to me, then," said I.
" Take it, then," says she, "and be sure you take care
of it." " I'll answer for it," said I, "if it were £20
value." "There, take it, then," says she, and away she
goes.

As soon as I got the bundle, and the maid was out of
sight, I goes on towards the ale-house, where the porter's
wife was, so that if I had met her, I had then only been
going to give her the bundle, and to call her to her business, as if I was going away, and could stay no longer ;
but as I did not meet her, I walked away, and turning
into Charterhouse Lane, made off through Charterhouse
Yard, into Long Lane, then into Bartholomew Close,
so into Little Britain, and through the Bluecoat Hospital,
to Newgate Street.

Daniel Defoe.

THE MAID OF THE ROSE AT WOKINGHAM

SAY, my Uncle, I pray you discover
   What has been the cause of your woes,
That you pine and you whine like a lover ?—
   I have seen Molly Mog of the Rose.

O Nephew ! your grief is but folly,
   In town you may find better prog ;
Half-a-crown there will get you a Molly,
   A Molly much better than Mog.

I know that by wits 'tis recited
   That women at best are a clog ;
But I am not so easily frightened
   From loving of sweet Molly Mog.

The school-boys delight in a play-day ;
    The school-master's joy is to flog ;
Fop is the delight of a lady,
    But mine is in sweet Molly Mog.

Will-a-wisp leads the trav'ller a gadding
    Thro' ditch, and thro' quagmire, and bog ;
No light can e'er set me a-padding
    But the eyes of my sweet Molly Mog.

For guineas in other men's breeches
    Your gamesters will palm and will cog ;
But I envy them none of their riches,
    So I palm my sweet Molly Mog.

The heart that's half wounded is changing,
    It here and there leaps like a frog ;
But my heart can never be ranging,
    It's so fix'd on my sweet Molly Mog.

Who follows all women of pleasure,
    In love has a taste like a hog ;
For no girl can give better measure
    Of joys than my sweet Molly Mog.

I feel I'm in love to distraction,
    My senses are all in a fog ;
And in nothing can find satisfaction
    But in thought of my sweet Molly Mog.

A letter when I am inditing,
    Comes Cupid and gives me a jog,
And I fill all my paper with writing
    Of nothing but sweet Molly Mog.

If I would not give up the three Graces,
    I wish I were hang'd like a dog,
And at court all the drawing-room faces,
    For a glance at my sweet Molly Mog.

For those faces want nature and spirit,
    And seem as cut out of a log ;
Juno, Venus, and Pallas's merit
    Unite in my sweet Molly Mog.

Those who toast all the Family Royal,
    In bumpers of Hogan and Nog,
Have hearts not more true or more loyal
    Than mine to my sweet Molly Mog.

Were Virgil alive with his Phillis,
    And writing another Eclogue ;
Both his Phillis and fair Amaryllis
    He'd give up for my sweet Molly Mog.

When Molly comes up with the liquor
    Then jealousy sets me agog,
To be sure she's a bit for the Vicar,
    And so I shall lose Molly Mog.

                             John Gay.

BETTY AND THE LANDLORD

ADAMS was going to answer, when a most hideous
uproar began in the inn. Mrs. Tow-wouse, Mr.
Tow-wouse, and Betty, all lifting up their voices together ; but Mrs. Tow-wouse's voice, like a bass-viol in
a concert, was clearly and distinctly distinguished among
the rest, and was heard to articulate the following
sounds :—" O you damn'd villain ! is this the return

to all the care I have taken of your family ? This the reward of my virtue ? Is this the manner in which you behave to one who brought you a fortune, and preferred you to so many matches, all your betters ? To abuse my bed, my own bed, with my own servant ! but I'll maul the slut, I'll tear her nasty eyes out ! Was ever such a pitiful dog, to take up with such a mean trollop ? If she had been a gentlewoman, like myself, it had been some excuse ; but a beggarly, saucy, dirty servant-maid. Get you out of my house, you whore." To which she added another name, which we do not care to stain our paper with. It was a monosyllable beginning with a b—, and indeed was the same as if she had pronounced the words, she-dog. Which term we shall, to avoid offence, use on this occasion, though indeed both the mistress and maid uttered the above-mentioned b—, a word extremely disgustful to females of the lower sort. Betty had borne all hitherto with patience, and had uttered only lamentations ; but the last appellation stung her to the quick. " I am a woman as well as yourself," she roared out, " and no she-dog ; and if I have been a little naughty, I am not the first ; if I have been no better than I should be," cried she, sobbing, " that's no reason you should call me out of my name ; my be-betters are wo-worse than me."—" Huzzy, huzzy," says Mrs. Tow-wouse, " have you the impudence to answer me ? Did I not catch you, you saucy "—and then again repeated the terrible word so odious to female ears. " I can't bear that name," answered Betty : " if I have been wicked, I am to answer for it myself in the other world ; but I have done nothing that's unnatural ; and I will go out of your house this moment, for I will never be called she-dog by any mistress in England." Mrs. Tow-wouse then armed herself with the spit, but was prevented from executing any dreadful purpose by Mr. Adams, who confined her arms with the strength of a wrist which Hercules would not have been ashamed of. Mr. Tow-wouse being caught, as our lawyers express it, with the manner and having no defence to make, very prudently withdrew himself; and Betty committed herself to the protection of the hostler, who, though she could not conceive him pleased with what had happened, was, in her opinion, rather a gentler beast than her mistress.

Betty, who was the occasion of all this hurry, had some good qualities. She had good nature, generosity, and compassion, but unfortunately her constitution was composed of those warm ingredients which, though the purity of courts or nunneries might have happily controlled them, were by no means able to endure the ticklish situation of a chambermaid at an inn; who is daily liable to the solicitations of lovers of all complexions; to the dangerous addresses of fine gentlemen of the army, who sometimes are obliged to reside with them a whole year together; and, above all, are exposed to the caresses of footmen, stage-coachmen, and drawers; all of whom employ the whole artillery of kissing, flattering, bribing, and every other weapon which is to be found in the whole armoury of love, against them.

Betty, who was but one-and-twenty, had now lived three years in this dangerous situation, during which she had escaped pretty well. An ensign of foot was the first person who made an impression on her heart; he did indeed raise a flame in her which required the care of a surgeon to cool.

While she burnt for him, several others burnt for her.

Officers of the army, young gentlemen travelling the western circuit, inoffensive squires, and some of graver character, were set a-fire by her charms !

At length, having perfectly recovered the effects of her first unhappy passion, she seemed to have vowed a state of perpetual chastity. She was long deaf to all the sufferings of her lovers, till one day, at a neighbouring fair, the rhetoric of John the hostler, with a new straw hat and a pint of wine, made a second conquest over her.

She did not, however, feel any of those flames on this occasion which had been the consequence of her former amour ; nor, indeed, those other ill effects which prudent young women very justly apprehend from too absolute an indulgence to the pressing endearments of their lovers. This latter, perhaps, was a little owing to her not being entirely constant to John, with whom she permitted Tom Whipwell the stage-coachman, and now and then a handsome young traveller, to share her favours.

Henry Fielding.

HUMPHREY CLINKER GETS A JOB

MRS. BRAMBLE, turning from him, said she had never seen such a filthy tatterdemalion, and bid him begone ; observing, that he would fill the room full of vermin. Her brother darted a significant glance at her, as she retired with Liddy into another apartment ; and then asked the man if he was known to any person in Marlborough ? When he answered, that the landlord of the inn had known him from his infancy, mine host was immediately called, and, being interrogated on the subject, declared that the young fellow's name was Humphrey Clinker. That he had been a love-begotten babe, brought up in the workhouse, and put out apprentice by the parish to a country blacksmith, who died before the boy's time was out. That he had worked for some time under his ostler, as a helper and extra postilion, till he was taken ill of the ague, which disabled him from getting his bread. That, having sold or pawned everything he had in the world for his cure and subsistence, he became so miserable and shabby, that he disgraced the stable, and was dismissed ; but that he never heard anything to the prejudice of his character in other respects. " So that the fellow being sick and destitute," said my uncle, " you turned him out to die in the streets."—" I pay the poor's rate," replied the other, " and I have no right to maintain idle vagrants, either in sickness or health ; besides, such a miserable object would have brought discredit upon my house."

" You perceive," said the Squire, turning to me, " our landlord is a Christian of bowels. Who shall presume to censure the morals of the age, when the very publicans exhibit such examples of humanity ? Hark ye, Clinker, you are a most notorious offender. You stand convicted of sickness, hunger, wretchedness, and want. But, as it does not belong to me to punish criminals, I will only take upon me the risk of giving you a word of advice. Get a shirt with all convenient despatch, that your nakedness may not henceforward give offence to travelling gentlewomen, specially maidens in years."

So saying, he put a guinea into the hand of the poor fellow, who stood staring at him in silence, with his mouth wide open, till the landlord pushed him out of the room.

Tobias Smollett.

THE BEDROOM BELL

EVERYTHING was now once more quiet, and most of the company returned again to their beds ; but the landlady, either from the natural activity of her disposition, or from her fear for her plate, having no propensity to sleep, prevailed with the officers, as they were to march within little more than an hour, to spend tha time with her over a bowl of punch.

Jones had lain awake all this while, and had heard great part of the hurry and bustle that had passed, of which he had now some curiosity to know the particulars. He therefore applied to his bell, which he rung at least twenty times without any effect : for my landlady was in such high mirth with her company, that no clapper could be heard there but her own ; and the drawer and chambermaid, who were sitting together in the kitchen (for neither durst he sit up nor she lie in bed alone), the more they heard the bell ring the more they were frightened, and as it were nailed down in their places.

At last, at a lucky interval of chat, the sound reached the ears of our good landlady, who presently sent forth her summons, which both her servants instantly obeyed. " Joe," says the mistress, " don't you hear the gentleman's bell ring ? Why don't you go up ? "—" It is not my business," answered the drawer, " to wait upon the chambers—it is Betty Chambermaid's."—" If you come to that," answered the maid, " it is not my business to wait upon gentlemen. I have done it indeed sometimes ; but the devil fetch me if ever I do again, since you make your preambles about it." The bell still ringing violently, their mistress fell into a passion, and swore, if the drawer did not go up immediately, she would turn him away that very morning. " If you do, madam," says he, " I can't help it. I won't do another servant's business." She then applied herself to the maid, and endeavoured to prevail by gentle means ; but all in vain : Betty was as inflexible as Joe. Both insisted it was not their business, and they would not do it.

The lieutenant then fell a laughing, and said, " Come, I will put an end to this contention " ; and then turning to the servants, commended them for their resolution in not giving up the point ; but added, he was sure, if one would consent to go the other would. To which proposal they both agreed in an instant, and accordingly went up very lovingly and close together.

Henry Fielding.

DICK OSTLER

THE Lady of the Seven Stars did not, indeed, ring a bell, because such was not the fashion of the time, but she whistled on a silver-call, which was hung by her side, and a tight serving-maiden entered the room.

" Tell Dick Ostler to come here," said Mrs. Bickerton.

Dick Ostler accordingly made his appearance ;—a queer, knowing, shambling animal, with a hatchet-face, a squint, a game-arm, and a limp.

" Dick Ostler," said Mrs. Bickerton, in a tone of authority that showed she was (at least by adoption) Yorkshire too, " thou knowest most people and most things o' the road."

" Eye, eye, God help me, mistress," said Dick, shrugging his shoulders betwixt a repentant and a knowing expression—" Eye ! I ha' know'd a thing or twa i' ma day, mistress." He looked sharp and laughed—looked grave and sighed, as one who was prepared to take the matter either way.

" Kenst thou this wee bit paper amang the rest, man ? " said Mrs. Bickerton, handing him the protection which Ratcliffe had given Jeanie Deans.

When Dick had looked at the paper, he winked with one eye, extended his grotesque mouth from ear to ear, like a navigable canal, scratched his head powerfully, and then said " Ken ?—ay—maybe we ken summat, an it werena for harm to him, mistress."

" None in the world," said Mrs. Bickerton ; " only a dram of Hollands to thyself, man, an thou will't speak."

" Why, then," said Dick, giving the head-band of his breeches a knowing hoist with one hand, and kicking out one foot behind him to accommodate the adjustment of that important habiliment, " I dares to say the pass will be kend well eneugh on the road, an that be all."

" But what sort of a lad was he ? " said Mrs. Bickerton, winking to Jeanie, as proud of her knowing ostler.

" Why, what ken I ?—Jim the Rat—why, he was Cock o' the North within this twelmonth—he and Scotch Wilson, Handie Dandie, as they called him—but he's been out o' this country a while, as I rackon ; but ony gentleman, as keeps the road o' this side Stamford, will respect Jim's pass."

Without asking farther questions, the landlady filled Dick Ostler a bumper of Hollands. He ducked with his head and shoulders, scraped with his more advanced hoof, bolted the alcohol, to use the learned phrase, and withdrew to his own domains.

Sir Walter Scott.

A CHARACTER

A REGULAR character was that old ostler ; he was a Yorkshireman by birth, but had seen a great deal of life in the vicinity of London, to which, on the death of his parents, who were very poor people, he went at a very early age. Amongst other places where he had served as ostler was a small inn at Hounslow, much frequented by highwaymen, whose exploits he was fond of narrating, especially those of Jerry Abershaw, who, he said, was a capital rider ; and on hearing his accounts of that worthy, I half regretted that the old fellow had not been in London, and I had not formed his acquaintance about the time I was thinking of writing the life of the said Abershaw, not doubting that with his assistance, I could have produced a book at least as remarkable as the life and adventures of that entirely imaginary personage Joseph Sell. My old friend, however, after talking of Abershaw, would frequently add, that, good rider as Abershaw certainly was, he was decidedly inferior to Richard Ferguson, generally called Galloping Dick, who was a pal of Abershaw's, and had enjoyed a career as long, and nearly as remarkable as his own. I learned from him that both were capital customers at the Hounslow inn, and that he had frequently drank with them in the corn-room. He said that no man could desire more jolly or entertaining companions over a glass of " summut " ; but that upon the road it was anything but desirable to meet them ; there they were terrible, cursing and swearing, and thrusting the muzzles of their pistols into people's mouths ; and at this part of his locution the old man winked, and said, in a somewhat lower voice, that upon the whole they were right in doing so, and that

when a person had once made up his mind to become a
highwayman, his best policy was to go the whole hog,
fearing nothing, but making everybody afraid of him.

George Borrow.

WILL WATERPROOF'S LYRICAL MONOLOGUE MADE
AT THE COCK

O PLUMP head-waiter at the Cock,
    To which I most resort,
How goes the time ?   'Tis five o'clock.
    Go fetch a pint of port :
But let it not be such as that
    You set before chance-comers,
But such whose father-grape grew fat
    On Lusitanian summers.

No vain libation to the Muse,
    But may she still be kind,
And whisper lovely words, and use
    Her influence on the mind,
To make me write my random rhymes,
    Ere they be half-forgotten ;
Nor add and alter, many times,
    Till all be ripe and rotten.

Head-waiter, honoured by the guest
    Half mused or reeling ripe,
The pint you brought me was the best
    That ever came from pipe.
But tho' the port surpasses praise,
    My nerves have dealt with stiffer.
Is there some magic in the place ?
    Or do my peptics differ ?

For since I came to live and learn,
   No pint of white or red
Had ever half the power to turn
   This wheel within my head,
Which bears a season'd brain about,
   Unsubject to confusion,
Tho' soaked and saturate, out and out,
   Thro' every convolution.

The Muse, the jolly Muse, it is !
   She answered to my call,
She changes with that mood or this,
   Is all-in-all to all :
She lit the spark within my throat,
   To make my blood run quicker,
Used all her fiery will, and smote
   Her life into the liquor.

And hence this halo lives about
   The waiter's hands, that reach
To each his perfect pint of stout,
   His proper chop to each.
He looks not like the common breed
   That with the napkin dally ;
I think he came like Ganymede
   From some delightful valley.

The Cock was of a larger egg
   Than modern poultry drop,
Stept forward on a firmer leg,
   And cramm'd a plumper crop ;
Upon an ampler dunghill trod,
   Crow'd lustier late and early,

Sipt wine from silver, praising God,
   And rak'd in golden barley.

A private life was all his joy,
   Till in a court he saw
A something-pottle-bodied boy,
   That knuckled at the taw :
He stoop'd and clutch'd him, fair and good,
   Flew over roof and casement ;
His brothers of the weather stood
   Stock-still for sheer amazement.

But he, by farmstead, thorpe and spire,
   And follow'd with acclaims,
A sign to many a staring shire,
   Came crowing over Thames.
Right down by smoky Paul's they bore,
   Till, where the street grows straighter,
One fixed for ever at the door,
   And one became head-waiter.

    .   .   .   .   .   .

Head-waiter of the chop-house here,
   To which I most resort,
I too must part : I hold thee dear
   For this good pint of port.
For this thou shalt from all things suck
   Marrow of mirth and laughter ;
And wheresoe'er thou move, good luck
   Shall fling her old shoe after.

But thou wilt never move from hence,
   The sphere thy fate allots :
Thy latter days increased with pence
   Go down among the pots :

Thou battenest by the greasy gleam
   In haunts of hungry sinners,
Old boxes larded with the steam
   Of thirty thousand dinners.

We fret, we fume, would shift our skins,
   Would quarrel with our lot ;
Thy care is, under polish'd tins,
   To serve the hot-and-hot ;
To come and go, and come again,
   Returning like the pewit,
And watch'd by silent gentlemen
   That trifle with the cruet.

Live long, ere from thy topmost head
   The thick-set hazel dies ;
Long, ere the hateful crow shall tread
   The corners of thine eyes :
Live long, nor feel in head or chest
   Our changeful equinoxes,
Till mellow death, like some late guest,
   Shall call thee from the boxes.

But when he calls, and thou shalt cease
   To pace the gritted floor,
And, laying down an unctuous lease
   Of life, shalt earn no more ;
No carved cross-bones, the types of Death,
   Shall show thee past to Heaven :
But carved cross-pipes, and, underneath,
   A pint-pot, neatly graven.

Alfred Tennyson.

A FAMOUS "BOOTS"

IN the Borough especially, there still remain some half
dozen old inns, which have preserved their external
features unchanged, and which have escaped alike the rage
for public improvement, and the encroachments of private
speculation. Great, rambling, queer, old places they
are, with galleries, and passages, and staircases, wide
enough and antiquated enough to furnish materials for
a hundred ghost stories, supposing we should ever be
reduced to the lamentable necessity of inventing any,
and that the world should exist long enough to exhaust
the innumerable veracious legends connected with old
London Bridge, and its adjacent neighbourhood on the
Surrey side.

It was in the yard of one of these inns—of no less celebrated a one than the White Hart—that a man was busily
employed in brushing the dirt off a pair of boots, early on
the morning succeeding the events narrated in the last
chapter. He was habited in a coarse-striped waistcoat,
with black calico sleeves, and blue glass buttons ; drab
breeches and leggings. A bright red handkerchief was
wound in a very loose and unstudied style round his neck,
and an old white hat was carelessly thrown on one side of
his head. There were two rows of boots before him, one
cleaned and the other dirty, and at every addition he made
to the clean row, he paused from his work, and contemplated its results with evident satisfaction.

The yard presented none of that bustle and activity
which are the usual characteristics of a large coach inn.
Three or four lumbering waggons, each with a pile of
goods beneath its ample canopy, about the height of the
second-floor window of an ordinary house, were stowed

away beneath a lofty roof which extended over one end of the yard : and another, which was probably to commence its journey that morning, was drawn out into the open space. A double tier of bedroom galleries, with old clumsy balustrades, ran round two sides of the straggling area, and a double row of bells to correspond, sheltered from the weather by a little sloping roof, hung over the door leading to the bar and coffee-room. Two or three gigs and chaise-carts were wheeled up under different little sheds and pent-houses ; and the occasional heavy tread of a cart-horse, or rattling of a chain at the further end of the yard, announced to anybody who cared about the matter, that the stable lay in that direction. When we add that a few boys in smock frocks were lying asleep on heavy packages, woolpacks, and other articles that were scattered about on heaps of straw, we have described as fully as need be the general appearance of the yard of the White Hart Inn, High Street, Borough, on the particular morning in question.

A loud ringing of one of the bells, was followed by the appearance of a smart chambermaid in the upper sleeping gallery, who, after tapping at one of the doors, and receiving a request from within, called over the balustrades—

" Sam ! "

" Hallo," replied the man with the white hat.

" Number twenty-two wants his boots."

" Ask number twenty-two, wether he'll have 'em now, or wait till he gets 'em," was the reply.

" Come, don't be a fool, Sam," said the girl, coaxingly, " the gentleman wants his boots directly."

" Well, you *are* a nice young 'ooman for a musical party, you are," said the boot-cleaner. " Look at these

here boots—eleven pair o' boots ; and one shoe as b'longs
to number six, with the wooden leg. The eleven boots is
to be called at half-past eight and the shoe at nine. Who's
number twenty-two, that's to put all the others out ? No,
no ; reg'lar rotation, as Jack Ketch said, wen he tied the
men up. Sorry to keep you a waitin', sir, but I'll attend to
you directly."

Charles Dickens.

SELLING A HORSE

I PROCEEDED, without delay, to the inn to which
my friend the surgeon had directed me. " It is of no
use coming here," said two or three ostlers, as I entered
the yard—"all full—no room whatever " ; whilst one
added in an under tone, " That ere a'n't a bad-looking
horse." " I want to see the master of this inn," said I, as
I dismounted from the horse. " See the master," said an
ostler—the same who had paid the negative kind of compliment to the horse—" a likely thing, truly ; my master
is drinking wine with some of the grand gentry, and can't
be disturbed for the sake of the like of you." " I bring a
letter to him," said I, pulling out the surgeon's epistle.
" I wish you would deliver it to him," I added, offering a
half-crown. " Oh, it's you, is it ? " said the ostler, taking
the letter and the half-crown ; " my master will be right
glad to see you ; why, you ha'n't been here for many a
year ; I'll carry the note to him at once." And with
these words he hurried into the house. " That's a nice
horse, young man," said another ostler, " what will you
take for it ? " to which interrogation I made no answer.
" If you wish to sell him," said the ostler, coming up to
me, and winking knowingly, " I think I and my partners
might offer you a summut under seventy pounds " ; to
which kind and half-insinuated offer I made no reply, save

by winking in the same kind of knowing manner in which I observed him wink. "Rather leary!" said a third ostler. "Well, young man, perhaps you will drink to-night with me and my partners, when we can talk the matter over." Before I had time to answer, the landlord a well-dressed, good-looking man, made his appearance with the ostler; he bore the letter in his hand. Without glancing at me, he betook himself at once to consider the horse, going round him, and observing every point with the utmost minuteness. At last, having gone round the horse three times, he stopped beside me, and keeping his eyes on the horse, bent his head towards his right shoulder. "That horse is worth some money," said he, turning towards me suddenly, and slightly touching me on the arm with the letter which he held in his hand; to which observation I made no reply, save by bending my head towards the right shoulder as I had seen him do. "The young man is going to talk to me and my partners about it to-night," said the ostler who had expressed an opinion that he and his friends might offer me somewhat under seventy pounds for the animal. "Pooh!" said the landlord, " the young man knows what he is about; in the meantime lead the horse to the reserved stall, and see well after him. My friend," said he, taking me aside after the ostler had led the animal away, "recommends you to me in the strongest manner, on which account alone I take you and your horse in. I need not advise you not to be taken in, as I should say, by your look, that you are tolerably awake; but there are queer hands at Horncastle at this time, and those fellows of mine, you understand me——; but I have a great deal to do at present, so you must excuse me." And thereupon went into the house.

George Borrow.

ROBERT, OF THE BOAR'S HEAD

ADJOINING the church, in a small cemetery, imme-diately under the back window of what was once the Boar's Head, stands the tombstone of Robert Preston, whilom drawer at the tavern. It is now nearly a century since this trusty drawer of good liquor closed his bustling career, and was thus quietly deposited within call of his customers. As I was clearing away the weeds from his epitaph, the little sexton drew me on one side with a mysterious air, and informed me in a low voice, that once upon a time, on a dark wintry night, when the wind was unruly, howling, and whistling, banging about doors and windows, and twirling weathercocks, so that the living were frightened out of their beds, and even the dead could not sleep quietly in their graves, the ghost of honest Preston, which happened to be airing itself in the church-yard, was attracted by the well-known call of " waiter " from the Boar's Head, and made its sudden appearance in the midst of a roaring club, just as the parish clerk was singing a stave from the " Mirre garland of Captain Death," to the discomfiture of sundry train-band cap-tains, and the conversion of an infidel attorney, who became a zealous Christian on the spot, and was never known to twist the truth afterwards, except in the way of business.

Be all this as it may, this Robert Preston seems to have been a worthy successor to the nimble-tongued Francis, who attended upon the revels of Prince Hal ; to have been equally prompt with his " Anon, anon, sir," and to have transcended his predecessor in honesty ; for Fal-staff, the veracity of whose taste no man will venture to impeach, flatly accuses Francis of putting lime in his sack ;

whereas honest Preston's epitaph lauds him for the sobriety
of his conduct, the soundness of his wine, and the fairness
of his measure :—

> " Bacchus, to give the toping world surprise,
> Produced one sober son, and here he lies,
> Tho' rear'd among full hogsheads, he defied
> The charms of wine and every one beside.
> O reader, if to justice thou'rt inclined,
> Keep honest Preston daily in thy mind.
> He drew good wine, took care to fill his pots,
> Had sundry virtues that excused his faults.
> You that on Bacchus have the like dependance
> Pray copy Bob in measure and attendance."

> *Washington Irving.*

THE CHAMBERMAID

WHEN clouds obscure the evening sky,
    And rains in torrents pour,
The inn with joy the travellers spy,
    And seek its welcome door.
'Tis there I stand to please them all,
    And follow still my trade ;
I smile and run whene'er they call,
    A merry little chambermaid.

But when appears the dawn of day,
    Farewell to every guest,
They take their leaves and onward stray,
    Some east and others west.
And when that horrid bore, the bill,
    Is call'd for, read, and paid,
I cry, " I hope, give what you will,
    You'll not forget the chambermaid."

Thus happy might I pass my life,
　　But love rules in my breast,
And till I'm made a happy wife,
　　I ne'er shall be at rest.
Then fortune's gifts in vain she sheds,
　　For love I leave my trade ;
And give my all to him who weds
　　The merry little chambermaid.

　　　　　　　　　　Theodore Hook.

A CRITICAL WAITER

I WAS now in the Strand, and, glancing about, I perceived that I was close by a hotel, which bore over the door the somewhat remarkable name of Holy Lands. Without a moment's hesitation I entered a well-lighted passage, and, turning to the left, I found myself in a well-lighted coffee-room, with a well-dressed and frizzled waiter before me. " Bring me some claret," said I, for I was rather faint than hungry, and I felt ashamed to give a humbler order to so well-dressed an individual. The waiter looked at me for a moment ; then, making a low bow, he bustled off, and I sat myself down in the box nearest to the window. Presently the waiter returned, bearing beneath his left arm a long bottle, and between the fingers of his right hand two large purple glasses ; placing the latter on the table, he produced a cork-screw, drew the cork in a twinkling, set the bottle down before me with a bang, and then, standing still, appeared to watch my movements. You think I don't know how to drink a glass of claret, thought I to myself. I'll soon show you how we drink claret where I come from ; and, filling one of the glasses to the brim, I flickered it for a moment between my eyes and the lustre, and then held it to my

nose ; having given that organ full time to test the
bouquet of the wine, I applied the glass to my lips, taking
a large mouthful of the wine, which I swallowed slowly
and by degrees, that the palate might likewise have an
opportunity of performing its functions. A second
mouthful I disposed of more summarily ; then, placing
the empty glass upon the table, I fixed my eyes upon
the bottle, and said—nothing ; whereupon the waiter
who had been observing the whole process with considerable attention, made me a bow yet more low than before,
and turning on his heel, retired with a smart chuck of his
head, as much as to say, It is all right ; the young man is
used to claret.

George Borrow.

THE STAGE-COACHMAN (ONE VIEW)

AND here, perhaps, it may not be unacceptable to my
untravelled readers, to have a sketch that may serve
as a general representation of this very numerous and
important class of functionaries, who have a dress, a
manner, a language, an air, peculiar to themselves, and
prevalent throughout the fraternity ; so that, wherever
an English stage-coachman may be seen, he cannot be
mistaken for one of any other craft or mystery.

He has commonly a broad, full face, curiously mottled
with red, as if the blood had been forced by hard
feeding into every vessel of the skin ; he is swelled into
jolly dimensions by frequent potations of malt liquors, and
his bulk is still further increased by a multiplicity of
coats, in which he is buried like a cauliflower, the upper
one reaching to his heels. He wears a broad-brimmed,
low-crowned hat ; a huge roll of coloured handkerchief
about his neck, knowingly knotted and tucked in at the
bosom ; and has in summer time a large bouquet of

flowers in his buttonhole ; the present, most probably, of some enamoured country lass. His waistcoat is commonly of some bright colour, striped, and his small-clothes extend far below the knees, to meet a pair of jockey-boots which reach about half-way up his legs.

All this costume is maintained with much precision ; he has a pride in having his clothes of excellent materials ; and, notwithstanding the seeming grossness of his appearance, there is still discernible that neatness and propriety of person which is almost inherent in an Englishman. He enjoys great consequence and consideration along the road ; has frequent conferences with the village housewives, who look upon him as a man of great trust and dependence ; and he seems to have a good understanding with every bright-eyed country lass. The moment he arrives where the horses are to be changed, he throws down the reins with something of an air, and abandons the cattle to the care of the ostler ; his duty being merely to drive from one stage to another. When off the box, his hands are thrust into the pockets of his great coat, and he rolls about the inn yard with an air of the most absolute lordliness. Here he is generally surrounded by an admiring throng of ostlers, stable-boys, shoeblacks, and those nameless hangers-on that infest inns and taverns, and run errands, and do all kinds of odd jobs, for the privilege of battening on the drippings of the kitchen and the leakage of the taproom. These all look up to him as to an oracle ; treasure up his cant phrases ; echo his opinions about horses and other topics of jockey lore ; and, above all, endeavour to imitate his air and carriage. Every ragamuffin that has a coat to his back thrusts his hands in the pockets, rolls in his gait, talks slang, and is an embryo Coachey.   *Washington Irving.*

THE STAGE-COACHMAN (ANOTHER VIEW)

I LIVED on very good terms, not only with the master and the old ostler, but with all the domestics and hangers on at the inn ; waiters, chambermaids, cooks, and scullions, not forgetting the " boots," of which there were three. As for the postillions, I was sworn brother with them all, and some of them went so far as to swear that I was the best fellow in the world ; for which high opinion entertained by them of me, I believe I was principally indebted to the good account their comrade gave of me, whom I had so hospitably received in the dingle. I repeat that I lived on good terms with all the people connected with the inn, and was noticed and spoken kindly to by some of the guests—especially by that class termed commercial travellers—all of whom were great friends and patronisers of the landlord, and were the principal promoters of the dinner, and subscribers to the gift of plate, which I have already spoken of, the whole fraternity striking me as the jolliest set of fellows imaginable, the best customers to an inn, and the most liberal to servants ; there was one description of persons, however, frequenting the inn, which I did not like at all, and which I did not get on well with, and these people were the stage-coachmen.

The stage-coachmen of England, at the time of which I am speaking, considered themselves mighty fine gentry, nay, I verily believe the most important personages of the realm, and their entertaining this high opinion of themselves can scarcely be wondered at ; they were low fellows, but masters at driving ; driving was in fashion, and sprigs of nobility used to dress as coachmen and imitate the slang and behaviour of the coachmen, from whom occasionally they would take lessons in driving as they sat beside them on the box, which post of honour any sprig of nobility who

happened to take a place on a coach claimed as his unques-
tionable right ; and these sprigs would smoke cigars and
drink sherry with the coachmen in bar-rooms, and on the
road ; and, when bidding them farewell, would give them
a guinea or a half-guinea, and shake them by the hand, so
that these fellows, being low fellows, very naturally
thought no small liquor of themselves, but would talk
familiarly of their friends lords so and so.

Truly the brutality and rapacious insolence of English
coachmen had reached a climax ; it was time that these
fellows should be disenchanted, and the time—thank
Heaven !—was not far distant. Let the craven dastards
who used to curry favour with them, and applaud their
brutality, lament their loss now that they and their vehicles
have disappeared from the roads ; I, who have ever been
an enemy to insolence, cruelty, and tyranny, loathe their
memory, and, what is more, am not afraid to say so, well
aware of the storm of vituperation, partly learnt from them,
which I may expect from those who used to fall down and
worship them.

George Borrow.

THE MORNING AFTER

MR. MANYLODES was, at any rate, right in this,
that that beverage, which men call bishop, is a
doctored tipple ; and Alaric Tudor, when he woke in the
morning, owned the truth. It had been arranged that
certain denizens of the mine should meet the two Commissioners at the pit-mouth at eight o'clock, and it had
been settled at dinner-time that breakfast should be on the
table at seven, sharp. Half an hour's quick driving would
take them to the spot.

At seven Mr. Fidus Neverbend, who had never yet
been known to be untrue to an appointment by the frac-

tion of a second, was standing over the breakfast-table alone. He was alone, but not on that account unhappy. He could hardly disguise the pleasure with which he asked the waiter whether Mr. Tudor was yet dressed, or the triumph which he felt when he heard that his colleague was not *quite ready*.

" Bring the tea and the eggs at once," said Neverbend, very briskly.

" Won't you wait for Mr. Tudor ? " asked the waiter, with an air of surprise. Now the landlord, waiter, boots, and chambermaid, the chambermaid especially, had all, in Mr. Neverbend's estimation, paid Tudor by far too much consideration ; and he was determined to show that he himself was first fiddle.

" Wait ! no ; quite out of the question—bring the hot water immediately—and tell the ostler to have the fly at the door at half-past seven exact."

" Yes, sir," said the man, and disappeared.

Neverbend waited five minutes, and then rang the bell impetuously. " If you don't bring me my tea imme-diately, I shall send for Mr. Boteldale." Now Mr. Botel-dale was the landlord.

" Mr. Tudor will be down in ten minutes," was the waiter's false reply ; for up to that moment poor Alaric had not yet succeeded in lifting his throbbing head from his pillow. The boots was now with him administering soda-water and brandy, and he was pondering in his sickened mind whether, by a manful effort, he could rise and dress himself ; or whether he would not throw him-self backwards on his coveted bed, and allow Neverbend the triumph of descending alone to the nether world.

Neverbend nearly threw the loaf at the waiter's head. Wait ten minutes longer ! what right had that vile Devon-

shire napkin-twirler to make to him so base a proposition?
"Bring me my breakfast, sir," shouted Neverbend, in
a voice that made the unfortunate sinner jump out of the
room, as though he had been moved by a galvanic battery.

In five minutes, tea made with lukewarm water, and
eggs that were not half boiled were brought to the impatient Commissioner. As a rule Mr. Neverbend, when
travelling on the public service, made a practice of enjoying
his meals. It was the only solace which he allowed himself; the only distraction from the cares of office which he
permitted either to his body or his mind. But on this
great occasion his country required that he should forget
his comforts; and he drank his tasteless tea, and ate
his uncooked eggs, threatening the waiter as he did so
with sundry pains and penalties, in the form of sixpences
withheld.

"Is the fly there?" said he, as he bolted a last morsel
of cold roast beef.

"Coming, sir," said the waiter, as he disappeared round
a corner.

In the meantime Alaric sat lackadaisical on his bedside,
all undressed, leaning his head upon his hand, and feeling
that his struggle to dress himself was all but useless. The
sympathetic boots stood by with a cup of tea—well-drawn
comfortable tea—in his hand, and a small bit of dry toast
lay near on an adjacent plate.

"Try a bit o' toast, sir," said boots.

"Ugh!" ejaculated poor Alaric.

"Have a leetle drop o' rum in the tea, sir, and it'll set
you all to rights in two minutes.'

The proposal made Alaric very sick, and nearly com-
pleted the catastrophe. "Ugh!" he said.

Anthony Trollope.

THE COMPLETE WAITER

YOUR thorough waiter has no ideas out of the sphere of his duty and the business ; and yet he is not narrow-minded either. He sees too much variety of character for that, and has to exercise too much consideration for the " drunken gentleman." But his world is the tavern, and all mankind but its visitors. His female sex are the maid-servants and his young mistress, or the widow. If he is ambitious, he aspires to marry one of the two latter : if otherwise, and Molly is prudent, he does not know but he may carry her off some day to be mistress of the Golden Lion at Chinksford, where he will " show off " in the eyes of Betty Laxon who refused him. He has no feeling of noise itself but as the sound of dining, or of silence but as a thing before dinner. Even a loaf with him is hardly a loaf ; it is so many " breads." His longest speech is the making out of a bill *viva voce*—" Two beefs—one potatoes—three ales—two wines—six-and-twopence "— which he does with an indifferent celerity, amusing to new-comers who have been relishing their fare, and not considering it as a mere set of items. He attributes all virtues to everybody, provided they are civil and liberal ; and of the existence of some vices he has no notion. Gluttony, for instance, with him, is not only inconceivable, but looks very like a virtue. He sees in it only so many more " beefs," and a generous scorn of the bill. As to wine, or almost any other liquor, it is out of your power to astonish him with the quantity you call for. His " Yes, sir," is as swift, indifferent, and official at the fifth bottle as at the first. Reform and other public events he looks upon purely as things in the newspaper, and the newspaper as a thing taken in at taverns, for gentlemen to read. His own reading is confined to " Accidents and Offences," and the advertisements for Butlers, which latter he peruses with an admiring fear, not choosing to give up " a certainty." When young he was always in a hurry, and exasperated his mistress by running against the other waiters, and breaking the " neguses." As he gets older, he learns to unite swiftness with caution ; declines wasting his breath in immediate answers to calls ; and knows, with a slight turn of his face and elevation of his voice, into what precise corner of the room to pitch his " Coming, sir." If you told him that, in Shakespeare's time, waiters said " Anon, anon, sir," he would be astonished at the repetition of the same word in one answer, and at the use of three words instead of two ; and he would justly infer that London could not have been so large, nor the chop-houses so busy, in those days. He would drop one of the two syllables of his " Yes, sir," if he could ; but business and civility will not allow it ; and therefore he does what he can by running them together in the swift sufficiency of his " Yezzir."

" Thomas ! "

" Yezzir."

" Is my steak coming ? "

" Yezzir."

" And the pint of port ? "

" Yezzir."

" You'll not forget the postman ? "

" Yezzir."

For in the habit of his acquiescence Thomas not seldom says " Yes, sir," for " No, sir," the habit itself rendering him intelligible.

Leigh Hunt.

THE INCOMPLETE WAITER

IN due sequence of events we drove up to the Temeraire, and alighted. A youth in livery received us on the doorstep. " Looks well," said Bullfinch confidentially. And then aloud, " Coffee-room ! "

The youth in livery (now perceived to be mouldy) conducted us to the desired haven, and was enjoined by Bullfinch to send the waiter at once, as we wished to order a little dinner in an hour. Then Bullfinch and I waited for the waiter, until, the waiter continuing to wait in some unknown and invisible sphere of action, we rang for the waiter ; which ring produced the waiter, who announced himself as not the waiter who ought to wait upon us, and who didn't wait a moment longer.

So Bullfinch approached the coffee-room door, and melodiously pitching his voice into a bar where two young ladies were keeping the books of the Temeraire, apologetically explained that we wished to order a little dinner in an hour, and that we were debarred from the execution of our inoffensive purpose by consignment to solitude.

Hereupon one of the young ladies rang a bell, which reproduced—at the bar this time—the waiter who was not the waiter who ought to wait upon us ; that extraordinary man, whose life seemed consumed in waiting upon people to say that he wouldn't wait upon them, repeated his former protest with great indignation, and retired.

Bullfinch, with a fallen countenance, was about to say to me, " This won't do," when the waiter who ought to wait upon us left off keeping us waiting at last. " Waiter," said Bullfinch piteously, " we have been a long time waiting." The waiter who ought to wait upon us laid the blame upon the waiter who ought not to wait upon us, and said it was all that waiter's fault.

" We wish," said Bullfinch, much depressed, " to order a little dinner in an hour.   What can we have ? "

" What would you like to have, gentlemen ? "

Bullfinch, with extreme mournfulness of speech and action, and with a forlorn old fly-blown bill of fare in his hand which the waiter had given him, and which was a sort of general manuscript index to any cookery-book you please, moved the previous question.

We could have mock-turtle soup, a sole, curry, and roast duck.   Agreed.   At this table by this window. Punctually in an hour.

I had been feigning to look out of this window ; but I had been taking note of the crumbs on all the tables, the dirty table-cloths, the stuffy, soupy, airless atmosphere, the stale leavings everywhere about, the deep gloom of the waiter who ought to wait upon us, and the stomach-ache with which a lonely traveller at a distant table in a corner was too evidently afflicted.   I now pointed out to Bull-finch the alarming circumstance that this traveller had *dined*.   We hurriedly debated whether, without infringe-ment of good breeding, we could ask him to disclose if he had partaken of mock-turtle, sole, curry, or roast duck ? We decided that the thing could not be politely done, and we had set our own stomachs on a cast, and they must stand the hazard of the die.

I hold phrenology, within certain limits, to be true ; I am much of the same mind as to the subtler expressions of the hand ; I hold physiognomy to be infallible ; though all these sciences demand rare qualities in the student. But I also hold that there is no more certain index to per-sonal character than the condition of a set of casters is to the character of any hotel. Knowing, and having often tested this theory of mine, Bullfinch resigned himself to the worst, when, laying aside any remaining veil of disguise, I held up before him, in succession, the cloudy oil and furry vinegar, the clogged cayenne, the dirty salt and the anchovy sauce in a flannel waistcoat of decomposition.

Charles Dicken .

ADVENTURE AND ENCOUNTER

OFT in your clothier's and your grazier's inn,
You shall have chamberlains that there have been
Plac'd purposely by thieves, or else consenting
By their large bribes, and by their often tempting,
That mark your purses drawn, and give a guess
What's there, within a little, more or less.
Then will they grip your cloak-bags, feel their weight ;
There's likewise in mine host sometimes deceit :
If it be left in charge with him all night,
Unto his roaring guests he gives a light,
Who spend full thrice as much in wine and beer
As you in those and all your other cheer.

John Clavel.

IF I be honest in keeping this " Light Heart,"
Where, I imagine, all the world's a play :
The state, and men's affairs, all passages
Of life, to spring new scenes ; come in, go out,
And shift and vanish ; and if I have got
A seat to sit at ease here, in mine inn,
To see the comedy, and laugh and chuck
At the variety and throng of humours
And dispositions that come justling in
And out still, as they one drove hence another ;
Why will you envy me my happiness ?

Ben Jonson.

THE POET'S TRICK

SKELTON was an Englishman, born as Scogin was, and he was educated and brought up in Oxford ; and there was he made a poet laureate. And on a time he had been at Abingdon to make merry, where that he had eat salt meats, and he did come late home to Oxford, and he did lie in an inn named Ye Tabere, which is now Ye Angel, and he did drink, and went to bed. About midnight he was so thirsty or dry that he was constrained to call to the tapster for drink, and the tapster heard him not. Then he cried to his host and his hostess, and to the ostler, for drink ; and no man would hear him ; alack, said Skelton, I shall perish for lack of drink ! what remedy ? At last he did cry out and said, Fire, fire, fire ! When Skelton heard every man bustle himself upward, and some of them were naked, and some were half asleep and amazed, and Skelton did cry Fire, fire, still, that every man knew not whither to resort. Skelton did go to bed, and the host and hostess, and the tapster with the ostler, did run to Skelton's chamber with candles lighted in their hands, saying, Where, where, where is the fire ? Here, here, here, said Skelton, and pointed his finger to his mouth, saying, Fetch me some drink to quench the fire and the heat and the dryness in my mouth ; and so they did. Wherefore it is good for every man to help his own self in time of need with some policy or craft.

The Merrie Tales of Master Skelton.

FREE ENTERTAINMENT

YOUR mayorship upon a horse whose hire is not paid for, with your page at your stirrup, like a Castilian Cavalier, lighted pennilesse at a pretie Inne, where that day sate certain Justices in Commission. Your high heart, carelesse of your present neede, would needes for your selfe share out one of the fairest chambers. Your page must be purveyer for your diet who in the kitchen found nothing for your liking. Beefe was grosse, veale was flashy, mutton fulsome, rabbets, hens and capons common. Wild foule for Will foole, or he will fast. But now a juggling tricke to pay the shot.

My imp, your man, while mistresse, men, and maids were busied about provision for the Justices that sate, slips into a private parlour, wherein stood good store of plate, and conveying a massy salt under his capouch, little lesse worth than twentie mark, got secretly to the back-side, and cast it into a filthie pond : which done, he acquaints your knaveship with the deed.

By then your diet was drest, the salt was mist, the good wife cryde out, the maydes were ready to runne madde.

Your man (making the matter strange) inquird the cause : which when they tolde, O (quoth hee) that my master would deale in the matter. I am sure he can do as much as any in the world.

Well, to you they come pitifully complaining, when very wrathfully (your choler rising) you demand reason why they should thinke yee bee able to deale in such cases. Your kind nature (bent alwayes to lenitie) yielded at the last to their importuning : only wisht them to stay till the nexte day, for that you would not deale while the Justices were in the house.

They must do as your discretion appoints : next day, calling the good-man and wife to your bedside, ye tell them the salt was stolen by one of their familiars, whom ye have forced by Art to bring it backe againe to the house, and in such a pond to cast it.

As you direct them, they search and find : then comes your name in rare admiration, the Host gives you four angels for a reward, the Hostess two French crowns ; the maides are double diligent to do your service, that they may learne their fortunes, the whole towne talks of the cunning man that, indeed, had only conny-catcht his Host.

Henrie Chettle.

FALSTAFF'S ESCAPE
The Boar's Head Tavern, Eastcheap.

BARDOLPH. O, my lord, my lord ! the sheriff with a most monstrous watch is at the door.

Falstaff. Out, ye rogue ! Play out the play : I have much to say in the behalf of that Falstaff.

(*Enter the* Hostess.)

Host.   O, Jesu, my lord, my lord !——

Prince.   Heigh, heigh ! the devil rides upon a fiddle-stick : what's the matter ?

Host.   The sheriff and all the watch are at the door : they are come to search the house. Shall I let them in ?

Fal.   Dost thou hear, Hal ? never call a true piece of gold a counterfeit : thou art essentially mad, without seeming so.

Prince.   And thou a natural coward, without instinct.

Fal.   I deny your major : if you will deny the sheriff, so ; if not, let him enter : if I become not a cart as well as another man, a plague on my bringing up ! I hope I shall as soon be strangled with a halter as another.

Prince.   Go, hide thee behind the arras : the rest walk up above. Now, my masters, for a true face and good conscience.

FAL. Both which I have had : but their date is out, and therefore I'll hide me.

PRINCE. Call in the sheriff.

(Enter SHERIFF *and the* CARRIER.*)*

Now, master sheriff, what is your will with me ?

SHER. First, pardon me, my lord.   A hue and cry
Hath follow'd certain men unto this house.

PRINCE. What men ?

SHER. One of them is well known, my gracious lord,
A gross fat man.

CAR.   As fat as butter.

PRINCE. The man, I do assure you, is not here ;
For I myself at this time have employ'd him.
And, sheriff, I will engage my word to thee
That I will, by to-morrow dinner-time,
Send him to answer thee, or any man,
For anything he shall be charged withal :
And so let me entreat you leave the house.

SHER. I will, my lord.   There are two gentlemen
Have in this robbery lost three hundred marks.

PRINCE. It may be so : if he have robb'd these men,
He shall be answerable ; and so farewell.

SHER. Good night, my noble lord.

PRINCE. I think it is good morrow, is it not ?

SHER. Indeed, my lord, I think it be two o'clock.

(Exeunt SHERIFF *and* CARRIER.*)*

PRINCE. This oily rascal is known as well as Paul's.
Go, call him forth.

PETO. Falstaff !—Fast asleep behind the arras, and snorting like a horse.

PRINCE. Hark, how hard he fetches breath.   Search his pockets. *(He searcheth his pockets, and findeth certain papers.)* What hast thou found ?

PETO. Nothing but papers, my lord.

PRINCE.   Let's see what they be : read them.

PETO. (*Reads.*) Item, A capon   .   .   2*s.* 2*d.*
                  Item, Sauce .   .   .   4*d.*
                  Item, Sack, two gallons .   5*s.* 8*d.*
                  Item, Anchovies and sack
                      after supper .   .   .   2*s.* 6*d.*
                  Item, Bread   .   .   .   ob.

PRINCE.   O monstrous ! but one half-pennyworth of
bread to this intolerable deal of sack !

William Shakespeare.

THE CONFIDENCE TRICK

THESE rank-riders (like butchers to Rumford
Market) seldom go under six or seven in a company, and these careers they fetch. Their purses being
warmly lined with some purchase gotten before, and they
themselves well booted and spur'd, and in reasonable good
outsides, arrive at the fairest Inn they can choose, either
in Westminster, the Strand, the City, or the Suburbs.
Two of them who have clothes of purpose to fit the play,
carrying the shew of Gentlemen : the other act their parts
in blue coats as they were their Servingmen, though indeed
they be all fellows.   They enter all dirtied or dusted
(according as it shall please the highway to use them) and the
first bridle they put into the Colts mouth (thats to say the
Innkeepers) is at their coming in to ask aloud if the footman
be gone back with the horses ? 'tis answered yes. Here the
rank-riders lie three or four days, spending moderately
enough, yet abating not a penny of any reckoning to show
of what house they come : in which space their counterfeit
followers learn what countryman the master of the house
is, where the Hostlers and Chamberlains were born, and

what other country Gentlemen are guests to the Inn? which lessons being presently gotten by heart, they fall in study with the general rules of their knavery : and those are, first to give out that their Master is a gentleman of such and such means, in such a shire (which shall be sure to stand far enough from those places where any of the house, or of other guests were born) that he is come to receive so many hundred pounds upon land which he hath sold, and that he means to Inn there some quarter of a year at least. . . .

In the middle of supper, or else very early in the following morning, comes in a counterfeit footman, sweatingly, delivering a message that such a Knight hath sent for the headmaster of these rank-riders, and that he must be with him by such an hour, the journey being not above twelve or fourteen miles. Upon delivery of this message (from so dear and noble a friend) he swears and chafes, because all his horses are out of town, curseth the sending of them back, offers any money to have himself, his couzen with him, and his men but reasonably horsed. Mine host being a credulous ass suffers them all to get up upon him, for he provides them horses either of his own (thinking his Guest to be a man of great account, and being loath to lose him, because he spends well) or else sends out to hire them of his neighbours, passing his word for their forthcoming within a day or two. Up they get and away gallop our rank-riders as far as the poor jades can carry them.

Thomas Dekker.

THE CRIMPING DEN

THE woman of the house conversed very freely, and conducted herself with such civility that we were emboldened to reveal our circumstances to her, and to entreat that she would procure us a passage from some of the collier masters. In the kindest manner possible she lamented that we had been a day late ; that a friend of hers had just fallen down to Shields, and that she would have had sufficient influence with him to have taken us all to London. " But," added she, " he is not yet, perhaps, gone ; he sometimes waits after the ship and follows her in the boat." We entreated her to send to inquire. To our great satisfaction he was not gone, and would call in a little time at this house. In an hour in the captain comes, " Where are those honest gentleman soldiers that are in such distress ? " We all stood up, and in a submissive manner paid our respects. " Well, gentlemen, and is all your money spent ? "—" Indeed, it is, and we will be infinitely obliged to you, sir, if you will give us a passage. We will be very willing to do any thing we can to the ship, though we are not seamen."—" For my good land-lady's sake here, I shall accommodate you. But are you all ready to go on board ? for I go on board myself this very night."—" Yes, sir, we are ready to go this very minute."—" No, no. We'll drink together. Come, land-lady, make these honest gentlemen a sneaker of punch." Conscious of empty pockets we stared at one another. " Come, come," said the captain, " don't be concerned at you having no money ; my landlady and me, here, never part with dry lips. Come, goodwife, make the punch as I bid you."

Our hearts were full with the generous captain's good-ness, and we thanked him, praying God to bless him. While we were drinking the punch, he told the landlady that he would go home and order his boy to bring the boat at high water, and in the meantime ordered some supper. In less than an hour he returned, and frowned that we had not drunk out the punch. " Come, don't be bashful, when that's out we can have another. When I am obliging poor men, I wish to do it handsomely." The bowl was emptied, and another brought ; then a good leg of mutton. We ate heartily, and were pressed by our kind captain, assuring us that we should have nothing to pay. After supper the captain inquired of the landlady if the boat was come ; she brought word that it was not yet high water. More punch was called, and something more somniferous than liquor put into it. It circulated very speedily —we were all intoxicated, and I fell sound asleep. . . .

When we came to move on deck we saw land at a very great distance. Thus we thought we were on our way to London, exulting in our good fortune. We now asked if we were not yet near the shore, and about to enter the river. " What river ? " said one of the sailors. " Why, the Thames," said Captain Jack. " The Thames— what d'ye mean by this ? What, han't you had time to be sober yet ? " Jack said no more, but looked sheepish. The same questions being repeated, the sailors began to smell a rat ; and turning to the other Englishman who came along with us, said : " Where do you fancy that you are going ? "—" Why, to London," replied he ; " where else should we be going ? We agreed with the captain to carry us to London."—" Not with the captain ; poor men, you are all deceived. I thought so when I saw you come on board with that infamous kidnapping rogue Gilliman. This ship is bound to Virginia."

Daniel Defoe.

CAREW'S PRANKS AT HIS INNS

DRESSING himself in a chequered shirt, jacket, and trousers, he went upon Exeter Key, and, with a rough but artless air and the behaviour of a sailor, enquired for some of the king's officers, whom he informed that he belonged to a vessel lately come from France, which had landed a large quantity of run goods, but the captain was a rascal, and had used him ill, and d—n his blood if he would not——.

They then ordered him to the sign of the Boot in St. Thomas's, Exeter, whither they soon followed him, having first sent Mr. Eastchurch, an exciseman, to ask what he would have for dinner, and what liquor he would have to drink. A fire was lighted up stairs in a private room, a couple of roasted ducks, and full glasses of wine and punch went cheerfully round ; they then thrust four guineas into his hand, which at first he seemed unwilling to accept of, which made them the more pressing. He now began to open his mind with great freedom, gave a particular account of the vessel, where they had taken in their cargo in France, and what it consisted of ; the day they sailed, and the time they were on the passage ; and at last concluded with acquainting them they had landed and concealed part of this valuable cargo in the outhouses of Squire Mallock of Cockington, and the remainder in those of Squire Cary of Tor-abbey, both which houses, upon account of their situation on the sea-side, were very noted for such concealments. The officers, having now got the scent, were like sagacious hounds for pursuing it forthwith, and also thought it proper the sailor should accompany them ; and to prevent all suspicion, resolved he should now change his habit ; they therefore dressed him in a ruffled shirt, a fine suit of broad cloth belonging to the collector, and put a gold-laced hat on his head ; then mounting him on a fine black mare, away they rode together, being in all seven or eight of them : they that night reached Newton Bushel, and slept at the Bull ;

nothing was wanting to make the night jovial ; the greatest delicacies the town afforded were served up at their table, the best liquors were broached for them, and music crowned the banquet : the officers' hearts being quite open and cheerful, as they already enjoyed, in imagination, all the booty they were to seize on the morrow. Thinking that they could not do enough for the honest sailor, they inquired if he knew anything of accounts ; promising, if he did, to get him a place in the customs. In the morning, after a good hearty breakfast, they set forward for Tor Abbey ; and, being arrived in Tor town, they demanded the constable's assistance, who was with the utmost reluctance prevailed on to accompany them in making this search, Squire Carey being a gentleman so universally beloved by the whole parish that everyone was very backward in doing anything to give him the least uneasiness.

Being come to the house, they all dismounted, and the collector desired the sailor to hold his horse, but he replied he would rather go round the garden, and meet them on the other side of the house, to prevent anything from being conveyed away, and that it would be proper he should be present to show the particular place where everything was deposited. This appeared quite right to the collector ; he therefore contented himself with fastening his horse to the garden rails, and proceeded with the rest of the officers in great form to search the dog-kennel, coal-house, dove-house, stables, and all other suspicious places, expecting every minute to see the informing sailor, who by this time had nearly got back to Newton Bushel, having turned his horse that way as soon as he was out of sight of the collector. He stopped at the Bull, where they had been the preceding night, and drank a bottle of wine ; then, ordering a handsome dinner to be got ready for his company, whom he said he had left behind, because his business called him with urgent haste to Exeter, he clapped spurs to his horse, and did not stop till he reached that city, where he put up at the Oxford inn, then kept by Mr. Buckstone, to whom both himself and friends were well known : he acquainted Mr. Buckstone that he was now reformed, and lived at home with his friends, and spent the night very jovially, calling for the best of every thing. In the morning he desired Mr. Buckstone to do him the favour of lending him a couple of guineas, till he could receive some of a merchant in the city upon whom he had a bill, for the merchant was gone out of town.   As Mr. Buckstone had a mare in his custody worth ten or twelve pounds, he made no scruple of doing it, and soon after Mr. Carew thought proper to change his quarters, without bidding the landlord good-bye.   Leaving the mare to discharge his reckoning and the money he had borrowed, he immediately repaired to a house of usual resort for his community, where he pulls off the fine clothes the collector had lent him, and rigged himself again in a jacket and trowsers ; then setting out for Topsham, about three miles from the city of Exeter, he there executed the stratagem upon Mr. Carter and the officers there ; informing them also of some great concealments at Sir Coppleston Bampfylde's house at Poltimore, for which they rewarded him with a good treat and a couple of guineas.

The Exeter officers (whom, as we have before said he left without the least ceremony at Squire Carey's) having searched all the outhouses, and even in the dwelling-house, very narrowly, without finding any prohibited goods, began to suspect the sailor had outwitted them ; therefore they returned in a great hurry to Newton-Bushel, all their mirth being turned into vexation, and their great expectations vanished into smoke. Soon after they had dismounted from their horses, the landlord brought in the dinner, which he said their companion had ordered to be got ready for them ; but though it was a very elegant one, yet they found abundance of fault with it ; for it is common with most people, when they are chagrined with one thing, to find fault with every thing ; however, as it was too late to reach Exeter that night, they were obliged to take up their quarters there ; but, instead of the jollity and good humour that reigned among them the night before, there now succeeded a sullen silence, interrupted now and then by some exclamations of revenge, and expressions of dislike of every thing that was brought them ; when they came into Exeter the next day, they had intelligence brought them of the mare, which was safe enough at the Oxford inn ; but they were obliged to disburse the money Mr. Carew had made her surety for.

Life of Bampfylde Moore Carew.

THE LADIES OF THE FRENCH HOUSE
GERRARD, MARTIN *and* MONSIEUR DE PARIS.

(Enter WAITER.*)*

WAITER.   Here are a couple of ladies coming up to you, sir.

GER.   To us ! Did you appoint any to come hither, Martin ?

MAR.   Not I.

GER.   Nor you, monsieur ?

MON.   Nor I.

GER.   Sirrah, tell your master, if he cannot protect us from the constable, and these midnight coursers, 'tis not a house for us.

MAR.   Tell 'em you have nobody in the house, and shut the doors.

WAIT.   They'll not be satisfied with that, they'll break open the door. They searched last night all over the house for my Lord Fisk, and Sir Jeffery Jantee, who were fain to hide themselves in the bar under my mistress' chair and petticoats.

MONS.   Wat, do the women hunt out the men so now ?

MAR.   Ay, ay, things are altered since you went to Paris ; there's hardly a young man in town dares be known of his lodging for 'em.

GER.   Bailiffs, pursuivants, or a city constable, are modest people in comparison of them.

MAR.   And we are not so much afraid to be taken up by the watch as by the tearing midnight ramblers, or huzza women.

MONS.   Jarni !   Ha ! ha ! ha !

GER.   Where are they ?   I hope they are gone again.

WAIT.   No, sir, they are below at the stair-foot, only swearing at their coachman.

GER.   Come, you rogue, they are in fee with you waiters, and no gentleman can come hither, but they have the intelligence straight.

WAIT.   Intelligence from us, sir !   They should never come here if we could help it.   I am sure we wish 'em choked when we see them come in ; for they bring such good stomachs from St. James's Park, or rambling about in the streets, that we poor waiters have not a bit left ; 'tis well if we can keep our money in our pockets for 'em.   I am sure I have paid seventeen-and-sixpence in half-crowns for coach-hire at several times for a little damned tearing lady, and when I asked her for it again one morning in her chamber, she bid me pay myself, for she had no money ; but I wanted the courage of a gentleman ; besides, the lord that kept her was a good customer to our house and my friend, and I made a conscience of wronging him.

GER. A man of honour ! Go, go, sirrah, shut the door, I hear 'em coming up.

WAIT. Indeed I dare not ; they'll kick me down stairs if I should.

GER. Go, you rascal, I say.

(*Enter* FLOUNCE *and* FLIRT, *striking the* WAITER, *and come up to the table.*)

GER. Flounce and Flirt, upon my life ! Ladies, I am sorry you have no volunteers in your service ; this is mere pressing, and argues a great necessity for men.

FLOU. You need not be afraid, sir ; we will use no violence to you ; you are not fit for our service ; we know you. . . .

FLIRT. Come, come ; pray leave this fooling ; sit down again, and let us bespeak supper.

GER. No, faith, I dare not.

MAR. Besides, we have supped.

FLOU. No matter, we only desire you should look on while we eat, and put the glass about, or so.

(GERRARD *and* MARTIN *offer to go.*)

FLIRT. Pray stay.

MONS. Wat ! must we leave the lady, then ? Dis is dam civility Englis, *ma foi !*

FLIRT. Nay, sir, you have too much of the French air to have so little honour and good breeding.

MONS. Dee you tinke so then, sweet madam, I have mush of de French eyre ?

FLIRT. More than any Frenchman breathing.

Mons.   Auh, you are the curtoise dame ; *morbleu !*
I shall stay then if you tink so.   Monsieur Gerrard, you
will be certain to see the lady to-morrow ?

Ger.   No, no, sir ?

(*Exeunt* Gerrard *and* Martin.)

Flou.   What will you eat, sir ?

Mons.   Wat you please, madam.

Flou.   D'ye hear, waiter ? then some young partridge.

Wait.   What else, madam ?

Flou.   Some ruffs.

Wait.   What else, madam ?

Flirt.   Some young pheasants.

Wait.   What else, madam ?

Flirt.   Some young rabbits.   I love rabbits.

Wait.   What else, madam ?

Flou.   Stay——

Mons.   Dis Englis waiter wit his Wat else, madam,
will ruin me, *tête non*.

Wait.   What else, madam.

Mons.   What else, madam, agen ! Call up the French
waiter.

Wait.   What else, madam ?

Mons.   Again !   Call up the French waiter or
cuisenier.   Auh, madam, the stupidity of the Englis
waiter.   I hate the Englis waiter, *ma foi !*

(*Enter French* Scullion.)

Cher Pierrot, serviteur, serviteur !   (*Kisses* Scullion.)
Or-ca à manger ?

Scull.   *En voulez-vous* de cram schiquin ?

Flou.   Yes.

Scull.   De partrish, de faysan, de quailles !

Mons.   This *bougre* vil ruine me too ; but he speak

wit dat bel eyre and grace, I cannot bid him hold his tongue, *ventre !   C'est assez, Pierrot, va-t'en.*

SCULL.   And de litel plate de——

MONS.   *Jarni ! va-t'en.*

SCULL.   And de litel plate de——

MONS.   *De grace*, go dy way.

SCULL.   And de litel de——

MONS.   *De fromage de Brie, va-t'en.*   Go, go.

(*Exit* SCULLION.)

FLOU.   But how shall we divertise ourselves till supper be ready ?

FLIRT.   Can we have better divertissement than this gentleman ?

FLOU.   But I think we had better carry the gentleman home with us, and because it is already late, sup at home, and divertise the gentleman at cards, till it be ready.   D'ye hear, waiter ?   Let it be brought, when 'tis ready, to my lodging hard by, in Mustard Alley, at the sign of the Crooked Billet.

William Wycherley.

A PLOT DISCOVERED

WHILE Cromwell was meditating how he could best " come in " with Charles, one of his spies— of the King's bedchamber—informed him that his final doom was decreed, and that what it was might be found out by intercepting a letter sent from the King to the Queen, wherein he declared what he would do.   The letter, he said, was sewed up in the skirt of a saddle, and the bearer of it would come with the saddle upon his head that night to the Blue Boar Inn, in Holborn ; for there he was to take horse and go to Dover with it.   This messenger knew nothing of the letter in the saddle ; but some persons at Dover did.   Cromwell and Ireton, disguised as troopers, taking with them a trusty fellow, went to the Inn in Holborn ; and this man watched at the wicket, and the troopers continued drinking beer till about ten o'clock, when the sentinel at the gate gave notice that the man with the saddle was come in. Up they got, and, as the man was leading out his horse saddled, they, with drawn swords, declared they were to search all who went in and out there ; but, as he looked like an honest man, they would only search his saddle. Upon this they ungirt the saddle, and carried it into the stall where they had been drinking, and left the horseman with the sentinel ; then, ripping up one of the skirts of the saddle, they found the letter, and gave back the saddle to the man, who, not knowing what he had done, went away to Dover. They then opened the letter, in which the King told the Queen that he thought he should close with the Scots. Cromwell and Ireton then took horse and went to Windsor ; and, finding they were not likely to have any tolerable terms with the King, they immediately from that time forward resolved his ruin.

Lord Orrery.

MOLL FLANDERS' MARRIAGE

HE could not reach Stony Stratford time enough to be with me at night, but he met me at a place called Brickhill the next morning, just as we were coming into the town. He took me out of the stage-coach immediately, which stopped at an inn in Brickhill ; and putting into the same inn, he set up his own coach, and bespoke his dinner. I asked him what he meant by that, for I was for going forward with the journey. He said No, I had need of a little rest upon the road, and that was a very good sort of a house ; so we would go no farther that night. I did not press him much, for since he had come so far to

meet me, and put himself to so much expense, it was but
reasonable I should oblige him a little too. After dinner
we walked to see the town, to see the church, and to view
the fields and the country, as is usual for strangers to do ;
and our landlord was our guide in going to see the church.
I observed my gentleman inquired pretty much about the
parson, and I took the hint immediately, that he certainly
would propose to be married. . . . But while these
thoughts ran round in my head, which was the work but
of a few moments, I observed my landlord took him aside
and whispered to him, though not very softly neither, for
so much I overheard : "Sir, if you shall have occasion
——" the rest I could not hear ; but my gentleman
answered loud enough for me to hear, "Very well, I
believe I shall."

I was no sooner come back to the inn, but he fell upon
me with irresistible words, that since he had had the good
fortune to meet me, and everything concurred, it would be
hastening his felicity if I would put an end to the matter
just there. "What do you mean ? " says I, colouring a
little. "What, in an inn, and on the road ! Bless us all,"
said I, "how can you talk so ? " "Oh, I can talk so very
well," says he ; "I came on purpose to talk so, and I'll
show you that I did ; " and with that he pulls out a great
bundle of papers. There was first the deed or sentence of
divorce from his wife, and the full evidence of her playing the whore ; then there was the certificates of the
minister and churchwardens of the parish where she lived,
proving that she was buried, and intimating the manner of
her death ; the copy of the coroner's warrant for a jury to
sit upon her, and the verdict of the jury. . . . There
were other papers rolled up, and I asked him what they
were. "Hold," says he ; "first look here ; " then he

took up the roll again, and read it, and behold ! it was a license for us to be married. " Why," says I, " are you distracted ? You were fully satisfied, sure, that I would yield at the first word, or resolved to take no denial." " The last is certainly the case," said he. " But you may be mistaken," said I. " No, no," says he, " I must not be denied, I can't be denied." I turned from him, for it filled my eyes with tears, and asked him leave to retire a little to my chamber. . . . He was impatient for my coming out of my chamber, but finding me long, he went downstairs and talked with my landlord about the parson.

My landlord, an officious though well-meaning fellow, had sent away for the clergyman ; and when my gentle-man began to speak to him of sending for him, " Sir," says he to him, " my friend is in the house ; " so without any more words he brought them together. . . . So up they brings the parson, and a merry, good sort of gentle-man he was. He had been told, it seems, that we had met there by accident ; that I came in a Chester coach, and my gentleman in his own coach to meet me ; that we were to have met last night at Stony Stratford, but that he could not reach so far. " Well, sir," says the parson, " every ill turn has some good in it. The disappoint-ment, sir," says he to my gentleman, " was yours, and the good turn is mine, for if you had met at Stony Stratford, I had not had the honour to marry you. Landlord, have you a Common Prayer Book ? "

I started as if I had been frighted. " Sir," says I, " what do you mean ? What, to marry in an inn, and at night too ! " " Madam," says the minister, " if you will have it be in the church, you shall ; but I assure you your marriage will be as firm here as in the church ; we are not tied by the canons to marry nowhere but in the church ; and as for the time of day, it does not at all weigh in this case ; our princes are married in their chambers, and at eight or ten o'clock at night."

I was a great while before I could be persuaded, and pretended not to be willing at all to be married but in the church. But it was all grimace ; so I seemed at last to be prevailed on, and my landlord, and his wife and daughter, were called up. My landlord was father and clerk and all together, and we were married, and very merry we were. . . . We enjoyed ourselves that evening completely, and yet all was kept so private in the inn that not a servant in the house knew of it, for my landlady and her daughter waited on me, and would not let any of the maids come upstairs. My landlady's daughter I called my bridemaid ; and sending for a shopkeeper the next morning, I gave the young woman a good suit of knots, as good as the town would afford, and finding it was a lace-making town, I gave her mother a piece of bone-lace for a head. One reason that my landlord was so close was that he was unwilling that the minister of the parish should hear of it ; but for all that somebody heard of it, so as that we had the bells set a-ringing the next morning early, and the music, such as the town would afford, under our window. But my landlord brazened it out, that we were married before we came thither, only that, being his former guests, we would have our wedding-supper at his house.

Daniel Defoe.

RANDOM AND THE HIGHWAYMAN

HAVING concerted the plan and settled our affairs that night, we departed next morning by daybreak, armed with a good cudgel each (my companion being charged with the furniture of us both, crammed into one knapsack), and our money sewed between the lining and waistband of our breeches, except some loose silver for our immediate expense on the road. We travelled all day at a round pace, but being ignorant of the proper stages, were benighted at a good distance from any inn, so that we were compelled to take up our lodging at a small hedge ale-house, that stood on a by-road, about half a mile from the highway. There we found a pedlar of our own country, in whose company we regaled ourselves with bacon and eggs, and a glass of good ale, before a comfortable fire, con-versing all the while very sociably with the landlord and his daughter, an hale buxom lass, who entertained us with great good humour, and in whose affection I was vain enough to believe I had made some progress. About eight o'clock, we were all three, at our own desire, shown into an apartment, furnished with two beds, in one of which Strap and I betook ourselves to rest, and the pedlar occupied the other, though not before he had prayed a considerable time extempore, searched into every corner of the room, and fastened the door on the inside with a strong iron screw, which he carried about with him for that use. I slept very sound till midnight, when I was disturbed by a violent motion of the bed, which shook under me with a continual tremor. Alarmed at this phenomenon, I jogged my companion, whom, to my no small amazement, I found drenched in sweat, and quaking through every limb ; he told me, with a low faltering voice, that we were undone ; for there was a bloody high-way man loaded with pistols in the next room ; then bidding me make as little noise as possible, he directed me to a small chink in the board partition, through which I could see a thick-set brawny fellow, with a fierce counten-ance, sitting at a table with our young landlady, having a bottle of ale and a brace of pistols before him. I listened with great attention, and heard him say in a terrible tone : " Damn that son of a bitch, Smack, the coachman ;—he has served me a fine trick, indeed !—but damnation seize me, if I don't make him repent it ! I'll teach the scoundrel to give intelligence to others, while he is under articles with me." Our landlady endeavoured to appease this exasperated robber, by saying he might be mistaken in Smack, who perhaps kept no correspondence with the other gentleman that robbed his coach ; and that, if an accident had disappointed him to-day, he might soon find opportunity enough to atone for his lost trouble. " I'll tell thee what, my dear Bett," replied he, " I never had, nor ever will, while my name is Rifle, have such a glorious booty as I missed to-day.—Zounds ! there was four hundred pounds in cash to recruit men for the king's service, besides the jewels, watches, swords, and money belonging to the passengers ;—had it been my fortune to have got clear off with so much treasure, I would have purchased a commission in the army, and made you an officer's lady, you jade, I would." " Well, well," cries Betty, " we must trust to Providence for that ;—but did you find nothing worth taking, which escaped the other gentlemen of the road ? " " Not much, faith," said the lover ; " I gleaned a few things, such as a pair of pops, silver mounted (here they are) ; I took them loaded from the captain who had the charge of the money, together with a gold watch, which he had concealed in his breeches. I likewise found ten Portugal pieces in the shoes of a Quaker, whom the spirit moved to revile me with great bitterness and devotion. But what I value myself mostly for, is this here purchase, a gold snuff-box, my girl, with a picture on the inside of the lid ; which I untied out of the tail of a pretty

lady's smock." Here, as the devil would have it, the
pedlar snored so loud, that the highwayman, snatching his
pistols, started up, crying : " Hell and damnation ! I am
betrayed ; who's that in the next room ? " Mrs. Betty
told him, he need not be uneasy ; there were only three
poor wearied travellers, who, missing the road, had taken
up their lodging in the house, and were asleep long ago.
" Travellers," says he, " spies, you b—ch ! but no matter
—I'll send them all to hell in an instant." He accordingly
ran towards our door ; when his sweetheart interposing,
assured him, there was only a couple of poor young Scotch-
men, who were too raw and ignorant to give him the
least cause of suspicion ; and the third was a Presbyterian
pedlar of the same nation, who had often lodged in the
house before. This declaration satisfied the thief, who
swore he was glad there was a pedlar, for he wanted some
linen. Then, in a jovial manner, he put about the glass,
mingling his discourse to Betty with caresses and fami-
liarities that spoke him very happy in his amours.

Tobias Smollett.

THE VICAR FINDS OLIVIA

NIGHT coming on, I put up at a little public-house
by the roadside, and asked for the landlord's company
over a pint of wine. We sat beside his kitchen fire, which
was the best room in the house, and chatted on politics
and the news of the country. . . . As we continued our
discourse, his wife, who had been out to get change,
returned, and perceiving that her husband was enjoying
a pleasure in which she was not a sharer, she asked him,
in an angry tone, what he did there ? to which he only
replied, in an ironical way, by drinking her health. " Mr.
Symmonds," cried she, " you use me very ill, and I'll bear

it no longer. Here three parts of the business is left for me to do, and the fourth left unfinished, while you do nothing but soak with the guests all day long; whereas, if a spoonful of liquor were to cure of a fever, I never touch a drop." I now found what she would be at, and immediately poured her out a glass, which she received with a courtesy; and, drinking towards my good health, "Sir," resumed she, "it is not so much for the value of the liquor I am angry, but one cannot help it when the house is going out of the windows. If the customers or guests are to be dunned, all the burden lies upon my back; he'd as lief eat that glass as budge after them himself. There, now, above stairs, we have a young woman who has come to take up her lodging here, and I don't believe she has got any money by her over-civility. I am certain she is very slow of payment, and I wish she were put in mind of it."—"What signifies minding her?" cried the host; "if she be slow, she is sure."—"I don't know that," replied the wife; "but I know that I am sure she has been here a fortnight, and we have not yet seen the cross of her money."—"I suppose, my dear," cried he, "we shall have it all in a lump."—"In a lump!" cried the other; "I hope we may get it any way; and that I am resolved we will this very night, or out she tramps, bag and baggage."—"Consider, my dear," cried the husband, "she is a gentlewoman, and deserves more respect." "As for the matter of that," returned the hostess, "gentle or simple, out she shall pack with a sussarara. Gentry may be good things where they take; but for my part I never saw much good of them at the sign of the Harrow."

Thus saying, she ran up a narrow flight of stairs that went from the kitchen to a room overhead; and I soon perceived, by the loudness of her voice, and the bitterness

of her reproaches, that no money was to be had from her
lodger. I could hear her remonstrances very distinctly :
" Out, I say ; pack out this moment ! Tramp, thou
infamous strumpet ; or I'll give thee a mark that won't
be the better for this three months. What ! you trum-
pery, to come and take up an honest house without cross
or coin to bless yourself with. Come along, I say ! "—
" Oh, dear Madam," cried the stranger, " pity me—pity
a poor abandoned creature, for one night, and death will
soon do the rest." I instantly knew the voice of my poor
ruined child, Olivia. I flew to her rescue, while the
woman was dragging her along by her hair, and I caught
the dear forlorn wretch in my arms.

                                   Oliver Goldsmith.

TRICKING THE TAPSTER

ONE evening, as I was passing through the Inner
Temple, very hungry, and very miserable, I heard
a voice on a sudden hailing me with great familiarity by
my Christian name ; and upon my turning about, I presently recollected the person who so saluted me to have
been my fellow-collegiate ; one who had left the univer-
sity above a year, and long before any of my misfortunes
had befallen me. This gentleman, whose name was
Watson, shook me heartily by the hand ; and expressing
great joy at meeting me, proposed our immediately drinking a bottle together. I first declined the proposal, and
pretended business, but as he was very earnest and pressing, hunger at last overcame my pride, and I fairly con-
fessed to him I had no money in my pocket ; yet not
without framing a lie for an excuse, and imputing it to my
having changed my breeches that morning. Mr. Watson
answered, " I thought, Jack, you and I had been too old

acquaintance for you to mention such a matter." He then took me by the arm, and was pulling me along ; but I gave him very little trouble, for my own inclinations pulled me much stronger than he could do.

We then went into the Friars, which you know is the scene of all mirth and jollity. Here, when we arrived at the tavern, Mr. Watson applied himself to the drawer only, without taking the least notice of the cook ; for he had no suspicion but that I had dined long since. However, as the case was really otherwise, I forged another falsehood, and told my companion I had been at the further end of the city on business of consequence, and had snapt up a mutton-chop in haste ; so that I was again hungry, and wished he would add a beef-steak to his bottle.

I began now to feel myself extremely happy. The meat and wine soon revived my spirits to a high pitch, and I enjoyed much pleasure in the conversation of my old acquaintance. . . .

We had now each drank our bottle, when Mr. Watson said, the board was sitting, and that he must attend, earnestly pressing me at the same time to go with him and try my fortune. I answered he knew that was at present out of my power, as I had informed him of the emptiness of my pocket. To say the truth, I doubted not from his many strong expressions of friendship, but that he would offer to lend me a small sum for that purpose, but he answered, " Never mind that, man ; e'en boldly run a levant ; but be circumspect as to the man. I will tip you the proper person, which may be necessary, as you do not know the town, nor can distinguish a rum cull from a queer one."

The bill was now brought, when Watson paid his share, and was departing. I reminded him, not without blushing, of my having no money. He answered, "That signifies nothing ; score it behind the door, or make a bold brush and take no notice.—Or—stay," says he ; " I will go down-stairs first, and then do you take up my money, and score the whole reckoning at the bar, and I will wait for you at the corner." I expressed some dislike at this, and hinted my expectations that he would have deposited the whole ; but he swore he had not another six-pence in his pocket.

He then went down, and I was prevailed on to take up the money and follow him, which I did close enough to hear him tell the drawer the reckoning was upon the table. The drawer past by me up-stairs ; but I made such haste into the street, that I heard nothing of his dis-appointment, nor did I mention a syllable at the bar, according to my instructions.

Henry Fielding.

THE TAVERN BEAU

WHEN they had finished their walk, and were returning by the corner of the Park, they observed a board hung out of a window signifying, " An excellent *ordinary* on Saturdays and Sundays." It happened to be Saturday, and the table was covered for the purpose.

"What if we should go in and dine here, if you happen not to be engaged, sir ? " said the young gentleman. " It is not impossible but we shall meet with some original or other ; it is a sort of humour I like hugely."

Harley made no objection, and the stranger showed him the way into the parlour.

He was placed, by the courtesy of his introductor, in an arm-chair that stood at one side of the fire. Over against him was seated a man of a grave considering aspect, with that look of sober prudence which indicates what is commonly called a warm man. He wore a pretty large wig, which had once been white, but was now of a brownish yellow ; his coat was one of those modest-coloured drabs which mock the injuries of dust and dirt ; two jack-boots concealed, in part, the well-mended knees of an old pair of buckskin breeches ; while the spotted handkerchief round his neck preserved at once its owner from catching cold and his neckcloth from being dirtied. Next him sat another man, with a tankard in his hand and a quid of tobacco in his cheek, whose eye was rather more vivacious, and whose dress was something smarter.

The first-mentioned gentleman took notice that the room had been so lately washed, as not to have had time to dry, and remarked that wet lodging was unwholesome for man or beast. He looked round at the same time for a poker to stir the fire with, which, he at last observed to the company, the people of the house had removed in order to save their coals. This difficulty, however, he overcame by the help of Harley's stick, saying, " that as they should, no doubt, pay for their fire in some shape or other, he saw no reason why they should not have the use of it while they sat."

The door was now opened for the admission of dinner. " I don't know how it is with you, gentlemen," said Harley's new acquaintance, " but I am afraid I shall not be able to get down a morsel at this horrid mechanical hour of dining." He sat down, however, and did not show any want of appetite by his eating. He took upon him the carving of the meat, and criticised on the goodness of the pudding.

When the table-cloth was removed, he proposed calling for some punch, which was readily agreed to ; he seemed at first inclined to make it himself, but afterwards changed his mind, and left that province to the waiter, telling him to have it pure West Indian, or he could not taste a drop of it.

While the punch lasted the conversation was wholly engrossed by the gentleman with the fine waistcoat, who told a great many " immense comical stories " and " confounded smart things," as he termed them, acted and spoken by lords, ladies, and young bucks of quality, of his acquaintance. At last, the grazier, pulling out a watch, of a very unusual size, and telling the hour, said that he had an appointment. " Is it so late ? " said the young gentleman ; " then I am afraid I have missed an appointment already ; but the truth is, I am cursedly given to missing of appointments."

When the grazier and he were gone, Harley turned to the remaining personage, and asked him if he knew that young gentleman. " A gentleman ! " said he ; " ay, he is one of your gentlemen at the top of an affidavit. I knew him, some years ago, in the quality of a footman ; and I believe he had some times the honour to be a pimp. At last, some of the great folks, to whom he had been serviceable in both capacities, had him made a gauger ; in which station he remains, and has the assurance to pretend an acquaintance with men of quality. The impudent dog ! with a few shillings in his pocket, he will talk you three times as much as my friend Mundy there, who is worth nine thousand if he's worth a farthing.

Henry Mackenzie.

SIR LAUNCELOT GREAVES LOSES HIS DULCINEA

IT was not without reason that our adventurer afflicted himself ; his fears were but too prophetic. When he alighted at the inn which he had left so abruptly the preceding evening, he ran directly to the apartment where he had been so happy in Aurelia's company ; but her he saw not—all was solitary. Turning to the woman of the house, who had followed him into the room, " Where is the lady ? " cried he, in a tone of impatience. Mine hostess screwing up her features into a very demure aspect, said she saw so many ladies she could not pretend to know who he meant. " I tell thee, woman," exclaimed the knight, in a louder accent, " thou never sawest such another—I mean that miracle of beauty." " Very like," replied the dame, as she retired to the room door. " Husband, here's one as axes concerning a miracle of beauty ; hi, hi, hi. Can you give him any information about this miracle of beauty ? O la ! hi, hi, hi."

Instead of answering this question, the innkeeper advancing and surveying Sir Launcelot, " Friend," said he, " you are the person that carried off my horse out of the stable."—" Tell me not of a horse—where is the young lady ? "—" Now, I will tell you of the horse, and I'll make you find him too before you and I part."— " Wretched animal ! how dar'st thou dally with my impatience ? Speak, or despair—what is become of Miss Meadows ? Say, did she leave this place of her own accord, or was she—hah ! speak—answer, or by the powers above."—" I'll answer you flat—she you call Miss Meadows is in very good hands—so you may make yourself easy on that score."—" Sacred Heaven ! explain your meaning, miscreant, or I'll make you a dreadful example to all the insolent publicans of the realm." So saying, he seized him with one hand and dashed him on the floor, set one foot on his belly, and kept him trembling in that prostate attitude. The hostler and waiter flying to the assistance of their master, our adventurer unsheathed his sword, declaring he would dismiss their souls from their bodies, and exterminate the whole family from the face of the earth, if they would not immediately give him the satisfaction he required.

The hostess being by this time almost terrified out of her senses, fell on her knees before him, begging he would spare their lives, and promising to declare the whole truth. He would not, however, remove his foot from the body of her husband until she told him, that in less than half an hour after he had sallied out upon the supposed robbers, two chaises arrived, each drawn by four horses ; that two men, armed with pistols, alighted from one of them, laid violent hands upon the young lady ; and, notwithstanding her struggling and shrieking, forced her into the other carriage, in which was an infirm gentleman, who called himself her guardian ; that the maid was left in the care of a third servant, to follow with a third chaise, which was got ready with all possible despatch, while the other two proceeded at full speed on the road to London. It was by this communicative lackey the people of the house were informed that the old gentleman, his master, was Squire Darnel, the young lady his niece and ward, and our adventurer a needy sharper who wanted to make a prey of her fortune.

Tobias Smollett.

THE FUTURE SIR THOMAS LAWRENCE

THE second day we slept at Speen Hill, and the third day we reached Devizes.

And here, Mrs. Thrale and I were much pleased with our hostess, Mrs. Lawrence, who seemed something above her station in her inn. While we were at cards before supper, we were much surprised by the sound of a pianoforte. I jumped up, and ran to listen whence it proceeded. I found it came from the next room, where the

overture to the " Buona Figliuola " was performing. The
playing was very decent, but as the music was not quite
new to me, my curiosity was not whole ages in satisfying,
and therefore I returned to finish the rubber.

Don't I begin to talk in an old-cattish manner of
cards !

Well, another deal was hardly played, ere we heard the
sound of a voice, and out I ran again. The singing, however, detained me not long, and so back I whisked : but
the performance, however indifferent in itself, yet surprised us at the Bear at Devizes, and, therefore, Mrs.
Thrale determined to know from whom it came. Accordingly, she tapped at the door. A very handsome girl, about
thirteen years old, with fine dark hair upon a finely-
formed forehead, opened it. Mrs. Thrale made an
apology for her intrusion, but the poor girl blushed and
retreated into a corner of the room : another girl, however, advanced, and obligingly and gracefully invited us
in, and gave us all chairs. She was just sixteen, extremely
pretty, and with a countenance better than her features,
though those were also very good. Mrs. Thrale made her
many compliments, which she received with a mingled
modesty and pleasure, both becoming and interesting. She
was, indeed, a sweetly-pleasing girl.

We found they were both daughters of our hostess, and
born and bred at Devizes. We were extremely pleased
with them, and made them a long visit, which I wished to
have been longer. But though those pretty girls struck us
so much, the wonder of the family was yet to be produced.
This was their brother, a most lovely boy of ten years of
age, who seems to be not merely the wonder of their
family, but of the times, for his astonishing skill in drawing. They protest he has never had any instruction, yet

showed us some of his productions that were really beautiful. Those that were copies were delightful—those of his own composition amazing, though far inferior. I was equally struck with the boy and his works. We found that he had been taken to town, and that all the painters had been very kind to him, and Sir Joshua Reynolds had pronounced him, the mother said, the most promising genius he had ever met with. Mr. Hoare has been so charmed with this sweet boy's drawings that he intends sending him to Italy with his own son.

The house was full of books, as well as paintings, drawings, and music ; and all the family seem not only ingenious and industrious, but amiable ; added to which, they are strikingly handsome.

Fanny Burney.

THE VIRAGO

MR. JONES and his fair companion no sooner entered the town, than they went directly to that inn which in their eyes presented the fairest appearance to the street. Here Jones, having ordered a servant to show a room above stairs, was ascending, when the dishevelled fair, hastily following, was laid hold on by the master of the house, who cried, "Heydey, where is that beggar wench going ? Stay below stairs, I desire you." But Jones at that instant thundered from above, "Let the lady come up," in so authoritative a voice, that the good man instantly withdrew his hands, and the lady made the best of her way to the chamber.

Here Jones wished her joy of her safe arrival, and then departed, in order, as he promised, to send the landlady up with some cloaths. The poor woman thanked him heartily for all his kindness, and said, she hoped she should see him again soon, to thank him a thousand times more.

During this short conversation, she covered her white bosom as well as she could possibly with her arms ; for Jones could not avoid stealing a sly peep or two, though he took all imaginable care to avoid giving any offence.

Our travellers had happened to take up their residence at a house of exceeding good repute, whither Irish ladies of strict virtue, and many northern lasses of the same predicament, were accustomed to resort in their way to Bath. The landlady therefore would by no means have admitted any conversation of a disreputable kind to pass under her roof. Indeed, so foul and contagious are all such proceedings, that they contaminate the very innocent scenes where they are committed, and give the name of a bad house, or of a house of ill repute, to all those where they are suffered to be carried on.

Not that I would intimate that such strict chastity as was preserved in the temple of Vesta can possibly be maintained at a public inn. My good landlady did not hope for such a blessing, nor would any of the ladies I have spoken of, or indeed any others of the most rigid note, have expected or insisted on any such thing. But to exclude all vulgar concubinage, and to drive all whores in rags from within the walls, is within the power of every one. This my landlady very strictly adhered to, and this her virtuous guests, who did not travel in rags, would very reasonably have expected of her.

Now it required no very blameable degree of suspicion to imagine that Mr. Jones and his ragged companion had certain purposes in their intention, which, though tolerated in some Christian countries, connived at in others, and practised in all, are however as expressly forbidden as murder, or any other horrid vice, by that religion which is universally believed in those countries. The landlady, therefore, had no sooner received an intimation of the entrance of the above-said persons than she began to meditate the most expeditious means for their expulsion. In order to this, she had provided herself with a long and deadly instrument, with which, in times of peace, the chambermaid was wont to demolish the labours of the industrious spider. In vulgar phrase, she had taken up the broomstick, and was just about to sally from the kitchen, when Jones accosted her with a demand of a gown and other vestments, to cover the half-naked woman upstairs.

Henry Fielding.

THE CHANCE BED-FELLOW

THE Doctor pac'd along the way
    Till it drew nigh the close of day,
When the fair town appear'd in sight,
Where he propos'd to pass the night :
But as he reach'd the destin'd inn,
The landlord, with officious grin,
At once declar'd he had no bed
Where Syntax could repose his head ;
At least, where such a reverend guest,
Would think it fit to take his rest ;
A main of cocks had fought that day,
And all the gentry chose to stay.
" Observe, my friend, I mind not cost,"
Says Syntax to his cringing host ;
" But still, at least, I may be able
To sleep with Grizzle in the stable ;
And many a Doctor, after all,
Is proud to slumber in a stall ;
In short, I only want to sleep
Where neither rogue nor knave can creep ;

I travel not with change of coats,
But in these bags are all my notes ;
Which, should I lose, would prove my ruin,
And be for ever my undoing."
Thus as he spoke, a lively blade,
With dangling queue and smart cockade,
Reply'd at once, " I have a room ;
The friend I look'd for is not come ;
And of two beds where we may rest,
You, my good sir, shall have the best ;
So you may sleep without alarm ;
No living wight shall do you harm ;
You may depend upon my word ;
I serve the King and wear a sword."
" Your offer, Sir, I kindly greet,"
Says Syntax, " but you'll let me treat
With what is best to drink and eat ;
And I request you will prepare,
To your own taste, the bill of fare."

The Doctor and the Captain sat,
Till tir'd of each other's chat,
They both agreed it would be best
To seek the balmy sweets of rest.
Syntax soon clos'd his weary eye,
Nor thought of any danger nigh ;
While, like the ever-watchful snake,
His sharp companion lay awake,
Impatient to assail his prey ;
When, soon as it was dawn of day,
He gently seiz'd the fancied store ;
But as he pass'd the creaking door,
Syntax awoke and saw the thief ;
When, loudly bawling for relief,

He forward rush'd in naked state,
And caught the culprit at the gate ;
Against that gate his head he beat,
Then kick'd him headlong to the street.

William Combe.

A BATTLE FOR A DINNER

ON the sixth day, while we were about to sit down to dinner, the innkeeper came and told us, that three gentlemen, just arrived, had ordered the victuals to be carried to their apartment, although he had informed them that they were bespoke by the passengers in the waggon. To which information they had replied, " The passengers in the waggon might be damned,—their betters must be served before them—they supposed it would be no hardship on such travellers to dine upon bread and cheese for one day." This was a terrible disappointment to us all ; and we laid our heads together how to remedy it ; when Miss Jenny observed, that Captain Weazel, being by profession a soldier, ought in this case to protect and prevent us from being insulted. But the captain excused himself, saying, he would not for all the world be known to have travelled in a waggon ; swearing at the same time, that, could he appear with honour, they should eat his sword sooner than his provision. Upon this declaration, Miss Jenny, snatching his weapon, drew it, and ran immediately into the kitchen, where she threatened to put the cook to death if he did not send the victuals into our chamber immediately. The noise she made brought the three strangers down, one of whom no sooner perceived her, than he cried, " Ha ! Jenny Ramper ! what the devil brought thee hither ? " " My dear Jack Rattle ! " replied she, running into his arms, " is it you ? Then Weazel may go to hell for a dinner—I shall dine with you." They consented to this proposal with a great deal of joy ; and we were on the point of being reduced to a very uncomfortable meal, when Joey, understanding the whole affair, entered the kitchen with a pitchfork in his hand, and swore he would be the death of any man who should pretend to seize the victuals prepared for the waggon. This menace had like to have produced fatal consequences ; the three strangers drawing their swords, and being joined by their servants, and we ranging ourselves on the side of Joey ; when the landlord interposing, offered to part with his own dinner to keep the peace, which was accepted by the strangers ; and we sat down at table without further molestation.

Tobias Smollett.

A POACHERS' SUPPER

MY horse being lamed with a stone in his foot, I was under the necessity of putting up at a small alehouse, with a stable and a yard behind it. The man received me very civilly, but when I inquired if he could accommodate me all night, he answered that he had no room. I requested him to put something to my horse's foot, and I would sit up all night. He was silent. The good wife was more rude, and insisted upon her husband's bringing my horse out instantly ; but putting a crown into her hand, and promising another in the morning, she became more accommodating. She then told me that there was a small bed upstairs, upon which she would lay a pair of clean sheets, and added that she supposed I was more of a gentleman than to take any notice of what I saw passing there. This created in me much uneasiness, and I concluded that I had fallen into a den of highwaymen ; that I would not only be robbed, but have my throat cut ; necessity, however, constrained me to submit.

It was now dark, and I heard three or four men dismount from their horses, lead them into the yard, and as they were coming into the room I heard the landlord say, " Indeed, brother, you need not be uneasy, I am positive the gentleman is a man of honour." Another said, " What good could our death do to a stranger ? The gentleman will be happy of our company. Hang fear ! I'll lead the way." So said and so done ; in came five, so effectually disguised, that unless it were in the same disguise, I should not be able to distinguish any one of them. Down they sat, and their captain accosted me with great civility, and requested me to honour them with my company at supper. Supposing that my landlord would not permit either a robbery or a murder in his house, I gradually became composed.

About ten I heard the noise of a number of horses arriving, and the feet of men stamping in an upper room. In a little time the landlord came to inform me that supper was upon the table. Upon this we all went upstairs, and the captain, with a ridiculous kind of ceremony, introduced me to a man more disguised than the rest, sitting at the head of the table ; at the same time adding that he hoped I would have no objections to pay my respects to Prince Oronooko, King of the Blacks. Then I began to perceive what kind of persons they were, and was astonished that the hurry and agitation I was in had prevented me from discovering sooner.

The supper consisted of eighteen dishes of venison in various shapes—roasted, boiled, with broth, hashed collops, pasties, umble pies, and a large haunch in the centre, larded. The table we sat at was large, and twenty-one sat down to supper. Each had a bottle of claret, and the man and woman of the house sat at the lower end of the table. A few of them had good musical voices, and the evening was spent with as great jollity as by the rakes at King's Arms or the city apprentices at Sadler's Wells. About two the company broke up, all of them assuring me that, upon any Thursday evening, they would be happy to see me at supper.

Johnson's " Lives of the Highwaymen."

WHERE SOPHIA SLEPT

WHEN Jones had taken leave of his friend the lieutenant, he endeavoured to close his eyes, but all in vain ; his spirits were too lively and wakeful to be lulled to sleep. So having amused, or rather tormented, himself with the thoughts of his Sophia till it was open daylight, he called for some tea ; upon which occasion my landlady herself vouchsafed to pay him a visit.

This was indeed the first time she had seen him, or at least had taken any notice of him ; but as the lieutenant had assured her that he was certainly some young gentleman of fashion, she now determined to show him all the respect in her power ; for, to speak truly, this was one of those houses where gentlemen, to use the language of advertisements, meet with civil treatment for their money.

She had no sooner begun to make his tea, than she likewise began to discourse :—" La ! sir," said she, " I think it is great pity that such a pretty young gentleman should under-value himself so, as to go about with these soldier fellows. They call themselves gentlemen, I warrant you ; but, as my first husband used to say, they should remember it is we that pay them. And to be sure it is very hard upon us to be obliged to pay them, and to keep 'um too, as we publicans are. I had twenty of 'um last night, besides officers : nay, for matter o' that, I had rather have the soldiers than officers : for nothing is ever good enough for those sparks ; and I am sure, if you was to see the bills ; la ! sir, it is nothing. I have had less trouble, I warrant you, with a good squire's family, where we take forty or fifty shillings of a night, besides horses. And yet I warrants me, there is narrow a one of those officer fellows but looks upon himself to be as good as arrow a squire of £500 a year. To be sure it doth me good to hear their men run about after 'um, crying your honour, and your honour. Marry come up with such honour, and an ordinary at a shilling a head. Then there's such swearing among 'um, to be sure it frightens me out o' my wits : I thinks nothing can ever prosper with such wicked people. And here one of 'um has used you in so barbarous a manner. I thought indeed how well the rest would secure him ; they all hang together ; for if you had been in danger of death, which I am glad to see you are not, it would have been all as one to such wicked people. They would have let the murderer go. Laud have mercy upon 'um ; I would not have such a sin to answer for, for the whole world. But though you are likely, with the blessing, to recover, there is laa for him yet ; and if you will employ lawyer Small, I darest be sworn he'll make the fellow fly the country for him ; though perhaps he'll have fled the country before ; for it is here to-day and gone to-morrow with such chaps. I hope, however, you will learn more wit for the future, and return back to your friends ; I warrant they are all miserable for your loss ; and if they was but to know what had happened—La, my seeming ! I would not for the world they should. Come, come, we know very well what all the matter is ; but if one won't, another will ; so pretty a gentleman need never want a lady. I am sure, if I was you, I would see the finest she that ever wore a head hanged, before I would go for a soldier for her.—Nay, don't blush so " (for indeed he did to a violent degree). "Why, you thought, sir, I knew nothing of the matter, I warrant you, about Madam Sophia ? "—"How," says Jones, starting up, "do you know my Sophia ? "—" Do I ! ay marry," cries the landlady ; " many's the time hath she lain in this house."

Henry Fielding.

THE NERVOUS STRANGER

ON the fifth day, about two o'clock, I arrived at a small town. Feeling hungry, I entered a decent-looking inn—within a kind of bar I saw a huge, fat, land-lord-looking person, with a very pretty, smartly-dressed maiden. Addressing myself to the fat man, " House ! " said I, " house ! Can I have dinner, house ? "

" Young gentleman," said the huge fat landlord, " you are come at the right time ; dinner will be taken up in a few minutes, and such a dinner," he continued, rubbing his hands, " as you will not see every day in these times."

" I am hot and dusty," said I, " and should wish to cool my hands and face."

" Jenny ! " said the huge landlord, with the utmost gravity, " show the gentleman into number seven that he may wash his hands and face."

" By no means," said I, " I am a person of primitive habits, and there is nothing like the pump in weather like this."

" Jenny," said the landlord, with the same gravity as before, " go with the young gentleman to the pump in the back kitchen, and take a clean towel along with you."

. . . Having set my dress to rights, and combed my hair with a pocket comb, I followed Jenny, who conducted me back through the long passage, and showed me into a neat sanded parlour on the ground floor.

I sat down by a window which looked out upon the dusty street ; presently in came the handmaid, and commenced laying the table-cloth. " Shall I spread the table for one, sir," said she, " or do you expect anybody to dine with you ? "

" I can't say that I expect anybody," said I, laughing inwardly to myself ; " however, if you please you can lay for two, so that if any acquaintance of mine should chance to step in, he may find a knife and fork ready for him."

So I sat by the window, sometimes looking out upon the dusty street, and now glancing at certain old-fashioned prints which adorned the wall over against me. I fell into a kind of doze, from which I was almost instantly awakened by the opening of the door. Dinner, thought I ; and I sat upright in my chair. No, a man of the middle age, and rather above the middle height, dressed in a plain suit of black, made his appearance, and sat down in a chair at some distance from me, but near to the table, and appeared to be lost in thought.

" The weather is very warm, sir," said I.

" Very," said the stranger laconically, looking at me for the first time.

" Would you like to see the newspaper ? " said I, taking up one which lay upon the window seat.

" I never read newspapers," said the stranger, " nor, indeed——" Whatever it might be that he had intended to say he left unfinished. Suddenly he walked to the mantelpiece at the farther end of the room, before which he placed himself with his back towards me. There he remained motionless for some time ; at length, raising his hand, he touched the corner of the mantelpiece with his finger, advanced towards the chair which he had left, and again seated himself.

" Have you come far ? " said he, suddenly looking towards me, and speaking in a frank and open manner, which denoted a wish to enter into conversation. " You do not seem to be of this place."

" I come from some distance," said I ; " indeed I am walking for exercise, which I find as necessary to the mind as the body. I believe that by exercise people would escape much mental misery."

" I wish you may be successful," said the stranger ; and here he touched one of the forks which lay on the table near him.

Here the door, which was slightly ajar, was suddenly pushed open with some fracas, and in came the stout landlord, supporting with some difficulty an immense dish, in which was a mighty round mass of smoking meat garnished all round with vegetables ; so high was the mass that it probably obstructed his view, for it was not until he had placed it upon the table that he appeared to observe the stranger ; he almost started, and quite out of breath exclaimed, " God bless me, your honour ; is your honour the acquaintance that the young gentleman was expecting ? "

" Is the young gentleman expecting an acquaintance ? " said the stranger.

There is nothing like putting a good face upon these matters, thought I to myself ; and, getting up, I bowed to the unknown. " Sir," said I, " when I told Jenny that she might lay the table-cloth for two, so that in the event of any acquaintance dropping in he might find a knife and fork ready for him, I was merely jocular, being an entire stranger in these parts, and expecting no one. Fortune, however, it would seem, has been unexpectedly kind to me ; I flatter myself, sir, that since you have been in this room I have had the honour of making your acquaintance ; and in the strength of that hope I humbly entreat you to honour me with your company to dinner, provided you have not already dined."

The stranger laughed outright.

" Sir," I continued, " the round of beef is a noble one, and seems exceedingly well boiled, and the landlord was just right when he said I should have such a dinner as is not seen every day. A round of beef, at any rate such a round of beef as this, is seldom seen smoking upon the table in these degenerate times. Allow me, sir," said I, observing that the stranger was about to speak, " allow me another remark. I think I saw you just now touch the fork. I venture to hail it as an omen that you will presently seize it, and apply it to its proper purpose, and its companion the knife also."

The stranger changed colour, and gazed upon me in silence.

" Do, sir," here put in the landlord ; " do, sir, accept the young gentleman's invitation. Your honour has of late been looking poorly, and the young gentleman is a funny young gentleman, and a clever young gentleman ; and I think it will do your honour good to have a dinner's chat with the young gentleman."

" It is not my dinner hour," said the stranger ; " I dine considerably later ; taking anything now would only discompose me ; I shall, however, be most happy to sit down with the young gentleman ; reach me that paper, and, when the young gentleman has satisfied his appetite, we may perhaps have a little chat together."

George Borrow.

THE WRONG BEDROOM

MR. PICKWICK seized the watch in triumph, and proceeded to re-trace his steps to his bed-chamber. If his progress downward had been attended with difficulties and uncertainty, his journey back was infinitely more perplexing. Rows of doors, garnished with boots of every shape, make, and size, branched off in every possible direction. A dozen times did he softly turn the handle of some bed-room door which resembled his own, when a gruff cry from within of " Who the devil's that ? " or " What do you want here ? " caused him to steal away, on tiptoe, with a perfectly marvellous celerity. He was reduced to the verge of despair, when an open door attracted his attention. He peeped in. Right at last ! There were the two beds, whose situation he perfectly remembered, and the fire still burning. His candle, not a long one when he first received it, had flickered away in the drafts of air through which he had passed, and sank into the socket as he closed the door after him. " No matter," said Mr. Pickwick, " I can undress myself just as well by the light of the fire."

The bedsteads stood one on each side of the door ; and on the inner side of each was a little path, terminating in a rush-bottomed chair, just wide enough to admit of a person's getting into, or out of bed, on that side, if he or she thought proper. Having carefully drawn the curtains of his bed on the outside, Mr. Pickwick sat down on the rush-bottomed chair, and leisurely divested himself of his shoes and gaiters. He then took off and folded up his coat, waistcoat, and neckcloth, and slowly drawing on his tasselled night-cap, secured it firmly on his head, by tying beneath his chin the strings which he always had attached to that article of dress. It was at this moment that the absurdity of his recent bewilderment struck upon his mind. Throwing himself back in the rush-bottomed chair, Mr. Pickwick laughed to himself so heartily, that it would have been quite delightful to any man of well-constituted mind to have watched the smiles that expanded his amiable features as they shone forth from beneath the night-cap.

"It is the best idea," said Mr. Pickwick to himself, smiling till he almost cracked the night-cap strings : "It is the best idea, my losing myself in this place, and wandering about those staircases, that I ever heard of. Droll, droll, very droll." Here Mr. Pickwick smiled again, a broader smile than before, and was about to continue the process of undressing, in the best possible humour, when he was suddenly stopped by a most unexpected interruption ; to wit, the entrance into the room of some person with a candle, who, after locking the door, advanced to the dressing table, and set down the light upon it.

The smile that played on Mr. Pickwick's features was instantaneously lost in a look of the most unbounded and wonder-stricken surprise. The person, whoever it was, had come in so suddenly and with so little noise, that Mr. Pickwick had had no time to call out, or oppose their entrance. Who could it be ? A robber ? Some evil-minded person who had seen him come up-stairs with a handsome watch in his hand, perhaps. What was he to do !

The only way in which Mr. Pickwick could catch a

glimpse of his mysterious visitor with the least danger of being seen himself, was by creeping on to the bed, and peeping out from between the curtains on the opposite side. To this manœuvre he accordingly resorted. Keeping the curtains carefully closed with his hand, so that nothing more of him could be seen than his face and night-cap, and putting on his spectacles, he mustered up courage, and looked out.

Mr. Pickwick almost fainted with horror and dismay. Standing before the dressing-glass was a middle-aged lady, in yellow curl-papers, busily engaged in brushing what ladies call their " back-hair."

Charles Dickens.

A NIGHT OF STORM

IT might be seven p.m. when first I entered upon my kingdom. About three hours later I rose from my chair, and with considerable interest looked out into the night. For nearly two hours I had heard fierce winds arising ; and the whole atmosphere had, by this time, become one vast laboratory of hostile movements in all directions. Such a chaos, such a distracting wilderness of dim sights, and of those awful " sounds that live in darkness " (Wordsworth's " Excursion "), never had I consciously witnessed. Rightly, and by a true instinct, had I made my farewell adieus to summer. All through the day Wales and her grand mountain ranges—Penmaenmawr, Snowdon, Cader Idris—had divided my thoughts with London. But now rose London—sole, dark, infinite—brooding over the whole capacities of my heart. Other object—other thought—I could not admit. Long before midnight, the whole household (with the exception of a solitary waiter) had retired to rest. Two hours, at least, were left to me, after twelve o'clock had struck, for heart-

shaking reflections. More than ever I stood upon the
brink of a precipice ; and the local circumstances around
me deepened and intensified these reflections, impressed
upon them solemnity and terror, sometimes even horror.
It is all but inconceivable to men of unyielding and
callous sensibilities, how profoundly others find their
reveries modified and overruled by the external characters
of the immediate scene around them. Many a suicide
that hung dubiously in the balances has been ratified, and
carried into summary effect, through the forlorn, soul-
revolting aspect of a crazy, dilapidated home. Oftentimes,
without extravagance, the whole difference between a mind
that spurns life and the same mind reconciled to life, turns
upon the outside features of that particular domestic
scenery which hourly besieges the eyes. I, in this Shrewsbury hotel, naturally contemplated a group of objects
tending to far different results. And yet in some respects
they agreed.

The unusual dimensions of the rooms, especially their
towering height, brought up continually and obstinately,
through natural links of associated feelings or images,
the mighty vision of London waiting for me afar off. An
altitude of nineteen or twenty feet showed itself unavoid-
ably upon an exaggerated scale in some of the smaller side-
rooms—meant probably for cards or for refreshments.
This single feature of the rooms—their unusual altitude,
and the echoing hollowness which had become the
exponent of that altitude—this one terrific feature (for
terrific it was in the effect), together with crowding and
evanescent images of the flying feet that so often had
spread gladness through these halls on the wings of youth
and hope at seasons when every room rang with music—
all this, rising in tumultuous vision, whilst the dead hours

of night were stealing along, all around me—household
and town—sleeping, and whilst against the windows more
and more the storm outside was raving, and to all appearance endlessly growing, threw me into the deadliest condition of nervous emotion under contradictory forces, high
over which predominated horror recoiling from that
unfathomed abyss in London into which I was now so
wilfully precipitating myself. Often I looked out and
examined the night. Wild it was beyond all description,
and dark as " the inside of a wolf's throat." But at
intervals, when the wind, shifting continually, swept in
such a direction as to clear away the vast curtain of vapour,
the stars shone out, though with a light unusually dim and
distant. Still, as I turned inwards to the echoing chambers,
or outwards to the wild, wild night, I saw London expand-
ing her visionary gates to receive me, like some dreadful
mouth of Acheron (*Acherontis avari*). Thou also, Whis-
pering Gallery ! once again in those moments of conscious and wilful desolation didst to my ear utter moni-
torial sighs. For once again I was preparing to utter an
irrevocable word, to enter upon one of those fatally
tortuous paths of which the windings can never be
unlinked.

Such thoughts, and visions without number corre-
sponding to them, were moving across the *camera obscura*
of my fermenting fancy, when suddenly I heard a sound
of wheels ; which, however, soon died off into some
remote quarter. I guessed at the truth—viz., that it was
the Holyhead Mail wheeling off on its primary duty of
delivering its bags at the post-office. In a few minutes
it was announced as having changed horses ; and off I
was to London.

Thomas de Quincey.

ARRANGING A DUEL

THEY went in at the bar of the tavern, and desired a private room and wine and cards, and when the drawer had brought these, they began to drink and called healths, and as long as the servants were in the room appeared very friendly.

Harry Esmond's plan was no other than to engage in talk with Lord Mohun, to insult him, and so get the first of the quarrel. So when cards were proposed he offered to play. " Psha," says my Lord Mohun (whether wishing to save Harry, or not choosing to try the *botte de Jesuite*, it is not to be known) " young gentlemen from college should not play these stakes. You are too young."

" Who dares say I am too young ? " broke out Harry. " Is your lordship afraid ? "

" Afraid ? " cries out Mohun.

But my good Lord Viscount saw the move. " I'll play you for ten moidores, Mohun," says he. " You silly boy, we don't play for groates here as you do at Cambridge " ; and Harry, who had no such sum in his pocket (for his half-year's salary was always pretty well spent before it was due) fell back with rage and vexation in his heart that he had not money enough to stake.

" I'll stake the young gentleman a crown," says the Lord Mohun's captain.

" I thought crowns were rather scarce with the gentle-men of the army," says Harry.

" Do they birch at college ? " says the Captain.

" They birch fools," says Harry, " and they cane bullies, and they fling puppies into the water."

" Faith, then, there's some escapes drowning," says the Captain, who was an Irishman ; and all the gentlemen began to laugh, and made poor Harry only more angry.

My Lord Mohun presently snuffed a candle. It was when the drawers brought in fresh bottles and glasses and were in the room—on which my Lord Viscount said, "The deuce take you, Mohun, how damned awkward you are ! Light the candle, you—drawer."

"Damned awkward is a damned awkward expression, my lord," says the other. "Town gentlemen don't use such words—or ask pardon if they do."

"I'm a country gentleman," says my Lord Viscount.

"I see it by your manner," says my Lord Mohun. "No man shall say damned awkward to me."

"I fling the words in your face, my lord," says the other ; "shall I send the cards too ? "

"Gentlemen, gentlemen ! before the servants ! " cry out Colonel Westbury and the Lord Warwick in a breath. The drawers go out of the room hastily. They tell the people below of the quarrel upstairs.

"Enough has been said," says Colonel Westbury. "Will your lordships meet to-morrow morning ? "

"Will my Lord Castlewood withdraw his words ? " asks the Earl of Warwick.

"My Lord Castlewood will be —— first," says Colonel Westbury.

"Then we have nothing for it. Take notice, gentle-men, there have been outrageous words—reparation asked and refused."

"And refused," says my Lord Castlewood, putting on his hat. "Where shall the meeting be ? and when ? "

"Since my lord refuses me satisfaction, which I deeply regret, there is no time so good as now," says my Lord

Mohun.   " Let us have chairs and go to Leicester
Field."

" Are your lordship and I to have the honour of exchanging a pass or two ? " says Colonel Westbury, with a
low bow to my Lord of Warwick and Holland.

" It is an honour for me," says my lord, with a profound
congee, " to be matched with a gentleman who has been
at Mons and Namur."

" Will your Reverence permit me to give you a lesson ? "
says the Captain.

" Nay, nay, gentlemen, two on a side are plenty," says
Harry's patron.   " Spare the boy, Captain Macartney,"
and he shook Harry's hand—for the last time, save one,
in his life.

At the bar of the tavern all the gentlemen stopped, and
my Lord Viscount said, laughing, to the barwoman, that
those cards set people sadly a-quarrelling ; but that the
dispute was over now, and the parties were all going away
to my Lord Mohun's house, in Bow Street, to drink a
bottle more before going to bed.   *W. M. Thackeray.*

MARGARET CATCHPOLE AT THE ALDGATE "BULL"

MARGARET took no notice of any one, but pushed
on her willing steed with the same indifference as if
she had been sent upon an errand of only a few miles ;
nor was the horse apparently fatigued in the least when
they arrived at the Bull Inn, which they did about half-
past nine o'clock.

She rode quietly down the yard, called for the ostler,
dismounted, shook her trousers down, and addressed
the man in as off-hand a manner as if she were a real
groom.

" Rub that horse down well, and get him cool and comfortable ; give him a sup of water and a mouthful of hay,
and I will come and see him fed."

" Have you rode far, young man ? " asked the
ostler.

" Not a very great way. I came out of Chelmsford
this morning. See and rub his ears dry, ostler. You
must make him look as well as you can, for I expect my
master up in town to-night ; and if I don't meet with a
customer for that horse he'll blow me up."

" He's a very fine horse ; and if as good as he looks,
would be worth any man's money."

" He's better than he looks, ostler : and 'tisn't any
man's money that will buy him. He must give a good
price for him, whoever buys him. But look well after
him. I must go and get a bait myself."

She went into the bar, ordered her breakfast, took
up the newspaper, and with all the airs of a consequential young jockey sat down to the perusal of it.
After taking some refreshment she got up to see her
horse fed.

The ostler, finding so fine a horse was for sale, apprised
a livery-stable-keeper of his acquaintance, who on hearing
his representation hastened to look at him. Margaret was
called out ; the animal exhibited ; under-valued by the
dealer in the style so characteristic of such gentry ; and
his good qualifications well vouched for by the young
groom.

" Did you ever see a better shape," exclaimed Margaret.
" Look at his fore-end ; there's a crest, there's a shoulder,
there's a head ! Look at his legs, as straight and clean as
a colt's ; and as for quarters, where will you find such for
strength and beauty ! He's six-year old next grass ; has

never done any hard work before this day ; and you won't find a puff as big as a pea in any of his sinews. Quiet to ride or drive, and without a fault. Now, what's the matter with him ? "

" I should like to see him down our ride ; I could better judge of his paces."

" Clap the saddle on him. I will ride him where you like ; or I will let you drive me with him ; but I do not trust any one else with him whilst he is in my care."

The saddle and bridle were put on, and Crop came out of the stable free, and ready to trot back again to Ipswich if his rider was so disposed. He was as fresh and joyous as a lark, and sprang up into the air with almost as light a heart. Margaret mounted awkwardly ; put her foot into the stirrup the wrong way ; and perceiving that this was noticed, she crossed the stirrups over the saddle in front of her, saying,

" My master always makes me ride without stirrups, and I like it best."

In truth she sat the horse better without them ; and had she had no saddle, it would have suited her even better still ; but this seemed to have the desired effect.

The dealer, however, entertained some suspicions from the awkward manner of the groom, and having already suffered for purchasing a stolen horse, he was more on his guard than he otherwise might have been.

They went out of the stable-yard together, and reached the ride belonging to the dealer, and Margaret turned her horse in as she was directed. The stable lads peeped out to see what kind of nag their master was buying, and were not satisfied with a glance, but looked with much admiration at him.

" Just trot him down the ride, young man."

Margaret dashed down the yard and back again.

" Soho ! my fine fellow ! Peter," he said to his head man, " just come and look at this nag."

Peter stepped forward, and gave his master a knowing look, as much as to say, " Am I to decry him ? "

" Look at his mouth ! "

Peter did so.

" How is it, Peter ? "

" All right, sir."

" What's his age ? "

" Rising six."

" What do you say to him ? "

Peter looked at every point, then scratched his head, and again looked at his master ; but he received no sign to manœuvre ; so he replied, " Why, master, if you ask for truth you shall have it. He's a right good one ; that is it. He's worth the money ; that's what I say. Buy him, master."

" Well, young man, I'll take the horse ; but you must give me a written warranty with him."

" That I'll do ; but perhaps you'll not like to conclude the bargain without master's warranty ; if so, we had better not exactly conclude the price."

This so took the dealer aback, that it drove away all suspicions, and he said, " No, no ; your warranty will do. I'll give you the money." He was in the act of going to the gateway as he saw one of his men come into the yard, with a paper in his hand, which proved to be one of the identical hand-bills, offering a reward of twenty guineas for the very horse he had just bought. " Peter," he called out, " tell the young man just to walk that horse once more up the yard, and come you here."

He showed Peter the bill, who said : " It's the very horse ! "

" Go you and fetch a constable ; I'll keep him in play a bit until he comes." . . .

By this time Peter returned with the constable ; but Margaret was joking about the saddle and bridle, and greatly rejoicing at her success, not the least conscious of the presence of the man of the law, or of the dreadful fate which awaited her.

" Did you say that horse came from Ipswich, young man ? " said the dealer.

" I did," said she.

" When did he leave Ipswich ? "

" Yesterday."

" Did you leave with him ? "

" Yes, I did ; I told you so."

" No, you didn't ; you told me you rode him from Chelmsford."

" So I did ; and from Ipswich too."

" What was your master's name ? "

" Mr. John Cook," said Margaret, who now began to feel a little uneasy.

" Are you sure it was not Mr. John Cobbold ? Look at that hand-bill, young man."

Margaret saw only her master's name, and all her fortitude forsook her ; she swooned away in a moment, and would have fallen from the horse, had not the constable caught her by her jacket as she was falling ; and in endeavouring to support her off the horse the jacket flew open, and to the astonishment of all around, lo, and behold, it was a woman !

Richard Cobbold.

JAN RIDD AT THE DULVERTON INN

IT was high noon before we got to Dulverton that day, near to which town the river Exe and its big brother Barle have union. The road from Bampton to Dulverton had not been very delicate, yet nothing to complain of much—no deeper, indeed, than the hocks of a horse, except in the rotten places. The day was inclined to be mild and foggy, and both nags sweated freely ; but Peggy carrying little weight (for my wardrobe was upon Smiler, and John Fry grumbling always), we could easily keep in front, as far as you may hear a laugh.

John had been rather bitter with me, which methought was a mark of ill taste at coming home for the holidays ; and yet I made allowance for John, because he had never been at school, and never would have chance to eat fry upon condition of spelling it ; therefore I rode on, thinking that he was hard-set, like a saw, for his dinner, and would soften after tooth-work. And yet at his most hungry times, when his mind was far gone upon bacon, *certes* he seemed to check himself and look at me as if he were sorry for little things coming over great.

But now, at Dulverton, we dined upon the rarest and choicest victuals that ever I did taste. Even now, at my time of life, to think of it gives me appetite, as once and awhile to think of my first love makes me love all goodness. Hot mutton pasty was a thing I had often heard of from very wealthy boys and men, who made a dessert of dinner ; and to hear them talk of it made my lips smack, and my ribs come inwards.

And now John Fry strode into the hostel, with the air and grace of a short-legged man, and shouted as loud as if he was calling sheep upon Exmoor,—

" Hot mooton pasty for twoo trarv'lers, at number vaive, in vaive minnits ! Dish un up in the tin with the grahvy, zame as I hardered last Tuesday."

Of course it did not come in five minutes, nor yet in ten or twenty ; but that made it all the better when it came to the real presence ; and the smell of it was enough to make an empty man thank God for the room there was inside him. Fifty years have passed me quicker than the taste of that gravy.

When the mutton pasty was done, and Peggy and Smiler had dined well also, out I went to wash at the pump, being a lover of soap and water, at all risk, except of my dinner. And John Fry, who cared very little to wash, save Sabbath days in his own soap, and who had kept me from the pump by threatening loss of the dish, out he came in a satisfied manner, with a piece of quill in his hand, to lean against a door-post, and listen to the horses feeding, and have his teeth ready for supper.

Then a lady's-maid came out, and the sun was on her face, and she turned round to go back again ; but put a better face upon it, and gave a trip and hitched her dress, and looked at the sun full body, lest the hostlers should laugh that she was losing her complexion. With a long Italian glass in her fingers very daintily, she came up to the pump in the middle of the yard, where I was running the water off all my head and shoulders, and arms, and some of my breast even, and though I had glimpsed her through the sprinkle, it gave me quite a turn to see her, child as I was, in my open aspect. But she looked at me, no whit abashed, making a baby of me, no doubt, as a woman of thirty will do, even with a very big boy when they catch him on a hayrick, and she said to me in a brazen manner, as if I had been nobody, while I was shrinking behind the pump, and craving to get my shirt on, " Good leetle boy, come hither to me. Fine heaven ! how blue your eyes are, and your skin like snow ; but some naughty man has beaten it black. Oh, leetle boy, let me feel it. Ah, how then it must have hurt you ! There now, and you shall love me."

All this time she was touching my breast, here and there, very lightly, with her delicate brown fingers, and I understood from her voice and manner that she was not of this country, but a foreigner by extraction. And then I was not so shy of her, because I could talk better English than she ; and yet I longed for my jerkin, but liked not to be rude to her.

" If you please, madam, I must go. John Fry is waiting by the tapster's door, and Peggy neighing to me. If you please, we must get home to-night ; and father will be waiting for me this side of the telling-house."

" There, there, you shall go, leetle dear, and perhaps I will go after you. I have taken much love of you. But the Baroness is hard to me. How far you call it now to the bank of the sea at Wash—Wash——"

" At Watchett, likely you mean, madam. Oh, a very long way, and the roads as soft as the road to Oare."

" Oh-ah, oh-ah—I shall remember ; that is the place where my leetle boy live, and some day I will come seek for him. Now make the pump to flow, my dear, and give me the good water. The Baroness will not touch unless a nebule be formed outside the glass."

I did not know what she meant by that ; yet I pumped for her very heartily, and marvelled to see her for fifty times throw the water away in the trough, as if it was not good enough. At last the water suited her, with a likeness of fog outside the glass, and the gleam of a crystal under it, and then she made a curtsey to me, in a sort of mocking manner, holding the long glass by the foot, not to take the cloud off ; and then she wanted to kiss me ; but I was out of breath, and have always been shy of that work, except when I come to offer it ; and so I ducked under the pump-handle, and she knocked her chin on the knob of it ; and the hostlers came out, and asked whether they would do as well.

Upon this, she retreated up the yard, with a certain dark dignity, and a foreign way of walking, which stopped them at once from going farther, because it was so different from the fashion of their sweethearts. One with another they hung back, where half a cart-load of hay was, and they looked to be sure that she would not turn round ; and then each one laughed at the rest of them.

R. D. Blackmore.

COBBETT ORDERED OUT

HAVING laid my plan to sleep at Andover last night, I went with two Farnham friends, Messrs. Knowles and West, to dine at the ordinary at the George Inn, which is kept by one Sutton, a rich old fellow, who wore a round-skirted sleeved fustian waistcoat, with a dirty white apron tied round his middle, and with no coat on ; having a look the eagerest and sharpest, that I ever saw in any set of features, in my whole life-time ; having an air of authority and of mastership, which, to a stranger, as I was, seemed quite incompatible with the meanness of his dress and the vulgarity of his manners : and there being, visible to every beholder, constantly going on in him, a pretty even contest between the servility of avarice and the insolence of wealth. A great part of the farmers, and other fair-people having gone off home, we found preparations made for dining only about ten people. But, after we sat down, and it was seen that we designed to dine, guests came in apace, the preparations were augmented, and as many as could dine came and dined with us.

After the dinner was over, the room became fuller and fuller ; guests came in from the other inns, where they had been dining, till, at last, the room became as full as possible in every part, the door being opened, the door way blocked up, and the stairs leading to the room crammed from bottom to top. In this state of things, Mr. Knowles, who was our chairman, gave my health, which, of course, was followed by a speech ; and, as the reader will readily suppose, to have an opportunity of making a speech was the main motive for my going to dine at an inn at any hour, and especially at seven o'clock at night. . . . Just at this time a noise was heard, and a sort of row was taking place in the passage, the cause of which was, upon inquiry, found to be no less a personage than our landlord, our host Sutton, who, it appeared, finding that my speech-making had cut off, or, at least, suspended, all intercourse between the dining, now become a drink, room, and the bar ; who, finding that I had been the cause of a great restriction in the exchange of our money for his " neat," " genuine " commodities downstairs, and being, apparently, an ardent admirer of the " liberal " system of " free trade " ; who, finding, in short, or rather, supposing, that if my tongue were not stopped from running, his taps would be, had, though an old man, fought, or, at least, forced his way up the thronged stairs and through the passage and doorway, into the room, and was, with what breath the struggle had left him, beginning to bawl out to me, when someone called to him, and told him that he was causing an interruption, to which he answered that that was what he had come to do ! And then he went on to say, in so many words, that my speech injured the sale of his liquor. . . .

After this I proceeded with my speech-making ; and, this being ended, the great business of the evening, namely, drinking, smoking and singing, was about to be proceeded in. But now behold, the old fustian-jacketed fellow, whose head was, I think, powdered, took it into that head not only to lay " restrictions " upon trade, but to impose an absolute embargo ; cut off entirely all supplies whatever from his bar to the room, *as long as I remained in that room.* A message to this effect having been, through the waiter, communicated to Mr. Knowles, and he having communicated it to the company, I addressed the company in nearly these words : " Gentlemen,—Born and bred, as you know I was, on the borders of this county, and fond as I am of bacon, Hampshire hogs have always with me been objects of admiration rather than of contempt ; but that which has just happened here induces me to observe that this feeling of mine has been confined to hogs of *four legs.* For my part, I like your company too well to quit it. I have paid this fellow six shillings for the wing of a fowl, a bit of bread, and a pint of small beer. I have a right to sit here ; I want no drink, and those who do, being refused it here, have a right to send to other houses for it, and to drink it here."

However, Mammon soon got the upper hand down-stairs, all the fondness for " free trade " returned, and up came the old fustian-jacketed fellow, bringing pipes, tobacco, wine, grog, sling, and seeming to be as pleased as if he had just sprung a mine of gold. Nay, he soon after this came into the room with two gentlemen, who had come to him to ask where I was. He actually came up to me, making me a bow, and, telling me that those gentlemen wished to be introduced to me, he, with a fawning look, laid his hand upon my knee. " Take away your paw," said I, and, shaking the gentlemen by the hand, I said, " I am happy to see you, gentlemen, even though introduced by this fellow. . . ." It was not politics ; it was not personal dislike to me ; for the fellow knew nothing of me. It was, as I told the company, just this : he looked upon their bodies as so many gutters to drain off the contents of his taps, and upon their purses, as so many small heaps from which to take the means of augmenting his great one ; and, finding that I had been, no matter how, the cause of suspending this work of " reciprocity," he wanted, and no matter how, to restore the reciprocal system to motion. All that I have to add is this : that the next time this old sharp-looking fellow gets six shillings from me for a dinner, he shall, if he choose, *cook me*, in any manner that he likes, and season me with hand so unsparing as to produce in the feeders thirst unquenchable.

William Cobbett.

VALENTINE VOX MAKES TROUBLE

HAVING tremblingly delivered himself thus, the gentleman in black turned exceedingly white, and as he prepared to leave the room, with the view of making certain necessary enquiries, Valentine, assuming his voice, ordered seven large glasses of brandy-and-water, and rump-steaks and onions for nine.

No sooner was this order given, than the whole of the domestic establishment of John Brown was in an uproar. Dan was sent out for the steaks ; Mary was told to peel the onions ; Roger was directed to wipe the bars of the gridiron, and Sally was ordered to make the fire clear with salt, while the hostess herself mixed the brandy-and-water, and scolded all about her with due bitterness and force.

While these preparations were making, the gentleman in black ascertained, to his unspeakable mortification, that there was not a single posting house within seven miles of the place. He, therefore, deemed it expedient to alter his tone, and having decided upon certain persuasive arguments, which he felt were too potent to fail, he returned to employ them as the hostess entered the parlour with the brandy-and-water on her best japanned tray. . . .

" Now, if you please, sir," said the hostess, bestowing one of her blandest smiles upon the gentleman in black, as she gracefully placed a chair for him at the head of the table. " Do'ee eat it while it's hot ; there's some more inguns doing."

" Not any for me, I thank you," said the gentleman with great politeness. " I have not the smallest appetite. I'll take a glass of sherry and a biscuit."

" Oh, do'ee eat a little," urged the fascinating hostess. " It's done very beautiful. Look'ee ! " added the tempter, as she took off the cover, and displayed a fine steak garnished with onions, the sight of which at once drew the rest of the passengers towards the table.

" Do have a bit with us, sir, do ! " cried the passengers in a chorus. " We shall not enjoy it half so much without you."

" Why not, my good people ? " enquired the pastor.

" 'Cause," replied the hostess, " you was kind enow to order it."

" *I*, my good woman ! " exclaimed the astonished gentleman, peering over his spectacles with a look of amazement. " I ordered ?   I ? "

"In course, sir, you did," replied the hostess, as the pleasing expression of her countenance vanished.

"Dear me! my good woman," rejoined the pastor, "you must have been dreaming!"

"I 'peal to the gentlemen and ladies present," said the hostess, "whether you didn't order seven glasses o' brandy-and-water, and rump-steaks and inguns for nine."

"Oh, that's right enough," said one of the passengers, "that wor the order ersackly, you doan't mean to go for to say as how it wasn't sir, do yer?"

"Upon my honour, my good people," returned the pastor; "believe me, you were never more mistaken in your lives."

"Not a bit on't," observed Tooler, "I heerd yow myself."

"God bless my soul! Impossible! impossible!" cried the pastor, as he strove with great energy of mind to ascertain what sentence in the English language, bore the slightest resemblance in point of sound to "seven glasses of brandy-and-water, and rump-steaks and onions for nine."

"Well, whether or no," observed the hostess, "there's what was ordered, and I 'spects to be paid for it at all events."

"Come," said the farmer, who had occupied a seat at the back of the coach, "let's tackle it together, for I feel rayther peckish," and he and Valentine with two other passengers commenced; the rest modestly keeping aloof from the table, lest payment should be demanded of them respectively as a social matter of course.

"Yow may as well just have a mouthful as not," said the farmer, "sin' yow do mean to pay all the same!"

"Really," observed the gentleman in black, "I am unconscious of having made such an arrangement."

"Well, well," said Valentine, in his natural voice; "suppose we compromise the matter, as there appears to be some slight misunderstanding on the subject: you settle for the steaks, and I'll pay for the brandy-and-water."

"Well, coom, that's handsome!" cried the farmer, "and to show that I doon't want to shirk from my share, why I'll be a couple o' bottles o' wine—coom, what say yow noo?"

"I cannot, under the circumstances, of course, object to join you," replied the puzzled pastor; "but I must be permitted to say that those circumstances are in my judgment perfectly inexplicable: I never in any case like to be *positive*; I know that human nature is but human nature, and therefore cannot pretend to claim entire exemption from those weaknesses which form its distinguishing characteristics: I may be mistaken: I confess that I may; but I nevertheless hold it to be utterly impossible for any man to give such an order as that without knowing it."

Henry Cockton.

WITH THE HIGH-TOBY MEN

TURNING to Augustus Tomlinson, he saluted him with—

"So, this is the youngster you present to us?—Welcome to the Jolly Angler! Give us thy hand, young sir; —I shall be happy to blow a cloud with thee."

"With all due submission," said Mr. Tomlinson, "I think it may first be as well to introduce my pupil and friend to his future companions."

"You speak like a leary cove," cried Gentleman

George, still squeezing our hero's hand ; and, turning round in his elbow-chair, he pointed to each member, as he severally introduced his guests to Paul :

" Here," said he,—" here's a fine chap at my right hand—(the person thus designated was a thin military-looking figure, in a shabby riding frock, and with a commanding, bold, aquiline countenance, a little the worse for wear)—here's a fine chap for you ; Fighting Attie we calls him : he's a devil on the road. ' Halt—deliver—must and shall—can't and shan't—do as I bid you, or go to the devil,'—that's all Fighting Attie's palaver ; and, 'sdeath, it has a wonderful way of coming to the point ! A famous cull is my friend Attie—an old soldier—has seen the world, and knows what is what ; has lots of gumption, and devil a bit of blarney. Howsomever, the highflyers doesn't like him ; and when he takes people's money, he need not be quite so cross about it !—Attie, let me introduce a new pal to you." Paul made his bow.

" Stand at ease, man ! " quoth the veteran, without taking the pipe from his mouth.

Gentleman George then continued ; and, after pointing out four or five of the company (among whom our hero discovered, to his surprise, his old friends, Mr. Eustace Fitzherbert and Mr. William Howard Russell), came, at length, to one with a very red face, and a lusty frame of body. " That gentleman," said he, " is Scarlet Jem ; a dangerous fellow for a *press*, though he says he likes robbing alone now, for a general press is not half such a good thing as it used to be formerly. You have no idea what a hand at disguising himself Scarlet Jem is. He has an old wig which he generally does business in ; and you would not go for to know him again, when he conceals

himself under the *wig*. Oh, he's a precious rogue, is
Scarlet Jem !—As for the cove on t'other side," continued
the host of the Jolly Angler, pointing to Long Ned, " all
I can say of him, good, bad, or indifferent, is, that he has
an unkimmon fine head of hair : and now, youngster, as
you knows him, spose you goes and sits by him, and he'll
introduce you to the rest ; for, split my wig ! if I ben't
tired, and so here's to your health ; and if so be as your
name's Paul, may you always rob Peter in order to pay
Paul."

This witticism of mine host's being exceedingly well
received, Paul went, amidst the general laughter, to take
possession of the vacant seat beside Long Ned. That tall
gentleman, who had hitherto been cloud-compelling (as
Homer calls Jupiter) in profound silence, now turned to
Paul with the warmest cordiality, declared himself overjoyed to meet his old friend once more, and congratulated
him alike on his escape from Bridewell and his admission
to the councils of Gentleman George. The conversation
of the convivialists now began to assume a most fascinating
bias. They talked with infinite *goût* of the sums they had
levied on the public, and the peculations they had committed for what one called the " *good of the community*,"
and another, the " *established order*,"—meaning themselves. It was easy to see in what school the dis-
cerning Augustus Tomlinson had learned the value of
words.

There was something edifying in hearing the rascals !
So nice was their language, and so honest their enthusiasm
for their own interests, you might have imagined you were
listening to a coterie of cabinet ministers conferring on
taxes, or debating on perquisites.

"Long may the *Commons* flourish !" cried punning

Georgie, filling his glass ; " it is by the commons we're fed, and may they never know cultiwation ! "

" Three time three ! " shouted Long Ned : and the toast was drunk as Mr. Pepper proposed.

" A little moderate cultivation of the commons, to speak frankly," said Augustus Tomlinson modestly, " might not be amiss ; for it would decoy people into the belief that they might travel safely ; and, after all, a hedge or a barley-field is as good for us as a barren heath, where we have no shelter if once pursued ! "

" You talks nonsense, you spooney ! " cried a robber of note, called Bagshot ; who, being aged, and having been a lawyer's footboy, was sometimes denominated " Old Bags." " You talks nonsense ; these innowating ploughs are the ruin of us. Every blade of corn in a common is an encroachment on the constitution and rights of the gemmen highwaymen. I'm old, and mayn't live to see these things ; but, mark my words, a time will come when a man may go from Lunnun to Johnny Groat's without losing a penny by one of us ; when Hounslow will be safe, and Finchley secure. My eyes, what a sad thing for us that'll be ! "

The venerable old man became suddenly silent, and the tears started to his eyes. Gentleman George had a great horror of blue devils, and particularly disliked all disagreeable subjects.

" Thunder and oons, Old Bags ! " quoth mine host of the Jolly Angler, " this will never do : we're all met here to be merry, and not to listen to your mullancolly taratarantarums. I says, Ned Pepper, spose you tips us a song, and I'll beat time with my knuckles."

Dashing away the drop of sensibility, the veteran knocked down Gentleman George himself.

" Oh, dang it ! " said George, with an air of dignity, " I ought to skip, since I finds the lush : but howsomever here goes."

GENTLEMAN GEORGE'S SONG

Air.—" Old King Cole."

" I be's the cove—the merry old cove,
    Of whose max all the *rufflers* sing.
And a lushing cove, I thinks, by Jove,
    Is as great as a sober king !

CHORUS.
    Is as great as a sober king.

Whatever the noise as is made by the boys,
    At the bar as they lush away :
The devil a noise my peace alloys,
    As long as the rascals pay !

CHORUS.
    As long as the rascals pay !

What if I sticks my stones and my bricks
    With mortar I takes from the snobbish ?
All who can feel for the public weal,
    Likes the public-house to be bobbish.

CHORUS.
    Likes the public-house to be bobbish."

" There, gemmen ! " said the publican, stopping short, " that's the pith of the matter, and split my wig but I'm short of breath now. So, send round the brandy, Augustus ; you sly dog, you keeps it all to yourself."

By this time the whole conclave were more than half-seas over, or, as Augustus Tomlinson expressed it, " their more austere qualities were relaxed by a pleasing and innocent indulgence." Paul's eyes reeled, and his tongue ran loose. By degrees the room swam round, the faces of his comrades altered, the countenance of Old Bags assumed an awful and menacing air. He thought Long Ned insulted him, and that Old Bags took the part of the assailant, doubled his fists, and threatened to put the plaintiff's nob into chancery, if he disturbed the peace of the meeting. Various other imaginary evils beset him. He thought he had robbed a mail-coach in company with Pepper ; that Tomlinson informed against him, and that Gentleman George ordered him to be hanged ; in short, he laboured under a temporary delirium, occasioned by a sudden reverse of fortune—from water to brandy ; and the last thing of which he retained any recollection, before he sunk under the table, in company with Long Ned, Scarlet Jem, and Old Bags, was, the bearing his part in the burthen, of what appeared to him a chorus of last dying speeches and confessions, but what in reality was a song made in honour of Gentleman George, and sung by his grateful guests as a finale of the festivities.

Lord Lytton.

THE END OF A JOURNEY

WHEN she had paid the fare for the last coach, she had only a shilling ; and as she got down at the sign of the Green Man in Windsor at twelve o'clock in the middle of the seventh day, hungry and faint, the coachman came up, and begged her to " remember him." She put her hand in her pocket, and took out the shilling, but the tears came with the sense of exhaustion and the thought that she was giving away her last means of getting food, which she really required before she could go in search of Arthur. As she held out the shilling, she lifted up her dark tear-filled eyes to the coachman's face and said, " Can you give me back sixpence ? "

" No, no," he said, gruffly, " never mind—put the shilling up again."

The landlord of the Green Man had stood near enough to witness this scene, and he was a man whose abundant feeding served to keep his good-nature, as well as his person, in high condition. And that lovely tearful face of Hetty's would have found out the sensitive fibre in most men.

" Come, young woman, come in," he said, " and have a drop o' something ; you're pretty well knocked up : I can see that."

He took her into the bar and said to his wife, " Here, missis, take this young woman into the parlour ; she's a little overcome,"—for Hetty's tears were falling fast. They were merely hysterical tears : she thought she had no reason for weeping now, and was vexed that she was too weak and tired to help it. She was at Windsor at last, not far from Arthur.

She looked with eager, hungry eyes at the bread and meat and beer that the landlady brought her, and for some minutes she forgot everything else in the delicious sensations of satisfying hunger and recovering from exhaustion. The landlady sat opposite to her as she ate, and looked at her earnestly. No wonder : Hetty had thrown off her bonnet, and her curls had fallen down : her face was all the more touching in its youth and beauty because of its weary look ; and the good woman's eyes presently wandered to her figure, which in her hurried dressing on her journey she had taken no pains to conceal ; moreover, the stranger's eye detects what the familiar unsuspecting eye leaves unnoticed.

" Why, you're not very fit for travelling," she said, glancing while she spoke at Hetty's ringless hand. " Have you come far ? "

" Yes," said Hetty, roused by this question to exert more self-command, and feeling the better for the food she had taken. " I've come a good long way, and it's very tiring. But I'm better now. Could you tell me which way to go to this place ? " Here Hetty took from her pocket a bit of paper : it was the end of Arthur's letter on which he had written his address.

While she was speaking, the landlord had come in, and had begun to look at her as earnestly as his wife had done. He took up the piece of paper which Hetty handed across the table, and read the address.

" Why, what do you want at this house ? " he said. It is in the nature of innkeepers, and all men who have no pressing business of their own, to ask as many questions as possible before giving any information.

" I want to see a gentleman as is there," said Hetty.

" But there's no gentlemen there," returned the landlord. " It's shut up—been shut up this fortnight. What gentleman is it you want ? Perhaps I can let you know where to find him."

" It's Captain Donnithorne," said Hetty, tremulously, her heart beginning to beat painfully at this disappointment of her hope that she should find Arthur at once.

" Captain Donnithorne ? Stop a bit," said the landlord, slowly. " Was he in the Loamshire Militia ? A tall young officer with a fairish skin and reddish whiskers —and had a servant by the name of Pym ? "

" Oh, yes," said Hetty ; " you know him ? Where is he ? "

" A fine sight o' miles away from here : the Loamshire Militia's gone to Ireland ; it's been gone this fortnight."

" Look there ! she's fainting," said the landlady.

George Eliot.

DESTRUCTION OF THE MAYPOLE

HE had not to wait long.   A dark mass, looming through a cloud of dust, soon became visible ; the mob quickened their pace ; shouting and whooping like savages, they came rushing on pell-mell ; and in a few seconds he was bandied from hand to hand, in the heart of a crowd of men.

" Halloa ! " cried a voice he knew, as the man who spoke came cleaving through the throng.   " Where is he ? Give him to me.   Don't hurt him.   How now, old Jack ! Ha ha ha ! "

Mr. Willet looked at him, and saw it was Hugh ; but he said nothing, and thought nothing.

" These lads are thirsty and must drink ! " cried Hugh, thrusting him back towards the house.   " Bustle, Jack, bustle.   Show us the best—the very best—the over-proof that you keep for your own drinking, Jack ! "

John faintly articulated the words, " Who's to pay ? "

" He says ' Who's to pay ? ' " cried Hugh, with a roar of laughter which was loudly echoed by the crowd.   Then turning to John, he added, " Pay !   Why, nobody."

John stared round at the mass of faces—some grinning, some fierce, some lighted up by torches, some indistinct, some dusky and shadowy ; some looking at him, some at his house, some at each other—and while he was, as he thought, in the very act of doing so, found himself, without any consciousness of having moved, in the bar ; sitting down in an arm-chair, and watching the destruction of his

Y 2

property, as if it were some queer play or entertainment, of an astonishing and stupefying nature, but having no reference to himself—that he could make out—at all.

Yes. Here was the bar—the bar that the boldest never entered without special invitation—the sanctuary, the mystery, the hallowed ground : here it was crammed with men, clubs, sticks, torches, pistols ; filled with a deafening noise, oaths, shouts, screams, hootings ; changed all at once into a bear-garden, a mad-house, an infernal temple : men darting in and out, by door and window, smashing the glass, turning the taps, drinking liquor out of china punch-bowls, sitting astride of casks, smoking private and personal pipes, cutting down the sacred grove of lemons, hacking and hewing at the celebrated cheese, breaking open inviolable drawers, putting things in their pockets which didn't belong to them, dividing his own money before his own eyes, wantonly wasting, breaking, pulling down and tearing up : nothing quiet, nothing private : men everywhere—above, below, overhead, in the bed-rooms, in the kitchen, in the yard, in the stables—clambering in at windows when there were doors wide open ; dropping out of windows when the stairs were handy ; leaping over the bannisters into chasms of passages : new faces and figures presenting themselves every instant—some yelling, some singing, some fighting, some breaking glass and crockery, some laying the dust with the liquor they couldn't drink, some ringing the bells till they pulled them down, others beating them with pokers till they beat them into fragments : more men still—more, more, more—swarming on like insects : noise, smoke, light, darkness, frolic, anger, laughter, groans, plunder, fear, and ruin !

Charles Dickens.

DEATH OF TOM KING

TOM'S presentiments of danger were not, it appeared, without foundation. Scarcely had the ostler brought forth our two highwaymen's steeds, when a post-chaise, escorted by two or three horsemen, drove furiously up to the door. The sole occupant of the carriage was a lady, whose slight and pretty figure was all that could be distinguished, her face being closely veiled. The landlord, who was busied in casting up Turpin's account, rushed forth at the summons. A word or two passed between him and the horsemen, upon which the former's countenance fell. He posted in the direction of the garden ; and the horsemen instantly dismounted.

" We have him now, sure enough," said one of them, a very small man, who looked, in his boots, like Buckle equipped for the Oaks.

" By the powers ! I begin to think so," replied the other horseman. " But don't spoil all, Mr. Coates, by being too precipitate."

" Never fear that, Mr. Tyrconnel," said Coates, for it was the gallant attorney : " he's sure to come for his mare. That's a *trap* certain to catch him, eh, Mr. Paterson ? With the chief constable of Westminster to back us, the devil's in it if we are not a match for him."

" And for Tom King, too," replied the chief constable ; " since his blowen's peached, the game's up with him too. We've long had an eye upon him, and now we'll have a finger. He's one of your dashing trouts to whom we always give a long line, but we'll land him this time, anyhow. If you'll look after Dick Turpin, gemmen, I'll make sure of Tom."

" I'd rather you would help us, Mr. Paterson," said

Coates ; " never mind Tom King ; another time will do for him."

" No such thing," said Paterson ; " one weighs just as much for that matter as t'other. I'll take Tom to myself, and surely you two, with the landlord and ostler, can manage Turpin amongst you."

" I don't know that," said Coates, doubtfully ; " he's a devil of a fellow to deal with."

As if conscious of what was passing around her, and of the danger that awaited her master, Black Bess exhibited so much impatience, and plunged so violently, that it was with difficulty the ostler could hold her. " The devil's in the mare," said he ; " what's the matter with her ? She was quiet enough a few minutes since. Soho, lass, stand."

Turpin and King, meanwhile, walked quickly through the house, preceded by the host, who conducted them, not without some inward trepidation, towards the door. Arrived there, each man rushed swiftly to his horse. Dick was in the saddle in an instant, and stamping her foot upon the ostler's leg, Black Bess compelled the man, yelling with pain, to quit his hold of the bridle. Tom King was not equally fortunate. Before he could mount his horse, a loud shout was raised, which startled the animal, and caused him to swerve, so that Tom lost his footing in the stirrup, and fell to the ground. He was instantly seized by Paterson, and a struggle commenced, King endeavouring, but in vain, to draw a pistol.

" Flip him, Dick ; fire, or I'm taken," cried King. " Fire ! damn you, why don't you fire ? " shouted he, in desperation, still struggling vehemently with Paterson, who was a strong man, and more than a match for a light weight like King.

" I can't," cried Dick ; " I shall hit you, if I fire."

" Take your chance," shouted King. " Is *this* your friendship ? "

Thus urged, Turpin fired. The ball ripped up the sleeve of Paterson's coat, but did not wound him.

" Again ! " cried King. " Shoot him, I say. Don't you hear me ? Fire again ! "

Pressed as he was by foes on every side, himself their mark, for both Coates and Tyrconnel had fired upon him, and were now mounting their steeds to give chase, it was impossible that Turpin could take sure aim ; added to which, in the struggle, Paterson and King were each moment changing their relative positions. He, however, would no longer hesitate, but again, at his friend's request, fired. The ball lodged itself in King's breast ! He fell at once.

                                   W. Harrison Ainsworth.

A MYSTERIOUS INN

THE house was a genuine old house of a very quaint description, teeming with old carvings and beams and panels, and having an excellent old staircase, with a gallery or upper staircase, cut off from it by a curious fence-work of old oak, or of the old Honduras Mahogany wood. It was and is and will be, for many a long year to come, a remarkably picturesque house ; and a certain grave mystery lurking in the depths of the old mahogany panels, as if they were so many deep pools of dark water—such, indeed, as they had been much among when they were trees—gave it a very mysterious character after nightfall.

When Mr. Goodchild and Mr. Idle had first alighted at the door, and stepped into the sombre handsome old hall, they had been received by half a dozen noiseless old men in black, all dressed exactly alike, who glided up the

stairs with the obliging landlord and waiter—but without
appearing to get into their way, or to mind whether they
did or no—and who had filed off to the right and left on
the old staircase, as the guests entered their sitting-room.
It was then broad bright day. But Mr. Goodchild had
said, when their door was shut, " Who on earth are those
old men ? " And afterwards, both on going out and coming in, he had noticed that there were no old men to be
seen. Neither had the old men, or any one of the old
men, reappeared since. The two friends had passed a
night in the house, but had seen nothing more of the old
men. Mr. Goodchild, in rambling about it, had looked
along passages and glanced in at doorways, but had encountered no old men ; neither did it appear that any old
men were, by any member of the establishment, missed or
expected.

Another odd circumstance impressed itself on their
attention. It was that the door of their sitting-room was
never left untouched for a quarter of an hour. It opened
with hesitation, opened with confidence, opened a little
way, opened a good way—always clapped to again without
a word of explanation. They were reading, they were
writing, they were eating, they were drinking, they were
talking, they were dozing ; the door was always opened
at an unexpected moment, and they looked towards it,
and it was clapped-to again, and nobody was to be seen.

Wilkie Collins.

A CELEBRATION

IT was now about eleven o'clock, at which hour the
" Cat and Whistle " generally does its most stirring
trade. This Charley knew ; but he also knew that the
little back parlour, even if there should be an inmate in

it at the time of his going in, would soon be made private for his purposes.

When he went in, Mrs. Davis was standing behind the counter, dressed in a cap of wonderful grandeur, and a red tabinet gown, which rustled among the pots and jars, sticking out from her to a tremendous width, inflated by its own magnificence and a substratum of crinoline. Charley had never before seen her arrayed in such royal robes. Her accustomed maid was waiting as usual on the guests, and another girl also was assisting ; but Norah did not appear to Charley's first impatient glance.

He at once saw that something wonderful was going on. The front parlour was quite full, and the ministering angel was going in and out quickly, with more generous supplies of the gifts of Bacchus than were usual at the " Cat and Whistle." Gin and water was the ordinary tipple in the front parlour ; and any one of its denizens inclined to cut a dash above his neighbours generally did so with a bottom of brandy. But now Mrs. Davis was mixing port-wine negus as fast as her hands could make it. . . .

" Of course you know what has happened, Mr. Tudor ? " said she.

" Devil a bit," said Charley.

" Laws, now—don't you indeed ? Well, that is odd."

" How the deuce should I know ? Where's Norah ? "

" Why, she's at Gravesend."

" At Gravesend—you don't mean to say she's——"

" I just do, then ; she's just gone and got herself spliced to Peppermint this morning. . . . And now, Mr. Tudor, come down and drink a glass to their healths, and wish 'em both well, and don't mind what them women says to you. You're well out of a mess ; and now it's all over, I'm glad it is as it is."

Charley went down and took his glass and drank " prosperity to the bride and bridegroom." The sarcastic rival barmaid said little snappish things to him, offered him a bit of green ribbon, and told him that if he " minded hisself," somebody might, perhaps, take him yet. But Charley was proof against this.

He sat there about half an hour, and then went his way, shaking hands with all the ladies and bowing to the gentlemen. On the following day, as soon as he left his office, he called at the " Cat and Whistle," and paid his little bill there, and said his last farewell to Mrs. Davis. He never visited the house again. Now that Norah was gone the attractions were not powerful. Reader, you and I will at the same time say our farewells to Mrs. Davis, to Mr. Peppermint also, and to his bride. If thou art an elegant reader, unaccustomed to the contamination of pipes and glasses, I owe thee an apology in that thou hast been caused to linger a while among things so un-savoury. But if thou art one who of thine own will hast taken thine ease in thine inn, hast enjoyed the freedom of a sanded parlour, hast known " that ginger is hot in the mouth," and made thyself light-hearted with a yard of clay, then thou wilt confess there are worse establish-ments than the " Cat and Whistle," less generous land-ladies than Mrs. Davis.

Anthony Trollope.

TAKING MINE EASE

AND now let's go to an honest ale-house, where we may have a cup of good barley-wine, and sing Old Rose, *and all of us rejoice together.*

Izaak Walton.

To the tavern, where Sir William Pen, and the Comptroller, and several others were, men and women ; and we had a great and merry dinner ; and after dinner the Comptroller begun some sports, among others, the naming of people round, and afterwards demanding questions of them that they are forced to answer their names to, which do make very good sport. And here I took pleasure to take forfeits of the ladies who would not do their duty by kissing of them : among others a pretty lady, who I found afterwards to be wife to Sir William Batten's son. We sat late, talking with my Lady and others, and Dr. Whistler, who I found good company and a very ingenious man : so home and to bed.

Samuel Pepys.

In contradiction to those who, having a wife and children, prefer domestic enjoyments to those which a tavern affords, I have heard him assert that a tavern chair was the throne of human felicity. As soon (said he) as I enter the door of a tavern, I experience an oblivion of care, and of freedom from solicitude : when I am seated I find the master courteous, and the servants obsequious to my call ; anxious to know and ready to supply my wants : wine there exhilarates my spirits, and prompts me to free conversation and an interchange of discourse with those whom I most love. I dogmatise and am contradicted, and in this conflict of opinion and sentiments I find delight.

Sir John Hawkins (of Dr. Johnson).

That nice little smoky room at the " Salutation," which is even now continually presenting itself to my recollection, with all its associated train of pipes, tobacco, egg-hot, welsh-rabbits, meta-physics, and poetry.

Charles Lamb, to Coleridge.

GLUTTON IN THE TAVERN

FORTH he went upon his way fasting, on a Friday,
But Betty the brewster bad him good morrow,
And asked of him withal whitherward he went.
"I go to church," says he, "for to hear mass,
"And then will I be shriven, and I shall no more sin."
"Gossip," says she, "I have good ale; wilt taste it,
    Glutton?"
"What hast thou?" says he, "any hot spice?"
"Pepper and peony seeds," says she, "and a pound of
    garlic,
"And a farthings worth of fennel, for your fasting day."
Then in goes Glutton and great oaths welcomed him.
Cis the shoemaker sat on the bench,
Watt the gamekeeper and his wife—drunk;
Tom the tinker and two of his 'prentices,
Hick the hackneyman, Hogg the needler,
Clarice of Cock Lane and the parish clerk;
Parson Piers of Pray-to-God and Pernel the Flemish
    woman,
Daw the ditcher and a dozen more of them;
A fiddler, a ratter, and a Cheapside scavenger,
A ropemaker, a trooper, and Rose of the Small Shop,
A watchman and a hermit, and the Tyburn hangman;
Godfrey the garlic seller, Griffin the Welshman,
All early in the morning welcomed Glutton gladly
To try the new good ale.
Then cobbler Clement threw down his cloak,
And said it was for sale at the New Fair Change.
Hick the hackneyman threw down his hood,

And bad Bet the butcher be speaker on his side ;
Two then were chosen the exchange to value—
He that had the hood should have somewhat with it.—
The two rose readily, and whispered together,
And went aside and valued the goods,
They could not in their conscience truly agree ;
Till Robin the ropemaker was bidden to arise,
And named an umpire that quarrel should be none.
Hick the ostler took the cloak,
And Clement took Hicks hood and a cup of ale,
And held him satisfied ; for if one should repent of it
Sir Glutton should be treated to a gallon of ale.
There was laughing and chattering, and, " Pass the cup
        round."
Bargains and toasts and songs, and so they sat—till even-
        song.
And Glutton had gulped down a gallon and a gill.
He could neither step nor stand till he had his staff,
Then gan he walk like a blind singers dog.
Now to this side, now to that, and sometimes backward,
Like a man who lays lines to catch wild birds ;
And when he drew to the doorstep, then his eyes grew
        dim,
He stumbled on the threshold and fell flat on the floor ;
Then Cobbler Clement caught him by the waist
To lift him up on high and get him to his knees ;
But Glutton was a heavy churl and groaned as he lifted
        him,
And coughed up his drink in Clements lap.
With all the trouble in the world his wife and his wench
Bore him home to his bed and laid him therein ;
And after all this surfeit he had a sleeping fit ;
All Saturday and Sunday slept till the sun went to rest.

Then waked he from his winking and wiped his eyes,
And the first word he threw was, "Where's the tankard?"
                                    William Langland.

GOOD HOSTESS

GOOD hostess, lay a crab in the fire, and broil a mess
of souse-a :

That we may toss the bowl to and fro, and brinks them all
carouse-a.

And I will pledge Tom Tosspot, till I be drunk as a
mouse-a.

Whoso will drink to me all day, I will pledge them all
carouse-a.

Then we will not spare for any cost, so long as we be in
house-a :

Then, hostess, fill the pot again, for I pledge them all
carouse-a.   *Ulpian Fulwell.*

IN THE TAVERN

A TAVERN is a degree, or (if you will) a pair of
stairs above an ale-house, where men are drunk with
more credit and apology. If the vintner's nose be at door,
it is a sign sufficient, but the absence of this is supplied by
the ivy-bush : the rooms are ill-breathed like the drinkers
that have been washt well over night, and are smelt-to
fasting next morning ; not furnished with beds apt to be
defiled, but more necessary implements. It is a broacher
of more news than hogsheads, and more jests than news,
which are suckt up here by some spungy brain, and from
thence squeezed into a comedy. Men come here to make
merry, but indeed make a noise, and this music above is
answered with the clinking below. The drawers are the
civilest people in it, men of good bringing up, and howso-
ever we esteem of them, none can boast more justly of

their high calling. 'Tis the best theatre of natures, where they are truly acted, not played, and the business as in the rest of the world up and down, to wit, from the bottom of the cellar to the great chamber. A melancholy man would find here matter to work upon, to see heads as brittle as glasses, and often broken ; men come hither to quarrel, and come hither to be made friends : and if Plutarch will lend me his simile, it is even Telephus his sword that makes wounds and cures them. It is the common consumption of the afternoon, and the murderer or maker-away of a rainy day. It is the torrid zone that scorches the face, and tobacco the gun-powder that blows it up. Much harm would be done if the charitable vintner had not water ready for these flames. A house of sin you may call it, but not a house of darkness, for the candles are never out ; and it is like those countries far in the North, where it is as clear at midnight as at mid-day. After a long sitting, it becomes like a street in a dashing shower, where the spouts are flushing above, and the conduits running below. To give you the total reckoning of it ; it is the busy man's recreation, the idle man's business, the melancholy man's sanctuary, the stranger's welcome, the inns-a-court man's entertainment, the scholar's kindness, and the citizen's courtesy. It is the study of sparkling wits, and a cup of canary their book, whence we leave them.

John Earle.

VERSES PLACED OVER THE DOOR AT
THE ENTRANCE INTO THE APOLLO

WELCOME all who lead or follow
　　To the Oracle of Apollo—
Here he speaks out of his pottle,
Or the tripos, his tower bottle :

All his answers are divine,
Truth itself doth flow in wine.
Hang up all the poor hop-drinkers,
Cries old Sim, the king of skinkers ;
He the half of life abuses,
That sits watering with the Muses.
Those dull girls no good can mean us ;
Wine, it is the milk of Venus,
And the poet's horse accounted :
Ply it and you all are mounted.
'Tis the true Phœbian liquor,
Cheers the brains, makes wit the quicker ;
Pays all debts, cures all diseases,
And at once the senses pleases.
Welcome all who lead or follow,
To the Oracle of Apollo !

Ben Jonson.

FALSTAFF MAKES MERRY
The Boar's-Head Tavern in Eastcheap.

(*Enter* Falstaff *and* Bardolph.)

FAL. Bardolph, am I not fallen away vilely since this last action ? do I not bate ? do I not dwindle ? Why my skin hangs about me like an old lady's loose gown ; I am withered like an old apple-john. Well, I'll repent, and that suddenly, while I am in some liking ; I shall be out of heart shortly, and then I shall have no strength to repent. An I have not forgotten what the inside of a church is made of, I am a peppercorn, a brewer's horse : the inside of a church ! Company, villanous company, hath been the spoil of me.

BARD. Sir John, you are so fretful, you cannot live long.

FAL. Why, there is it : come sing me a bawdy song ; make me merry. I was as virtuously given as a gentleman need to be ; virtuous enough ; swore little ; diced not above seven times a week ; went to a bawdy-house not above once in a quarter—of an hour ; paid money that I borrowed, three or four times ; lived well, and in good compass : and now I live out of all order, out of all compass.

BARD. Why, you are so fat, Sir John, that you must needs be out of all compass, out of all reasonable compass, Sir John.

FAL. Do thou amend thy face, and I'll amend my life : thou art our admiral, thou bearest the lantern in the poop, but 'tis in the nose of thee ; thou art the Knight of the Burning Lamp.

BARD. Why, Sir John, my face does you no harm.

FAL. No, I'll be sworn ; I make as good use of it as many a man doth of a Death's-head or a memento mori : I never see thy face but I think upon hell-fire, and Dives that lived in purple ; for there he is in his robes, burning, burning. If thou wert any way given to virtue, I would swear by thy face ; my oath should be, " By this fire, that's God's angel : " but thou art altogether given over ; and wert indeed, but for the light in thy face, the son of utter darkness. When thou rannest up Gadshill in the night to catch my horse, if I did not think thou hadst been an ignis fatuus or a ball of wildfire, there's no purchase in money. O, thou art a perpetual triumph, an everlasting bonfire-light ! Thou hast saved me a thousand marks in links and torches, walking with thee in the night betwixt tavern and tavern : but the sack that thou hast drunk me would have bought me lights as good cheap at the dearest chandler's in Europe. I have maintained that salamander of yours with fire any time this two and thirty years ; God reward me for it !

BARD.   'Sblood, I would my face were in your belly !

FAL.   God-a-mercy ! so should I be sure to be heart-burned.

(*Enter* HOSTESS.)

How now, Dame Partlet the hen ! have you inquired yet who picked my pocket ?

HOST.   Why, Sir John, what do you think, Sir John ? do you think I keep thieves in my house ? I have searched, I have inquired, so has my husband, man by man, boy by boy, servant by servant : the tithe of a hair was never lost in my house before.

FAL.   Ye lie, hostess : Bardolph was shaved, and lost many a hair ; and I'll be sworn my pocket was picked. Go to, you are a woman, go.

HOST.   Who, I ? no ; I defy thee : God's light, I was never called so in mine own house before.

FAL.   Go to, I know you well enough.

HOST.   No, Sir John ; you do not know me, Sir John. I know you, Sir John : you owe me money, Sir John ; and now you pick a quarrel to beguile me of it : I bought you a dozen of shirts to your back.

FAL.   Dowlas, filthy dowlas : I have given them away to bakers' wives, and they have made bolters of them.

HOST.   Now, as I am a true woman, holland of eight shillings an ell.   You owe money here besides, Sir John, for your diet and by-drinkings, and money lent you, four and twenty pound.

FAL.   He had his part of it ; let him pay.

HOST.   He ? alas, he is poor ; he hath nothing.

FAL. How ! poor ? look upon his face ; what call you rich ? let them coin his nose, let them coin his cheeks : I'll not pay a denier. What, will you make a younker of me ? shall I not take mine ease in mine inn but I shall have my pocket picked ? I have lost a seal-ring of my grandfather's worth forty mark.

HOST. O Jesu, I have heard the prince tell him, I know not how oft, that ring was copper !

FAL. How ! the prince is a Jack, a sneak-cup : 'sblood, an he were here, I would cudgel him like a dog, if he would say so.

(*Enter the* PRINCE *and* PETO, *marching, and* FAL-STAFF *meets them playing on his truncheon like a fife.*) How now, lad ! is the wind in that door, i' faith ? must we all march ?

BARD. Yea, two and two Newgate fashion.

HOST. My lord, I pray you, hear me.

PRINCE. What sayest thou, Mistress Quickly ? How doth thy husband ? I love him well ; he is an honest man.

HOST. Good my lord, hear me.

FAL. Prithee, let her alone, and list to me.

PRINCE. What sayest thou, Jack ?

FAL. The other night I fell asleep here behind the arras, and had my pocket picked : this house is turned bawdy-house ; they pick pockets.

PRINCE. What didst thou lose, Jack ?

FAL. Wilt thou believe me, Hal ? three or four bonds of forty pound a-piece, and a seal-ring of my grand-father's.

PRINCE. A trifle, some eight-penny matter.

HOST. So I told him, my lord ; and I said I heard your grace say so : and, my lord, he speaks most vilely of you, like a foul-mouthed man as he is ; and said he would cudgel you.

PRINCE.   What ! he did not ?

HOST.   There's neither faith, truth, nor womanhood in me else.

FAL.   There's no more faith in thee than in a stewed prune ; nor no more truth in thee than in a drawn fox ; and for womanhood, Maid Marian may be the deputy's wife of the ward to thee.   Go, you thing, go.

HOST.   Say, what thing ? what thing ?

FAL.   What thing ! why, a thing to thank God on.

HOST.   I am no thing to thank God on, I would thou shouldst know it ; I am an honest man's wife : and, setting thy knighthood aside, thou art a knave to call me so.

William Shakespeare.

THE BEGGARS' INN

AND these (quoth the Hostess of the Beggars) are all or the chiefest (both he-devils and she-devils) that daunce in this large circle.   I have brought you acquainted with their names, their natures, their tradings, and their traffic : if you have a desire to know more of them, you shall find whole congregations of them at Saint Quintens, The three-Cranes in the Vintry, Saint Tybs, and at Knapsbury, which four places are four several barns within one mile compass near London, being but nicknames given to them by the Upright-men : In those inns do they lodge every night ; in those do Upright-men lie with Morts, and turns Dels into Doxies (that is to say, ravish young wenches) whilst the Rogue is glad to stand at Reversion and to take the others leavings.   In Middlesex likewise stand four other harbours for them, namely, Draw the pudding out of the fire, (which is in the parish of Harrow on the Hill) ; The Cross Keys, (which is in

Cranford parish), Saint Julians, (which is in Thistleworth parish) and the house of Pity in Northall parish. The King's Barn, near Dartford, and Ketbrooke near Blackheath, are likewise houses of good receipt for them : In all shires have they such inns as these ; and in all of them and these recited, shall you find sometimes 40 Upright-men together ingendering beggars with their Morts. No sin but is here committed without shame. Adultery is common amongst them, Incest but laughed at, S—— made a jest : At these Havens do they cast anchor boldly, because none are by to bar their entrance ; yea, they that are owners of these Barns and Back-houses, dare not but give welcome to these unruly guests ; for if they should not they would at one time or other set fire of their houses, or by bloody and treacherous practises take away their lives. For this cause, sir, (quoth she) am I glad to look smilingly upon them, and to play the Hostess, because my abiding stands so far from company, yet I protest (quoth she) I hate the sight of them, as knowing them to be hellhounds, and have made discovery of their devilish conditions, because you may teach others how to avoid them.

Thomas Dekker.

AT THE PENNY CLUB
(*Enter* JUG, BARNABY *and* JORDAN.)

JUG. O Barnaby !

JOR. Welcome, Barnaby ! where hast thou been ?

BAR. In the foul weather.

JUG. Which has wet thee, Barnaby.

BAR. As dry as a chip. Good Jug, a cast of thy name As well as thy office : two jugs.

JUG. By and by. (*Exit.*)

JOR. What lady's this thou hast brought here ?

Bar. A great lady !
I know no more ; one that will try you, Jordan ;
She'll find your gage, your circle, your capacity.
How does old Staggers the smith, and Tree the sadler ?
Keep they their penny club still ?
 Jor. And the old catch too,
Of *Whoop-Barnaby !*
 Bar. Do they sing at me ?
 Jor. They are reeling at it in the parlour now.
     (Re-enter Jug *with wine.)*
 Bar. I'll to them : give me a drink first. *(Drinks.)*
 Jor. Where's thy hat ?
 Bar. I lost it by the way—Give me another.
 Jug. A hat !
 Bar. A drink.   *(Drinks.)*
 Jug. Take heed of taking cold, Bar——
 Bar. The wind blew 't off at Highgate, and my lady
Would not endure me light to take it up ;
But made me drive bareheaded in the rain.
 Jor. That she might be mistaken for a countess ?
 Bar. Troth, like enough : she might be an o'er-
  grown dutchess,
For aught I know.
 Jug. What, with one man !
 Bar. At a time,
They carry no more, the best of them.
 Jor. Nor the bravest.
 Bar. And she is very brave.
 Jor. A stately gown
And petticoat, she has on !
 Bar. Have you spied that, Jordan ?
You are a notable peerer, an old rabbi,
At a smock's hem, boy.

Jug. As he is chamberlain,
He may do that by his place.
 Jor. What is her squire ?
 Bar. A toy, that she allows eight pence a day,
A slight mannet, to port her up and down :
Come, show me to my play-fellows, old Staggers,
And father Tree.

Ben Jonson.

AN ODE FOR BEN JONSON

Ah Ben !
Say how or when
Shall we, thy guests,
Meet at those lyric feasts
Made at the Sun,
The Dog, the Triple Tun ?
Where we such clusters had,
As made us nobly wild, not mad ;
And yet each verse of thine
Out-did the meat, out-did the frolic wine.

My Ben !
Or come again,
Or send to us
Thy wit's great overplus ;
But teach us yet
Wisely to husband it,
Lest we that talent spend,
And having once brought to an end
That precious stock, the store
Of such a wit the world should have no more.

Robert Herrick.

AT THE MERMAID

In this warm shine
I lie, and dream of your full Mermaid wine.
Oh, we have water mix'd with claret-lees,
Drink apt to bring in drier heresies
Than beer, good only for the sonnet's strain,
With fustian metaphors to stuff the brain ;
So mix'd, that, given to the thirstiest one,
'Twill not prove alms unless he have the stone. . . .
'Tis this that keeps our minds fit for our states,
A medicine to obey our magistrates ;
For we do live more free than you ; no hate,
No envy at one another's happy state
Moves us ; we are all equal, every whit
Of land that God gives men here, is their wit,
If we consider fully ; for our best
And gravest man will with his main house-jest
Scarce please you ; we want subtlety to do
The city-tricks, lie, hate, and flatter too.
Methinks the little wit I had is lost
Since I saw you ; for wit is like a rest
Held up at tennis, which men do the best
With the best gamesters.   What things have we seen
Done at the Mermaid ! heard words that have been
So nimble, and so full of subtle flame,
As if that every one from whence they came
Had meant to put his whole wit in a jest,
And had resolv'd to live a fool the rest
Of his dull life ; then when there hath been thrown
Wit able enough to justify the town
For three days past ; wit that might warrant be
For the whole city to talk foolishly

Till that were cancell'd ; and when that was gone,
We left an air behind us, which alone
Was able to make the two next companies
(Right witty, though but downright fools) more wise.

Francis Beaumont.

TROLL THE BOWL

COLD'S the wind, and wet's the rain,
  Saint Hugh be our good speed !
Ill is the weather that bringeth no gain,
  Nor helps good hearts in need.

Troll the bowl, the jolly nut-brown bowl,
  And here, kind mate, to thee !
Let's sing a dirge for Saint Hugh's soul,
  And down it merrily.

Down-a-down, hey, down-a-down,
  Hey derry derry down-a-down !
Ho ! well done, to me let come,
  Ring compass, gentle joy !

Troll the bowl, the nut-brown bowl,
  And here, kind mate, to thee, etc.

*Repeat as often as there be men to drink ; and when at
    last all have drunk, this verse :—*

Cold's the wind, and wet's the rain,
  Saint Hugh be our good speed !
Ill is the weather that bringeth no gain,
  Nor helps good hearts in need.

Thomas Dekker.

A RHAPSODIS

*Occasionally written upon a meeting with some of his friends
at the Globe Tavern, in a chamber painted overhead
with a cloudy sky and some few dispersed stars, and
on the sides with landscapes, hills, shepherds, and
sheep.*

DARKNESS and stars i' the mid-day ! they invite
Our active fancies to believe it night :
For taverns need no sun, but for a sign,
Where rich tobacco and quick tapers shine ;
And royal, witty sack, the poet's soul,
With brighter suns than he doth gild the bowl ;
As though the pot and poet did agree,
Sack should to both illuminator be.
That artificial cloud with its curl'd brow
Tells us 'tis late ; and that blue space below
Is fired with many stars : mark ! how they break
In silent glances o'er the hills, and speak
The evening to the plains, where shot from far,
They meet in dumb salutes, as one great star.

The room, methinks, grows darker, and the air
Contracts a sadder colour, and less fair.
Or is't the drawer's skill ? hath he no arts
To blind us so we can't know pints from quarts ?
No, no, 'tis night : look where the jolly clown
Musters his bleating herd and quits the down.
Hark ! how his rude pipe frets the quiet air,
Whilst ev'ry hill proclaims Lycoris fair.
Rich, happy man ! that canst thus watch and sleep,
Free from all cares, but thy wench, pipe, and sheep.
But see, the moon is up : view where she stands
Sentinel o'er the door, drawn by the hands

Of some base painter, that for gain hath made
Her face the landmark to the tippling trade.
'Twas wit at first and wine that made them live.
Choke may the painter ! and his box disclose
No other colours than his fiery nose ;
And may we no more of his pencil see
Than two churchwardens and Mortality.

    Should we go now a-wand'ring, we should meet
With catchpolls, whores, and carts in every street :
Now when each narrow lane, each nook and cave
Sign-posts and shop-doors, pimp for ev'ry knave,
When riotous sinful plush and tell-tale spurs
Walk Fleet Street and the Strand, when the soft stirs
Of bawdy, ruffled silks turn night to day ;
And the loud whip and coach scolds all the way ;
When lust of all sorts, and each itchy blood
From the Tower-wharf to Cymbeline and Lud,
Hunts for a mate, and the tired footman reels
'Twixt chair-men, torches, and the hackney wheels.

    Come, take the other dish ; it is to him
That made his horse a senator ; each brim
Look big as mine.   The gallant, jolly beast
Of all the herd—you'll say—was not the least.

    Now crown the second bowl, rich as his worth
I'll drink it to ; he, that like fire broke forth
Into the Senate's face, crost Rubicon,
And the state's pillars, with their laws thereon,
And made the dull grey beards and furr'd gowns fly
Into Brundusium to consult and lie.

    This, to brave Sylla ! why should it be said
We drink more to the living than the dead ?
Flatt'rers and fools do use it.   Let us laugh
At out own honest mirth ; for they that quaff

To honour others, do like those that sent
Their gold and plate to strangers to be spent.

    Drink deep : this cup be pregnant, and the wine,
Spirit of wit to make us all divine,
That, big with sack and mirth, we may retire
Possessors of more souls and nobler fire ;
And by the influx of this painted sky
And labour'd forms, to higher matters fly ;
So, if a nap shall take us, we shall all,
After full cups, have dreams poetical.

    Let's laugh now and the press'd grape drink,
Till the dowsy day-star wink,
And in our merry, mad mirth run
Faster and further than the sun ;
And let none his cup forsake,
Till that star again doth wake ;
So we men below shall move
Equally with the gods above.

                     Henry Vaughan.

THE ALE HOUSE AT HODDESDON

CORIDON : I will sing a song, if anybody will sing another ; else, to be plain with you, I will sing none : I am none of those that sing for meat, but for company : I say, 'Tis merry in hall, when men sing all.

PISCATOR. I'll promise you I'll sing a song that was lately made at my request by Mr. William Basse, one that hath made the choice songs of The Hunter in his Career, and of Tom of Bedlam, and many others of note ; and this that I will sing is in praise of angling.

COR. And then mine shall be, the praise of a countryman's life ; what will the rest sing of ?

PETER. I will promise you, I will sing another song in praise of angling to-morrow night ; for we will not part till then, but fish to-morrow, and sup together, and the next day every man leave fishing, and fall to his business.

VENATOR. 'Tis a match; and I will provide you a song or a catch against then too, which shall give some addition of mirth to the company; for we will be civil and as merry as beggars.

PISC. 'Tis a match, my masters; let's e'en say grace, and turn to the fire, drink the other cup to wet our whistles, and so sing away all sad thoughts. . . .

COR. Well sung, brother, you have paid your debt in good coin. We anglers are all beholden to the good man that made this song : come, hostess, give us more ale, and let's drink to him. And now let's every one go to bed, that we may rise early ; but first let's pay our reckoning, for I will have nothing to hinder me in the morning, for my purpose is to prevent the sun rising.

PETER. A match. Come, Coridon, you are to be my bed-fellow. I know, brother, you and your scholar will lie together. But where shall we meet to-morrow night ? for my friend Coridon and I will go up the water towards Ware.

PISC. And my scholar and I will go down towards Waltham.

COR. Then let's meet here, for here are fresh sheets that smell of lavender ; and I am sure we cannot expect better meat or better usage in any place.

Izaak Walton.

A TAVERN TOUR

THENCE to Holloway, Mother Redcap,
   In a troop of trulls I did hap ;
Whores of Babylon me impalled,
And me their Adonis called.

Thence to Islington, at Lion,
Where a-juggling I did spy one,
Nimble with his mates consorting,
Mixing cheating with his sporting ;
Creeping into the case of's viol,
Spoiled his juggling, made them fly all.
Country left I in a fury,
To the Axe in Aldermanbury
First arrived, that place slighted,
I at the Rose in Holborn lighted ;
From the Rose in flagons sail I
To the Griffin, i'th' Old Bailey ;
Where no sooner do I waken
Than to Three Cranes I am taken ;
Where I lodge and am no starter
Till I see the summer quarter.
Yea, my merry mates and I too
Oft the Cardinal's Hat do fly to,
Where at Hart's horn we carouse it,
As Minerva doth infuse it.

Drunken Barnaby.

AT A QUAKERS' TAVERN

MY friend recollected a little sanctified Aminidab in
Finch Lane, whose purple nectar had acquired a
singular reputation among the staggering zealots of the
Sober Fraternity, who are allowed of late to be as good
judges of the comfortable creature as a Protestant priest or
a Latitudinarian fuddle-cap, who (as rooks play) drink
wine on Sundays.

To this salutiferous fountain of Nature's choicest
juleps, our inclinations led us, though we knew the little
ruler of the mansion intended it chiefly for watering the

Lambs of Grace, and not to succour the evil offspring of a reprobate generation.

When we had entered our land of promise, which overflow'd with more healthful riches than either milk or honey, we found all things were as silent as the mourning attendance at a rich man's funeral ; no ringing of barbell, bawling of drawers, or rattling of pot-lids ; but a general hush ordered to be kept thro' the whole family, as a warning to all tipplers at their entrance, how they make a noise to awake the Spirit, lest it move the masters and drawers to stand still when you call 'em ; and refuse to draw any more wine, for fear the inward man should break out into open disorder.

A drunken-look'd drawer, disguis'd in a sober garb, like a wolf in sheep's clothing, or the devil in a friar's habit, shew'd us into the kitchen, which we told him we were desirous of being in, as crickets covet ovens, for the sake of their warmth. Several of Father Ramsey's slouching disciples sat hovering over their half-pints, like so many coy gossips over their quarterns of brandy, as if they were afraid any body should see 'em ; they cast as many froward looks upon us swordsmen as so many misers would be apt to do upon a couple of spunging acquaintances ; staring as if they took us for some of the wild Irish, that should have cut their throats in the beginning of the revolution.

However, we bid ourselves welcome into their company ; and were forc'd, for want of room, the kitchen being well fill'd, to mix higgle-depiggle-de, as the rooks among the jackdaws upon the battlements of a church steeple ; they leering at us under their Bongraces, with as much contempt as so many primitive Christians at a couple of Pagans.

We, like true Protestant topers, scorning the hypocrisy

of tippling by half-pints, as if we drank rather to wash away our sins than our sorrows, appear'd bare-fac'd, called for a quart at once, and soon discover'd our religion by our drinking ; whilst they, like true Puritans, gifted with abundance of Holy Cheats, were unwilling to be catch'd over more than half a pint, tho' they'll drink twenty at a sitting.

The drawer now was constantly employ'd in replenishing their scanty measures ; for once warm'd they began to drink so fast, 'twas the business of one servant to keep them doing. When they were desirous to elevate their lethargic spirits with the circulation of a bumper, one fills it, and offers the prevailing temptation to his left-hand companion, in these words, saying, " Friend, does the Spirit move thee to receive the good creature thus plentifully ? " The other replies, " Yea, do thou take and enjoy the fruits of thy own labour, and by the help of Grace I will drink another as full." Thus did the liquorish Saints quaff it about as merrily, after their precise canting manner, as so many country parsons over a tub of ale, when freed from the remarks of their censorious parishioners ; till, like reprobate sinners, who have not the fear of Providence before their eyes, they were deluded by Satan into a wicked state of drunkenness.

By this time the subtile spirits of the noble juice had given us a fresh motion to the wheels of life, and corroborated those springs which impart vigour and activity to the whole engine of mortality ; insomuch that my friend must needs be so frolicsome to tune his pipes, and entertain us with a song ; in order to try whether those who were deaf to reason and good manners, had any ears towards music with their wine, which are usually held to be such inseparable companions, that the true relish of the one can never be enjoyed without the assistance of the other.

Just as my friend had ended his Sonnet, in came the little lord of the tippling tenement, about the height of a nine-pin, with his head in a hat of such capacious dimensions that his body was as much drown'd under the disproportion'd brim of this unconscionable castor as a pigmy under the umbrage of a Giant's Bongrace. He waited a little while the motion of the Spirit ; and when he had compos'd his countenance, and put himself into a fit posture for reproof, he breaks into this following oration : " Pray, Friend, forbear this profane hollowing and hooting in my house, the wicked noise thou makest among my sober friends is neither pleasing to them nor me ; and since I find the wine is too powerful for thy inward-man, I must needs tell thee I will draw thee no more of it ; I therefore desire thee to pay for what thou hast had, and depart my house, for I do not like thy ways, nor does any body here approve of thy ranting doings."

Ned Ward.

STRANDED AT HOLYHEAD

WE left the guide to shoe the horses and walked to a hedge inn three miles from Holyhead. There I stayed an hour with no ale to be drunk. A boat offered, and I went by sea and sailed in it to Holyhead. The guide came about the same time. I dined with an old innkeeper, Mrs. Welch, about 3, on a Loyne of mutton, very good, but the worst ale in the world, and no wine, for the day before I came here a vast number went to Ireland after having drunk out all the wine.

Monday.—I had a raw chicken for dinner and brandy with water for my drink. I walked morning and after-

noon among the rocks. This evening Watt tells me that
my landlady whispered him that the Grafton packet-boat
just come in had brought her 18 bottles of Irish claret. I
secured one, and supped on part of a neat's tongue which
a friend at London had given Watt to put up for me, and
drank a pint of the wine, which was bad enough. Not a
soul is yet come to Holyhead, except a young fellow who
smiles when he meets me and would fain be my companion, but it has not come to that yet. . . .

Tuesday.—I am forced to wear a shirt three days for
fear of being lowsy. I was sparing of them all the way.
It was a mercy there were 6 clean when I left London—
otherwise Watt (whose blunders would bear an history)
would have got them all in the great box of goods which
went by the Carrier to Chester. . . . I got a small loyn
of mutton but so tough I could not chew it, and drank my
second pint of wine. It rained all night and hath rained
since dinner. But now the sun shines and I will take my
afternoon walk. It was fiercer and wilder weather than
yesterday, yet the Captain now dreams of sailing. Is this
strange stuff ? Why, what would you have me do ? I
see no creature. I cannot read by candle-light. Sleeping
will make me sick.

Sept. 26th.—Thoughts upon being confined at Holyhead. If this were to be my settlement during life I could
content myself a while by forming new conveniences to be
easy, and should not be frightened either by the solitude or
the meanness of lodging, eating or drinking. I dare not
send my linen to be washed for fear of being called away
at half an hour's warning, and then I must leave them
behind. I live at great expense without one comfortable
bit or sup. I am afraid of joyning with passengers for fear
of getting acquaintance with Irish. The days are short

and I have five hours a night to spend by myself before I
go to Bed. . . . Oh for a dozen bottles of Deanery wine
and a slice of bread and butter !

Wednesday.——Watt and I walked up the mountain
Marucia, properly called Holyhead ; returning we were
overtaken by a furious shower. Watt (otherwise called
unfortunate Jack) ran home for my coat, but stayed so long
that I came home in worse rain without him, and he was
so lucky to miss me, but took good care to convey the key
of my room where a fire was ready for me. So I cooled
my heels in the Parlour till he came, but called for a glass of
Brandy. I have been cooking myself dry, and am now in
my night-gown. And so I wait for dinner. I shall dine
like a King all alone, as I have done these six days. . . .
My room smokes into the bargain, but the weather is too
cold and moist to be without a fire. There is or should be
a proverb here : When Mrs. Welch's chimney smokes,
'Tis a sign she'll keep her folks, But when of smoke the
room is clear, It is a sign we shan't stay here. Tell me,
am I not a comfortable wag ? Here is a young Jaka-
napes in the Inn waiting for a wind who would fain be my
companion, and if I stay here much longer I am afraid all
my pride and grandeur will truckle to comply with him,
especially if I finish these leaves that remain.

Jonathan Swift.

A HALT BY THE WAY

PISCATOR. Being you have abandoned yourself
to my conduct, we will only call and drink a glass on
horseback at the Talbot, and away.

VIATOR. I attend you. But what pretty river is this,
that runs under this stone bridge ? Has it a name ?

PISC. Yes, it is called Henmore ; and has in it both

trout and grayling. . . . But we are now come to the
Talbot.   What will you drink, sir, ale or wine?

VIAT.   Nay, I am for the country liquor, Derbyshire
ale, if you please; for a man should not, methinks, come
from London to drink wine in the Peak.

PISC.   You are in the right; and yet, let me tell you,
you may drink worse French wine in many taverns in
London than they have sometimes at this house.   What
ho! bring us a flagon of your best ale; and now, sir, my
service to you, a good health to the honest gentleman you
know of, and you are welcome into the Peak.

VIAT.   I thank you, sir, and present you my service
again, and to all the honest brothers of the angle.

PISC.   I'll pledge you, sir; so, there's for your ale, and
farewell.

Charles Cotton.

LINES WRITTEN AT AN INN

TO thee, fair Freedom, I retire,
        From flattery, feasting, dice and din;
Nor art thou found in domes much higher
        Than the lone cot or humble Inn.

'Tis here with boundless power I reign,
        And every health which I begin,
Converts dull port to bright champagne;
        For Freedom crowns it, at an Inn.

I fly from pomp, I fly from plate,
        I fly from falsehood's specious grin;
Freedom I love, and form I hate,
        And choose my lodgings at an Inn.

Here, waiter! take my sordid ore,
        Which lacqueys else might hope to win;

It buys what Courts have not in store,
　　It buys me Freedom, at an Inn.

And now once more I shape my way
　　Through rain or shine, through thick and thin,
Secure to meet, at close of day,
　　With kind reception at an Inn.

Whoe'er has travelled life's dull round,
　　Where'er his stages may have been,
May sigh to think how oft he found
　　The warmest welcome—at an Inn.

William Shenstone.

A FREE FEAST AT THE KING'S HEAD

GENTLEMEN, says he, I have seen such a sight
to-day, would make a Spaniard change his pace, and
turn his stately steps into a dog-trot, to run after it ; nay,
make a Dutchman, in surprise, pluck his hands out of his
pockets, and hold 'em up like an Englishman going to be
hang'd ; or put a Frenchman into as great an amazement
as the snow did the Bantum ambassador. Pray, Sir, said
a grave gentleman, would it make an Englishman do
nothing ? Yes, Sir, answered the other, it would make
an Englishman whet his knife, if it were drest, and fall on
without grace, and stuff his belly till it was as hard as a
foot-ball, before he would rise from the table. But, Sir,
says the old gentleman, you'll forget, I'm afraid, to tell us
what it was. Why, Sir, says he, then I'll tell you. It was
a piece of roasting beef, but of such an extraordinary size
that ten men might ride upon 't, without incommoding
themselves ; and but turn it on its back, and it will carry
as many people withinside as a Gravesend wherry ; which

magnificent piece of beef, notwithstanding its ponderosity, will certainly, on a day appointed, be taken up by the teeth. Pray, Sir, where is this Leviathan of beef to be devoured, that a man may view this gluttonous prodigy before the cooks have mangled it out of all shape ? Why, Sir, says he, at the King's Head Tavern, at Chancery Lane, where, at this time, the Honestest Vintner in London lives ; where the best wine in England is to be drank, and the stateliest piece of beef in Christendom is to be roasted. . . .

When the morning came, my friend and I having a great desire to discover what an attractive influence such a magnificent piece of beef had upon the stomachs of this town, resolv'd not to lose the opportunity of gratifying our palates, as well as feasting our eyes, and of coming in for our share of the benefit, as well as the rest of the town epicures. When we came to the door we had more difficulty to get admittance than we had before, for as many people were crowding to see it at the fire as there were to see the ox roasted upon the ice. When we had squeez'd sideways through the entry, with as much pains as a fat man takes to shove his guts thro' a narrow turn-stile, we got into the yard, where such a litter of drawers were scampering from cellar to bar, and from bar to company, that it was difficult to believe that the whole house could have entertain'd guests sufficient to have required such a number of attendance ; as many bells rattling at a time as o'er a green bird's cage, when the feathered animal rings Whittington ; the servants all puffing and blowing like greyhounds after a course, sweating like a couple of chair-men in the dog-days, who have just set down a bulky nobleman. The kitchen being now as hot as Guinea at noon-day, yet we concluded there we should be best

attended, being near the bar, and the least incommoded
for want of room, could we but reconcile our bodies to the
extraordinary heat. The poor carcase of the beast was by
this time so lamentably mangled by the cuts and slashes of
the broiling carvers, that had Sir Courtly Nice, or my
Lady Squeamish been to have taken a view of the roasting rarity, they would scarce have long'd to have been
partakers of the feast ; for the shoulders and the ribs were
soon stripp'd as bare of their flesh as if the Tower lions
had been just at breakfast on't ; and the buttock and more
fleshy parts were cut and digg'd so full of holes and furrows,
that it look'd as disfigur'd as the carcase of a goose after a
couple of tun-bellied churchwardens have had the picking
of her.

By this time a generous plateful of the good creature
was brought as a present to my friend and I, with all the
rest of the appurtenances at once, without the trouble of
calling ; which encourag'd our appetite and gave us a
better liking to our treat ; which in justice, I must say,
according to the old English way of praising beef, was as
rich, fat, young, well-fed, delicious meat as ever was taken
into the mouth and swallowed into the belly of a true
Englishman. By the time we had made an end of our
plentiful commons, the bones of the whole carcase were
pared as clean as the sharp whetted weapons of the blunt
dissectors could well pick 'em, insomuch that the Vintner
found himself under a necessity of sending for two barons
more, or half his guests would have been disappointed of
their breakfasts.

Having now well freighted the hold of our vessels with
excellent food and delicious wine, at a small expense, we
scribbled these following lines with chalk upon the wall,*

* The landlord of the King's Head was Ned Ward himself.

so took our departure from thence, and steer'd our course
to a more temperate climate :—

> To speak but the truth of my honest friend Ned,
> The best of all vintners that ever God made ;
> He's free of his beef, and as free of his bread,
> And washes both down with a glass of rare Red,
> That tops all the town and commands a good trade ;
> Such wine as will cheer up the drooping King's Head,
> And brisk up the soul though the body's half dead.
> He scorns to draw bad, as he hopes to be paid,
> And now his name's up, he may e'en lie a-bed,
> For he'll get an estate, there's no more to be said.
>
> *Ned Ward.*

LOVE LETTERS FROM A TAVERN

DEAR Prue,—I have partly succeeded in my business
to-day, and enclose two guineas as earnest of more.

Dear Prue, I cannot come home to dinner. I languish
for your welfare, and will never be a moment careless
more.—Your faithful Husband.

Dear Wife,—Mr. Edgecomb, Ned Ask, and Mr.
Lumley have desired me to sit an hour with them at the
George, in Pall Mall, for which I desire your patience till
twelve o'clock, and that you will go to bed.

Madam,—I beg pardon that my paper is not finer, but
I am forced to write from a coffee-house, where I am
attending about businesse. There is a croud of busie faces
all around me talking of money ; while all my Ambition,
all my wealth is Love ! Love, which animates my Heart,
sweetens my Humour, enlarges my Soul, and affects every
action of my Life.

Richard Steele.

MRS. ABIGAIL AT UPTON

THE lady had no sooner laid herself on her pillow than the waiting-woman returned to the kitchen to regale with some of those dainties which her mistress had refused.

The company, at her entrance, showed her the same respect which they had before paid to her mistress, by rising ; but she forgot to imitate her, by desiring them to sit down again. Indeed, it was scarce possible they should have done so, for she placed her chair in such a posture as to occupy almost the whole fire. She then ordered a chicken to be broiled that instant, declaring, if it was not ready in a quarter of an hour, she would not stay for it. Now, though the said chicken was then at roost in the stable, and required the several ceremonies of catching, killing, and picking, before it was brought to the gridiron, my landlady would nevertheless have undertaken to do all within the time ; but the guest, being unfortunately admitted behind the scenes, must have been witness to the *fourberie ;* the poor woman was therefore obliged to confess that she had none in the house ; " but, madam," said she, " I can get any kind of mutton in an instant from the butcher's."

" Do you think, then," answered the waiting-gentle-woman, " that I have the stomach of a horse, to eat mutton at this time of night ? Sure you people that keep inns imagine your betters are like yourselves. Indeed, I expected to get nothing at this wretched place. I wonder my lady would stop at it. I suppose none but tradesmen and grasiers ever call here." The landlady fired at this indignity offered to her house ; however, she suppressed her temper, and contented herself with saying, " Very good quality frequented it, she thanked heaven ! " " Don't tell me," cries the other, " of quality ! I believe I know more of people of quality than such as you.—But, prithee, without troubling me with any of your impertinence, do tell me what I can have for supper ; for, though I cannot eat horse-flesh, I am really hungry." " Why, truly, madam," answered the landlady, " you could not take me again at such a disadvantage ; for I must confess I have nothing in the house, unless a cold piece of beef, which indeed a gentleman's footman and the post-boy have almost cleared to the bone." " Woman," said Mrs. Abigail (so for shortness we will call her), " I entreat you not to make me sick. If I had fasted a month, I could not eat what had been touched by the fingers of such fellows. Is there nothing neat or decent to be had in this horrid place ? " " What think you of some eggs and bacon, madam ? " said the landlady. " Are your eggs new laid ? are you certain they were laid to-day ? and let me have the bacon cut very nice and thin ; for I can't endure anything that's gross.— Prithee try if you can do a little tolerably for once, and don't think you have a farmer's wife, or some of those creatures, in the house."—The landlady began then to handle her knife ; but the other stopt her, saying, " Good woman, I must insist upon your first washing your hands ; for I am extremely nice, and have been always used from my cradle to have everything in the most elegant manner."

The landlady, who governed herself with much difficulty, began now the necessary preparations ; for as to Susan, she was utterly rejected, and with such disdain, that the poor wench was as hard put to it to restrain her hands from violence as her mistress had been to hold her tongue. This indeed Susan did not entirely ; for, though she literally kept it within her teeth, yet there it muttered

many " marry-come-ups, as good flesh and blood as yourself " ; with other such indignant phrases.

While the supper was preparing, Mrs. Abigail began to
lament she had not ordered a fire in the parlour ; but, she
said, that was now too late. " However," said she, " I
have novelty to recommend a kitchen ; for I do not
believe I ever eat in one before." Then, turning to the
post-boys, she asked them, " Why they were not in the
stable with their horses ? If I must eat my hard fare here,
madam," cries she to the landlady, " I beg the kitchen may
be kept clear, that I may not be surrounded with all the
blackguards in town : as for you, sir," says she to Partridge, " you look somewhat like a gentleman, and may sit
still if you please ; I don't desire to disturb anybody but
mob."

Henry Fielding.

THE INNS OF ALDEBURGH

DETERMINE, ye, who on your shining nags
Wear oil-skin beavers and bear seal-skin bags ;
Or ye, grave topers, who with coy delight
Snugly enjoy the sweetness of the night ;
Ye travellers all, superior inns denied
By moderate purse, the low by decent pride ;
Come and determine—will ye take your place
At the *full* orb, or *half* the lunar face ?
With the Black Boy or Angel will ye dine ?
Will ye approve the Fountain or the Vine ?
Horses the white or black will ye prefer ?
The Silver Swan, or swan opposed to her—
Rare bird ! whose form the raven plumage decks,
And graceful curve her three alluring necks ?
All these a decent entertainment give,
And by their comforts comfortably live.

Shall I pass by the Boar ?   There are who cry
" Beware the Boar," and pass determin'd by :
Those dreadful tusks, those little peering eyes
And churning chaps, are tokens to the wise.
There dwells a kind old aunt, and there you see
Some kind young nieces in her company ;
Poor village nieces, whom the tender dame
Invites to town, and gives their beauty fame ;
The grateful sisters feel th'important aid,
And the good aunt is flatter'd and repaid.
What though it may some cool observers strike,
That such fair sisters should be so unlike ;
That still another and another comes,
And at the matron's table smiles and blooms ;
That all appear as if they meant to stay
Time undefin'd, nor name a parting day ;
And yet, though all are valued, all are dear,
Causeless, they go, and seldom more appear.
Yet let Suspicion hide her odious head,
And Scandal vengeance from a burgess dread.
A pious friend, who, with the ancient dame,
At sober cribbage takes an evening game ;
His cup beside him, through their play he quaffs,
And oft renews, and innocently laughs ;
Or growing serious, to the text resorts,
And from the Sunday sermon makes reports ;
While all, with grateful glee, his wish attend,
A grave protector and a powerful friend.
But Slander says, who indistinctly sees,
Once he was caught with Silvia on his knees.
A cautious burgess with a careful wife
To be so caught ?   'Tis false, upon my life.

George Crabbe.

A BOWL OF RUMBO

IT was on the great northern road from York to London, about the beginning of October, and the hour of eight in the evening, that four travellers were, by a violent shower of rain, driven for shelter into a little public-house on the side of the highway, distinguished by a sign which was said to exhibit the figure of a black lion. The kitchen, in which they were assembled, was the only room for entertainment in the house, paved with red bricks, remarkably clean, furnished with three or four Windsor chairs, adorned with shining plates of pewter, and copper saucepans, nicely scoured, that even dazzled the eyes of the beholder ; while a cheerful fire of sea-coal blazed in the chimney. Three of the travellers, who arrived on horseback, having seen their cattle properly accommodated in the stable, agreed to pass the time, until the weather should clear up, over a bowl of rumbo, which was accordingly prepared. But the fourth, refusing to join their company, took his station at the opposite side of the chimney, and called for a pint of twopenny, with which he indulged himself apart. At a little distance, on his left hand, there was another group, consisting of the landlady, a decent widow, her two daughters, the elder of whom seemed to be about the age of fifteen, and a country lad who served both as waiter and ostler.

The social triumvirate was composed of Mr. Fillet, a country practitioner in surgery and midwifery, Captain Crowe, and his nephew Mr. Thomas Clarke, an attorney. Fillet was a man of some education, and a great deal of experience, shrewd, sly, and sensible. Captain Crowe had commanded a merchant ship in the Mediterranean trade for many years, and had saved some money by dint of frugality and traffic. He was an excellent seaman, brave, active, friendly in his way, and scrupulously honest ; but as little acquainted with the world as a sucking child ; whimsical, impatient, and so impetuous, that he could not help breaking in upon the conversation, whatever it might be, with repeated interruptions, that seemed to burst from him by involuntary impulse. . . .

Captain Crowe, having remarked that it was squally weather, asked how far it was to the next market-town ; and understanding that the distance was not less than six miles, said he had a good mind to come to an anchor for the night, if so be as he could have a tolerable berth in this here harbour. Mr. Fillet, perceiving by his style that he was a seafaring gentleman, observed that their landlady was not used to lodge such company ; and expressed some surprise that he, who had no doubt endured so many storms and hardships at sea, should think much of travelling five or six miles a-horseback by moonlight. " For my part," said he, " I ride in all weathers, and at all hours, without minding cold, wet, wind, or darkness. My constitution is so case-hardened that I believe I could live all the year at Spitzbergen. With respect to this road, I know every foot of it so exactly that I'll engage to travel forty miles upon it blindfold, without making one false step ; and if you have faith enough to put yourselves under my auspices, I will conduct you safe to an elegant inn, where you will meet with the best accommodation." " Thank you, brother," replied the captain, " we are much beholden to you for your courteous offer ; but, howsomever, you must not think I mind foul weather more than my neighbours. I have worked hard aloft and alow in many a taut gale ; but this here is the case, d'ye see ; we have run down a long day's reckoning ; our beasts have had a hard spell ; and as for my own hap, brother, I doubt my bottom-planks have lost some of their sheathing, being as how I ain't used to that kind of scrubbing."

The doctor, who had practised aboard a man-of-war in his youth, and was perfectly well acquainted with the captain's dialect, assured him that if his bottom was damaged he would new pay it with an excellent salve, which he always carried about him to guard against such accidents on the road. But Tom Clarke, who seemed to have cast the eyes of affection upon the landlady's eldest daughter, Dolly, objected to their proceeding farther without rest and refreshment, as they had already travelled fifty miles since morning.   *Tobias Smollett.*

THE GERMAN PASTOR AT OXFORD

WE went on, a few houses further, and then knocked at a door. It was then nearly twelve. They readily let us in ; but how great was my astonishment, when, on our being shown into a room on the left, I saw a great number of clergymen, all with their gowns and bands on, sitting round a large table, each with his pot of beer before him. My travelling companion introduced me to them, as a German clergyman, whom he could not sufficiently praise, for my correct pronunciation of the Latin, my orthodoxy, and my good walking.

I now saw myself, in a moment as it were, all at once transported into the midst of a company, all apparently, very respectable men, but all strangers to me. And it appeared to me extraordinary, that I should, thus at midnight, be in Oxford, in a large company of Oxonian clergy, without well knowing how I had got there. Meanwhile, however, I took all the pains in my power to recommend myself to my company, and, in the course of conversation, I gave them as good an account as I could of our German Universities, neither denying, nor concealing, that, now and then, we had riots and disturbances. " O we are very unruly here too," said one of the clergymen, as he took a hearty draught out of his pot of beer, and knocked on the table with his hand. The conversation now became louder, more general, and a little confused : they enquired after Mr. Bruns, at present Professor at Helmstadt, and who was known by many of them.

Before Mr. Maud went away, he invited me to go and see him in the morning ; and very politely offered himself to show me the curiosities of Oxford. The rest of the company now also dispersed ; and as I had once (though in so singular a manner) been introduced into so reputable a society, the people of the house made no difficulty of giving me lodging, but, with great civility, showed me a very decent bed-chamber.

I am almost ashamed to own that, next morning, when I awoke, I had got so dreadful an headach, from the copious and numerous toasts of my jolly and reverend friends, that I could not possibly get up ; still less could I wait on Mr. Maud at his College.

The inn where I was, goes by the name of The Mitre. Compared to Windsor, I there found Prince-like attendance. Being, perhaps, a little elevated, the preceding evening, I had, in the gaiety, or perhaps, in the vanity of my heart, told the waiter, that he must not think, because I came on foot, that therefore I should give him less than others gave. I assured him of the contrary. It was probably not a little owing to this assurance, that I had so much attention shown to me.

Carl Philip Moritz.

INN-YARD DIVERSIONS

THOMAS DALE, drawer at the Crown Tavern at Aldgate, keepeth the Turk's Head Musik Booth, in Smithfield Rounds, Where is a glass of good Wine, Mum, Syder, Beer, Ale, and all other Sorts of Liquors, to be Sold ; and where you will likewise be entertained with good Musick, Singing, and Dancing. You will see a Scaramouch Dance, the Italian Punch's Dance, the Quarter Staff, the Antick, the Countryman and Countrywoman's Dance, and the Merry Cuckolds of Hogsden.

Also, a Young Man that dances an Entry, Salabrand, and Jigg, and a Woman that dances with Six Naked Rapiers. There is likewise a young woman that dances with Fourteen Glasses on the backs and palms of her Hands, and turns round with them above an Hundred Times, as fast as a Windmill turns ; and another Young Man that dances a Jigg incomparably well, to the Admiration of all Spectators.

·   ·   ·   ·   ·

At Hippisley's and [Henry] Fielding's
Booth in the George Inn Yard, will be presented a Dramatick Entertainment (never perform'd there before) call'd
Love and Jealousy,
or,
The Downfall of Alexander the Great.
To which will be added a Ballad Opera call'd
A Cure for Covetousness
or,
The Cheats of Scapin
Done from the French of Molière.
With several Entertainments of Dancing between the Acts ; and farther to divert the Audience during the

Filling of the Booth, the famous Mr. Phillips will perform his surprising Postures on the Stage.

An Extraordinary Band of Music is provided, consisting of violins, hautboys, bassoons, kettle drums, trumpets and French horns.

Note.—The Passage to the Booth will be commodiously illuminated with several large Moons, for the conveniency of the Company ; and Persons of Quality's Coaches may drive up the Yard. To begin every day at one o'clock and continue till eleven at night.

Two Advertisements of 1730.

A MORNING SNACK

BUT thought, as well as grief, is dry
And lo ! a friendly cot was nigh,
Whose sign, high dangling in the air,
Invites the trav'ller to repair,
Where he in comfort may regale,
With cooling pipe and foaming ale.
The Doctor gave the loud command,
And sees the Host beside him stand ;
Then quits his steed with usual state,
And passes through the wicket-gate ;
The Hostess opes the willing door,
And then recounts the humble store
Which her poor cottage could afford,
To place upon the frugal board.
The home-spun napkin soon was laid,
The table all its ware display'd ;
The well-broil'd rasher then appear'd,
And with fresh eggs his stomach cheer'd ;
The crusty pie with apples lin'd,
Sweeten'd the feast on which he din'd,

And liquor, that was brew'd at home,
Among the rest was seen to foam.
The Doctor drank, the Doctor eat,
Well pleas'd to find so fair a treat ;
Then to his pipe he kindly took,
And with a condescending look,
Call'd on the Hostess to relate
What was the village name and state.

William Combe.

TONY LUMPKIN IN HIS ELEMENT

(*An Alehouse room. Several shabby fellows, with punch and tobacco. TONY at the head of the table, a little higher than the rest: a mallet in his hand.*)

OMNES. Hurrea, hurrea, hurrea, bravo !
FIRST FELLOW. Now, gentlemen, silence for a song. The Squire is going to knock himself down for a song.

OMNES. Ay, a song, a song.

TONY. Then I'll sing you, gentlemen, a song I made upon this ale-house, the Three Pigeons.

SONG.

Let school-masters puzzle their brains,
    With grammar, and nonsense, and learning ;
Good liquor, I stoutly maintain,
    Gives *genus* a better discerning ;
Let them brag of their Heathenish Gods,
    Their Lethes, their Styxes, and Stygians ;
Their Quis, and their Quæs, and their Quods,
    They're all but a parcel of Pigeons.
        Toroddle, toroddle, toroll !

When Methodist preachers come down,
 A-preaching that drinking is sinful,
I'll wager the rascals a crown,
 They always preach best with a skinful.
But when you come down with your pence,
 For a slice of their scurvy religion,
I'll leave it to all men of sense,
 But you, my good friend, are the pigeon.
   Toroddle, toroddle, toroll !

Then come, put the jorum about,
 And let us be merry and clever,
Our hearts and our liquors are stout,
 Here's the Three Jolly Pigeons for ever.
Let some cry up woodcock or hare,
 Your bustards, your ducks, and your widgeons ;
But of all the birds in the air,
 Here's a health to the Three Jolly Pigeons.
   Toroddle, toroddle, toroll !

OMNES. Bravo, bravo !

FIRST FELLOW. The Squire has got spunk in him.

SECOND FELLOW. I loves to hear him sing, bekeays he never gives us nothing that's *low*.

THIRD FELLOW. O damn anything that's *low*, I cannot bear it.

FOURTH FELLOW. The genteel thing is the genteel thing at any time. If so be that a gentleman bees in a concatenation accordingly.

THIRD FELLOW. I like the maxum of it, Master Muggins. What, though I am obligated to dance a bear, a man may be a gentleman for all that. May this be my poison if my bear ever dances but to the very gentellest of tunes—Water Parted, or the minuet in Ariadne.

SECOND FELLOW. What a pity it is the Squire is not come to his own. It would be well for all the publicans within ten miles round of him.

TONY. Ecod, and so it would, Master Slang. I'd then show what it was to keep choice of company.

SECOND FELLOW. O, he takes after his own father for that. To be sure, old Squire Lumpkin was the finest gentleman I ever set my eyes on. For winding the straight horn, or beating a thicket for a hare or a wench, he never had his fellow. It was a saying in the place, that he kept the best horses, dogs, and girls in the whole county.

TONY. Ecod, and when I'm of age I'll be no bastard, I promise you. I have been thinking of Bet Bouncer and the miller's grey mare to begin with. But come, my boys, drink about and be merry, for you pay no reckoning. Well, Stingo, what's the matter?

(*Enter* LANDLORD.)

LANDLORD. There be two gentlemen in a post-chaise at the door. They have lost their way upon the forest ; and they are talking something about Mr. Hardcastle.

TONY. As sure as can be, one of them must be the gentleman that's coming down to court my sister. Do they seem to be Londoners ?

LANDLORD. I believe they may. They look woundily like Frenchmen.

TONY. Then desire them to step this way, and I'll set them right in a twinkling. (*Exit* LANDLORD.) Gentlemen, as they mayn't be good enough company for you, step down for a moment, and I'll be with you in the squeezing of a lemon.

Oliver Goldsmith.

THE WAGGONER'S SONG

WHEN first I went a-waggoning, a-waggoning did
　　go,
I filled my parents' heart with grief, with sorrow and with
　　woe,
And many are the hardships that I have since gone thro',
　　　　Sing wo, my lads, sing wo !
　　　　Drive on, my lads, heigh-ho,
And who won't lead the merry life we jolly waggoners
　　do ?

It is a cold and stormy night, I'm wetted to the skin,
But I'll bear it with contentment until I reach the inn,
And then I'll get a-drinking with the landlord and his kin,
　　　　Sing wo, my lads, sing wo !
　　　　Drive on, my lads, heigh-ho,
And who won't lead the merry life we jolly waggoners
　　do ?
　　　　　　　　　　　　　　　　　Traditional.

THE POWER OF GOOD ALE

I ENTERED a well-sanded kitchen, and seated
myself on a bench, on one side of a long white table ;
the other side, which was nearest the wall, was occupied
by a party, or rather family, consisting of a grimy-looking
man, somewhat under the middle size, dressed in faded
velveteens, and wearing a leather apron—a rather pretty-
looking woman, but sun-burnt, and meanly dressed, and
two ragged children, a boy and a girl, about four or five
years old.   The man sat with his eyes fixed upon the table,
supporting his chin with both his hands ; the woman who
was next to him, sat quite still, save that occasionally she
turned a glance upon her husband with eyes that appeared
to have been lately crying.   The children had none of the

vivacity so general at their age. A more disconsolate family I had never seen ; a mug, which, when filled, might contain half a pint, stood empty before them ; a very disconsolate party indeed.

" House ! " said I ; " House ! " and then as nobody appeared, I cried again as loud as I could, " House ! do you hear me, House ! "

" What's your pleasure, young man ? " said an elderly woman, who now made her appearance from a side apartment.

" To taste your ale," said I.

" How much ? " said the woman, stretching out her hand towards the empty mug upon the table.

" The largest measure-full in your house," said I, putting back her hand gently. " This is not the season for half-pint mugs."

" As you will, young man," said the landlady ; and presently brought in an earthen pitcher which might contain about three pints, and which foamed and frothed withal.

" Will this pay for it ? " said I, putting down sixpence.

" I have to return you a penny," said the landlady, putting her hand into her pocket.

" I want no change," said I, flourishing my hand with an air.

" As you please, young gentleman," said the landlady, and then making a kind of curtsey, she again retired to the side apartment.

" Here is your health, sir," said I to the grimy-looking man, as I raised the pitcher to my lips.

The tinker, for such I supposed him to be, without altering his posture, raised his eyes, looked at me for a moment, gave a slight nod, and then once more fixed his eyes upon the table. I took a draught of the ale, which I found excellent. "Won't you drink?" said I, holding the pitcher to the tinker.

The man again lifted his eyes, looked at me, and then at the pitcher, and then at me again. I thought at one time that he was about to shake his head in sign of refusal, but no, he looked once more at the pitcher, and the temptation was too strong. Slowly removing his head from his arms, he took the pitcher, sighed, nodded, and drank a tolerable quantity, and then set the pitcher down before me upon the table.

"You had better mend your draught," said I to the tinker, "it is a sad heart that never rejoices."

"That's true," said the tinker, and again raising the pitcher to his lips, he mended his draught as I had bidden him, drinking a larger quantity than before.

"Pass it to your wife," said I.

The poor woman took the pitcher from the man's hand; before, however, raising it to her lips, she looked at the children. True mother's heart, thought I to myself, and taking the half-pint mug, I made her fill it, and then held it to the children, causing each to take a draught. The woman wiped her eyes with the corner of her gown, before she raised the pitcher and drank to my health.

In about five minutes none of the family looked half so disconsolate as before, and the tinker and I were in deep discourse.

Oh, genial and gladdening is the power of good ale, the true and proper drink of Englishmen. He is not deserving of the name of Englishman who speaketh against ale, that is good ale, like that which has just made merry the hearts of this poor family; and yet there are beings, calling themselves Englishmen, who say that it is a sin to

THE BOOK OF THE INN

drink a cup of ale, and who, on coming to this passage, will be tempted to fling down the book and exclaim, "The man is evidently a bad man, for behold, by his own confession, he is not only fond of ale himself, but is in the habit of tempting other people with it." Alas ! alas ! what a number of silly individuals there are in this world ; I wonder what they would have had me do in this instance —given the afflicted family a cup of cold water ? go to ! They could have found water in the road, for there was a pellucid spring only a few yards distant from the house, as they were well aware—but they wanted not water ; what should I have given them ? meat and bread ? go to ! They were not hungry ; there was stifled sobbing in their bosoms, and the first mouthful of strong meat would have choked them. What should I have given them ? Money! what right had I to insult them by offering them money ? Advice ! words, words, words ; friends, there is a time for everything ; there is a time for a cup of cold water ; there is a time for strong meat and bread ; there is a time for advice, and there is a time for ale ; and I have generally found that the time for advice is after a cup of ale.

George Borrow.

AT THE RED HORSE

TO a homeless man, who has no spot on this wide world which he can truly call his own, there is a momentary feeling of something like independence and territorial consequence, when, after a weary day's travel, he kicks off his boots, thrusts his feet into slippers, and stretches himself before an inn fire. Let the world without go as it may ; let kingdoms raise or fall, so long as he has the wherewithal to pay his bill, he is, for the time being, the very monarch of all he surveys. The arm-chair is his throne, the poker his sceptre, and the little parlour, some twelve feet square, his undisputed empire. It is a morsel of certainty, snatched from the midst of the uncertainties of life ; it is a sunny moment gleaming out kindly on a cloudy day : and he who has advanced some way on the pilgrimage of existence knows the importance of husbanding even morsels and moments of enjoyment. " Shall I not take mine ease in mine inn ? " thought I, as I gave the fire a stir, lolled back in my elbow-chair, and cast a complacent look about the little parlour of the Red Horse, at Stratford-on-Avon.

The words of sweet Shakespeare were just passing through my mind as the clock struck midnight from the tower of the church in which he lies buried. There was a gentle tap at the door, and a pretty chambermaid, putting in her smiling face, inquired, with a hesitating air, whether I had rung. I understood it as a modest hint that it was time to retire. My dream of absolute dominion was at an end ; so abdicating my throne, like a prudent potentate, to avoid being deposed, and putting the Stratford Guide Book under my arm, as a pillow companion, I went to bed and dreamt all night of Shakespeare.

Washington Irving.

NED KILDERKIN'S HOUSE

" SIR MUNKO MALCROWTHER ?—yes, sir, I dare say he is at this moment in Ned's eating-house, for few folks ask him out, now Lord Huntinglen is gone to London. You will get touched again—yes, sir—there you shall find him with his can of single ale, stirred with a sprig of rosemary, for he never drinks strong potations, sir, unless to oblige Lord Huntinglen—take heed, sir—or any other person who asks him forth to breakfast—but single beer he always drinks at Ned's, with his broiled bone of beef or mutton—or, it may be, lamb at the season—but not pork, though Ned is famous for his griskins. But the Scots never eat pork—strange that ! some folk think they are a sort of Jews. There is a semblance, sir,—Do you not think so ? Then they call our most gracious Sovereign the Second Solomon, and Solomon, you know, was King of the Jews ; so the thing bears a face, you see. I believe, sir, you will find yourself trimmed now to your content. I will be judged by the fair mistress of your affections. Crave pardon—no offence, I trust. Pray, consult the glass—one touch of the crisping tongs, to reduce this straggler.—Thank your munificence, sir—hope your custom while you stay in Greenwich. Would you have a tune on that glittern, to put your temper in concord for the day ?—Twang, twang—twang, twang, dillo. Something out of tune, sir—too many hands to touch it—we cannot keep these things like artists. Let me help you with your cloak, sir—yes, sir—You would not play yourself, sir, would you ?—Way to Sir Munko's eating-house ? —Yes, sir ; but it is Ned's eating-house, not Sir Munko's. —The knight, to be sure, eats there, and makes it his eating-house in some sense, sir—ha, ha ! Yonder it is, removed from over the way, new whitewashed posts, and red lattice—fat man in his doublet at the door—Ned himself, sir—worth a thousand pounds, they say—better singeing pigs' faces than trimming courtiers—but ours is the less mechanical vocation.—Farewell, sir ; hope your custom." So saying, he at length permitted Nigel to depart, whose ears, so long tormented with continued babble, tingled when it had ceased, as if a bell had been rung close to them for the same space of time.

Upon his arrival at the eating-house, where he proposed

to meet with Sir Mungo Malagrowther, from whom, in
despair of better advice, he trusted to receive some information as to the best mode of introducing himself into the
royal presence, Lord Glenvarloch found, in the host with
whom he communed, the consequential taciturnity of an
Englishman well to pass in the world. Ned Kilderkin
spoke as a banker writes, only touching the needful. Being
asked if Sir Mungo Malagrowther was there ? he replied,
No. Being interrogated whether he was expected ? he
said, Yes. And being again required to say when he was
expected, he answered, Presently. As Lord Glenvarloch
next inquired, whether he himself could have any breakfast ? the landlord wasted not even a syllable in reply, but,
ushering him into a neat room where there were several
tables, he placed one of them before an armchair, and
beckoning Lord Glenvarloch to take possession, he set
before him, in a very few minutes, a substantial repast of
roast-beef, together with a foaming tankard, to which
refreshment the keen air of the river disposed him, notwithstanding his mental embarrassments, to do much
honour.

While Nigel was thus engaged in discussing his commons, but raising his head at the same time whenever he
heard the door of the apartment open, eagerly desiring the
arrival of Sir Mungo Malagrowther, (an event which had
seldom been expected by any one with so much anxious
interest,) a personage, as it seemed, of at least equal
importance with the knight, entered into the apartment,
and began to hold earnest colloquy with the publican, who
thought proper to carry on the conference on his side un-
bonneted. This important gentleman's occupation might
be guessed from his dress. A milk-white jerkin, and hose
of white kersey ; a white apron twisted around his body

in the manner of a sash, in which, instead of a war-like dagger, was stuck a long-bladed knife, hilted with buck's-horn ; a white nightcap on his head, under which his hair was neatly tucked, sufficiently pourtrayed him as one of those priests of Comus whom the vulgar call cooks ; and the air with which he rated the publican for having neglected to send some provisions to the Palace, showed that he ministered to royalty itself.

Sir Walter Scott.

PRAISE OF THE CHOP-HOUSE

A CHOP-HOUSE is productive of all the pleasures in life ; it is a combination of the most agreeable and satisfying amusements ; the heart, the mind, and the constitution are to be mended upon crossing its threshold. It is, in a word, a little world within itself, possessing a system peculiar to itself, of planets and satellites and fixed stars and revolutions, in all its extensive diversity of waiters, cooks, saucepans, frying-pans, gridirons, salamanders, stoves and smoke-jacks.

Within the doors of a chop-house are to be found food for both body and soul, nourishment at once for the faculties both of mind and body ; while the palate is satisfied by devouring a mutton chop, a veal cutlet or a beef steak. In this delightful place of amusement and convenience there is provender for philosophers or fools, stoics or epicureans ; contemplation for genius of all denominations ; and it embraces every species of science and art, having an especial eye to the important art of cookery. The name, the very name alone, is sufficient to excite all that is pleasant to our senses. A Chop-house ! at that word what delightful prospects are presented to the mind's eye —what a clashing of knives and forks and plates and pewter pots, and rushing of footsteps and murmurings of expectant hosts enter into our delighted ears—what gay scenes of varied beauty, and many-natured viands and viscous soups, tarts, puddings and pies, rise before our visual nerves—what fragrant perfumes, sweet-scented odours, and grateful gales of delicate dainties ! It is creative of the lordiest independence of spirit. It excites the best passions of the heart—it calls into action every kind and generous feeling of our nature—it begets fraternal affection and unanimity and cordiality of soul, and excellent neighbourhood among men—it will correct antipodes, for its ministerial effects will produce a Radical advantage—its component parts go down with the world, and are well digested. From among its innumerable excellencies, I will mention one which deserves to be held in recollection and kept in contemplation—what is more delightful than a fine beef-steak ? spite of Lexicographers, there is something of harmony even in its name ; it circles all that is full, rich and sonorous.

Pierce Egan.

THE SUPERANNUATED INN

IF the Dodo were only a gregarious bird—if he had only some confused idea of making a comfortable nest—I could hope to get through the hours between this and bed-time, without being consumed by devouring melancholy. But, the Dodo's habits are all wrong. It provides me with a trackless desert of sitting-room, with a chair for every day in the year, a table for every month, and a waste of sideboard where a lonely China vase pines in a corner for its mate long departed, and will never make a match with the candlestick in the opposite corner if it live till Dooms-day. The Dodo has nothing in the larder. Even now, I behold the Boots returning with my sole in a piece of paper ; and with that portion of my dinner, the Boots, perceiving me at the blank bow window, slaps his leg as he comes across the road, pretending it is something else. The Dodo excludes the outer air. When I mount up to my bedroom, a smell of closeness and flue gets lazily up my nose like sleepy snuff. The loose little bits of carpet writhe under my tread, and take wormy shapes. I don't know the ridiculous man in the looking-glass, beyond having met him once or twice in a dish-cover—and I can never shave *him* to-morrow morning! The Dodo is narrow-minded as to towels; expects me to wash on a freemason's apron without the trimming: when I asked for soap, gives me a stony-hearted something white, with no more lather in it than the Elgin marbles. The Dodo has seen better days, and possesses interminable stables at the back, —silent, grass-grown, broken-windowed, horseless.

This mournful bird can fry a sole, however, which is much. Can cook a steak, too, which is more. I wonder where it gets its Sherry? If I were to send my pint of wine to some famous chemist to be analysed, what would it turn out to be made of? It tastes of pepper, sugar, bitter-almonds, vinegar, warm knives, any flat drinks, and a little brandy. Would it unman a Spanish exile by re-minding him of his native land at all? I think not. If there really be any townspeople out of the churchyards, and if a caravan of them ever do dine, with a bottle of wine per man, in this desert of the Dodo, it must make good for the doctor next day!

Where was the waiter born? How did he come here? Has he any hope of getting away from here? Does he ever receive a letter, or take a ride upon the railway, or see anything but the Dodo? Perhaps he has seen the Berlin Wool. He appears to have a silent sorrow on him, and it may be that. He clears the table; draws the dingy cur-

tains of the great bow window, which so unwillingly consent to meet, that they must be pinned together ; leaves
me by the fire with my pint decanter, and a little thin
funnel-shaped wine-glass, and a plate of pale biscuits—in
themselves engendering desperation.

Charles Dickens.

A COMMON HOME

THE forest inn was also a farmhouse. There was a
comfortable-looking kitchen enough ; but the ingle
nook was full of smokers, and Coningsby was glad to avail
himself of the only private room for the simple meal which
they offered him. Only eggs and bacon ; but very welcome to a pedestrian and a hungry one.

As he stood at the window of his little apartment, watching the large drops that were the heralds of the coming
hurricane, and waiting for his repast, a flash of lightning
illumined the whole country, and a horseman at full speed,
followed by his groom, galloped up to the door.

The remarkable beauty of the animal so attracted
Coningsby's attention, that it prevented him catching even
a glimpse of the rider, who rapidly dismounted and entered
the inn. The host shortly after came in and asked Coningsby whether he had any objection to a gentleman, who
was driven there by the storm, sharing his room until it
subsided. The consequence of the immediate assent of
Coningsby was, that the landlord retired and soon returned
ushering in an individual, who though perhaps ten years
older than Coningsby, was still, according to Hippocrates,
in the period of lusty youth. He was above the middle
height, and of a distinguished air and figure ; pale, with
an impressive brow, and dark eyes of great intelligence.

" I am glad that we have both escaped the storm," said

the stranger ; " and I am greatly indebted to you for your courtesy." He slightly and graciously bowed as he spoke in a voice of remarkable clearness ; and his manner, though easy, was touched with a degree of dignity that was engaging.

" The inn is a common home," replied Coningsby returning his salute.

" And free from cares," added the stranger. Then looking through the window, he said : " A strange storm this. I was sauntering in the sunshine, when suddenly I found I had to gallop for my life. 'Tis more like a white squall in the Mediterranean than anything else."

" I never was in the Mediterranean," said Coningsby. " There is nothing that I should like so much as to travel." . . .

At this moment, a pretty serving-maid entered the room. She laid the dapper-cloth and arranged the table with a self-possession quite admirable. She seemed unconscious that any being was in the chamber except herself, or that there were any other duties to perform in life beyond filling a salt-cellar or folding a napkin.

" She does not even look at us," said Coningsby when she had quitted the room, " and I dare say only a prude."

" She is calm," said the stranger, " because she is mistress of her subject ; 'tis the secret of self-possession. She is here, as a duchess at court."

They brought in Coningsby's meal, and he invited the stranger to join him. The invitation was accepted with cheerfulness.

" 'Tis but simple fare," said Coningsby as the maiden uncovered the still hissing bacon and the eggs that looked like tufts of primroses.

" Nay, a national dish," said the stranger, glancing quickly at the table, " whose fame is a proverb. And what more should we expect under a simple roof ! How much better than an omelette or a greasy olla, that they would give us in a posada ! 'Tis a wonderful country this England ! What a napkin ! How spotless ! And so sweet I declare 'tis a perfume. There is not a princess throughout the south of Europe served with the cleanliness that meets us in this cottage."

Benjamin Disraeli.

HONEYBALL'S ORDINARY

THE Masons' Arms is kept by Master Edward Honeyball. It is one of those little taverns which abound in the heart of the city, and form the centre of gossip and intelligence of the neighbourhood. We entered the bar-room, which was narrow and darkling ; for in these close lanes but few rays of reflected light are enabled to struggle down to the inhabitants, whose broad day is at best but a tolerable twilight. The room was partitioned into boxes, each containing a table spread with a clean white cloth for dinner. At the lower end of the room was a clear coal fire, before which a breast of lamb was roasting. A row of bright brass candlesticks and pewter mugs glistened along the mantelpiece, and an old-fashioned clock ticked in one corner. There was something primitive in this medley of kitchen, parlour, and hall, that carried me back to earlier times, and pleased me. The place, indeed, was humble, but everything had that look of order and neatness, which bespeaks the superintendence of a notable English housewife. A group of amphibious-looking beings, who might be either fishermen or sailors, were regaling themselves in one of the boxes. As I was a visitor of rather higher pretensions, I was ushered into a little

misshapen backroom, having at least nine corners. It
was lighted by a sky-light, furnished with antiquated
leather chairs, and ornamented with the portrait of a fat
pig. It was evidently appropriated to particular customers, and I found a shabby gentleman, in a red nose
and oil-cloth hat, seated in one corner, meditating on a
half-empty pot of porter.   *Washington Irving.*

THE MERMAID TAVERN

SOULS of Poets dead and gone,
What Elysium have ye known,
Happy field or mossy cavern,
Choicer than the Mermaid Tavern ?
Have ye tippled drink more fine
Than mine host's Canary wine ?
Or are fruits of Paradise
Sweeter than those dainty pies
Of venison ?   O generous food !
Drest as though bold Robin Hood
Would, with his Maid Marian,
Sup and browse from horn and can.

I have heard that on a day
Mine host's signboard flew away,
Nobody knew whither, till
An astrologer's old quill
To a sheepskin gave the story,
Said he saw you in your glory,
Underneath a new old sign
Sipping beverage divine,
And pledging with contented smack
The Mermaid in the Zodiac.

Souls of Poets dead and gone,
What Elysium have ye known,
Happy field or mossy cavern,
Choicer than the Mermaid Tavern ?

John Keats.

TRICKS OF THE ROAD

WELL, I walked away, cursing all the Eton boys and all their tutors, who did not teach them honesty as well as Latin and Greek, and put up at a very humble sort of abode, where they sold small beer, and gave beds at twopence per night, and I may add, with plenty of fleas in the bargain. There I fell in with some ballad singers and mumpers, who were making very merry, and who asked me what was the matter. I told them how I had been treated, and they laughed at me, but gave me some supper, so I forgave them. An old man, who governed the party, then asked me whether I had any money. I produced my enormous capital of eightpence. "Quite enough, if you are clever," said he ; "quite enough—many a man with half that sum has ended in rolling in his carriage. A man with thousands has only the advance of you a few years. You will pay for your lodging, and then spend this sixpence in matches, and hawk them about the town. If you are lucky, it will be a shilling by to-morrow night. Besides, you go down into areas, and sometimes enter a kitchen when the cooks is above stairs. There are plenty of things to be picked up." "But I am not dishonest," said I. "Well, then, every man to his liking ; only if you were, you would ride in your own coach the sooner." "And suppose I should lose all this, or none would buy my matches, what then ? " replied I ; "I shall starve." "Starve—no, no—no one starves in this country ; all you have to do is to get into gaol—committed for a month—you will live better, perhaps, than you ever did before. I have been in every gaol in England, and I know the good ones, for even in gaols there is a great difference. Now the one in this town is one of the best in all England, and I patronises it during the winter." I was much amused with the discourse of this mumper, who appeared to be one of the merriest old vagabonds in England. I took his advice, bought sixpennyworth of matches, and commenced my new vagrant speculation.

Frederick Marryat.

" INSIDES " AND " OUTSIDES "

IT was the fixed assumption of the four inside people that they, the illustrious quaternion, constituted a porcelain variety of the human race, whose dignity would have been compromised by exchanging one word of civility with the three miserable delf-ware outsides. Even to have kicked an outsider might have been held to attaint the foot concerned in that operation, so that perhaps it would have required an Act of Parliament to restore its purity of blood. What words, then, could express the horror and the sense of treason in that case, which *had* happened, where all three outsides (the trinity of pariahs) made a vain attempt to sit down at the same breakfast-table or dinner-table with the consecrated four ? I myself witnessed such an attempt ; and on that occasion a benevolent old gentleman endeavoured to soothe his three holy associates by suggesting that if the outsides were indicted for this criminal attempt at the next assizes, the court would regard it as a case of lunacy or delirium tremens rather than that of treason. England owes much of her grandeur to the depth of the aristocratic element in her social composition when pulling against her own strong democracy. I am not the man to laugh at it. But sometimes, undoubtedly, it expressed itself in comic shapes. The course taken with the infatuated outsides, in the particular attempt which I have noticed, was that the waiter, beckoning them away from the privileged *salle-à-manger*, sang out, " This way, my good men," and then enticed these good men away to the kitchen. But that plan had not always answered. Sometimes, though rarely, cases occurred where the intruders, being stronger than usual, or more vicious than usual, resolutely refused to budge, and so far carried their point as to have a separate table arranged for themselves in a corner of the general room. Yet, if an Indian screen could be found ample enough to plant them out from the very eyes of the high table or dais, it then became possible to assume as a fiction of law that the three delf fellows after all were not present. They could be ignored by the porcelain men, under the maxim that objects not appearing and not existing are governed by the same logical construction.

Thomas de Quincey.

THE HIGHWAYMEN AT EASE

THE present straggling suburb at the north-west of the metropolis, known as Kilburn, had scarcely been called into existence a century ago, and an ancient hostel, with a few detached farmhouses, were the sole habitations to be found in the present populous vicinage. The place of refreshment for the ruralising cockney of 1737 was a substantial-looking tenement of the good old stamp, with great bay windows, and a balcony in front, bearing as its ensign the jovial visage of the lusty knight Jack Falstaff. Shaded by a spreading elm, a circular bench embraced the aged trunk of the tree, sufficiently tempting, no doubt, to incline the wanderer on those dusty ways to " rest and be thankful," and to cry *encore* to a frothing tankard of the best ale to be obtained within the chimes of Bow Bells.

Upon a table, green as the privet and holly that formed the walls of the bower in which it was placed, stood a great china bowl, one of those leviathan memorials of bygone wassailry which we may sometimes espy (reversed, in token of its desuetude) perched on the top of an old japanned closet, but seldom, if ever, encounter in its proper position at the genial board. All the appliances of festivity were at hand. Pipes and rummers strewed the board. Perfume, subtle yet mellow, as of pine and lime, exhaled from out the bowl, and, mingling with the scent of a neighbouring bed of mignonette, and the subdued odour of the Indian weed, formed altogether as delectable an atmosphere of sweets as one could wish to inhale on a melting August afternoon. So, at least, thought the inmates of the arbour ; nor did they by any means confine themselves to the gratification of a single sense. The ambrosial contents of the china bowl proved as delicious to the taste as its bouquet was grateful to the smell ; while the eyesight was soothed by reposing on the smooth sward of a bowling-green spread out immediately before it, or in dwelling upon gently undulating meads, terminating, at about a mile's distance, in the woody, spire-crowned heights of Hampstead.

Dick had been called upon to act as president of the board, and an excellent president he made, sedulously devoting himself to the due administration of the punch-bowl. Not a rummer was allowed to stand empty for an instant. Toast, sentiment, and anacreontic song, succeeded each other at speedy intervals ; but there was no speechifying—no politics. He left church and state to take care of themselves. Whatever his politics might be,

Dick never allowed them to interfere with his pleasures. His maximum was to make the most of the passing moment ; the *dum vivimus vivamus* was never out of his mind ; a precautionary measure which we recommend to the adoption of all gentlemen of the like, or any other precarious profession.

Notwithstanding all Dick's efforts to promote conviviality, seconded by the excellence of the beverage itself, conversation, somehow or other, began to flag ; from being general, it became particular. Tom King, who was no punch-bibber, especially at that time of day, fell into a deep reverie ; your gamesters often do so ; while the Magnus, who had smoked himself drowsy, was composing himself to a doze.
W. Harrison Ainsworth.

THOUGHTS AT AN INN

THIS inn is one of the nicest, and, in summer, one of the pleasantest, in England ; for, I think, that my experience in this way will justify me in speaking thus positively. The house is large, the yard and the stables good, the landlord a farmer also, and, therefore, no cribbing your horses in hay or straw and yourself in eggs and cream. The garden, which adjoins the south side of the house, is large, of good shape, has a terrace on one side, lies on the slope, consists of well-disposed clumps of shrubs and flowers, and of short grass very neatly kept. In the lower part of the garden there are high trees, and, amongst these, the tulip tree and the live-oak. Beyond the garden is a large clump of lofty sycamores, and, in these a most populous rookery, in which, of all things in the world, I delight. The village, which contains 301 souls, lies to the north of the inn but adjoining its premises. All the rest, in every direction, is bare down or open arable. I am now sitting at one of the southern windows of this inn, looking across the garden towards the rookery. It is nearly sun-setting ; the rooks are skimming and curving over the tops of the trees ; while, under the branches, I see a flock of several hundred sheep, coming nibbling their way in from the Down, and going to their fold.

Now, what ill-natured devil could bring Old Nick Grimshaw into my head in company with these innocent sheep ? Why, the truth is this : nothing is so swift as thought : it runs over a life-time in a moment ; and, while I was writing the last sentence of the foregoing paragraph, thought took me up at the time when I used to wear a smock-frock and to carry a wooden bottle like that shepherd's boy ; and, in an instant, it hurried me along through my no very short life of adventure, of toil, of peril, of pleasure, of ardent friendship and not less ardent enmity ; and after filling me with wonder, that a heart and mind so wrapped up in everything belonging to the gardens, the fields and the woods, should have been con-demned to waste themselves away amidst the stench, the noise and the strife of cities, it brought me to the present moment, and sent my mind back to what I have yet to perform about Nicholas Grimshaw and his ditches !

William Cobbett.

AN EXCITING EVENING

THE Rainbow, in Marner's view, was a place of luxuri-ous resort for rich and stout husbands, whose wives had superfluous stores of linen ; it was the place where he was likely to find the powers and dignities of Raveloe, and where he could most speedily make his loss public. He lifted the latch, and turned into the bright bar or kitchen on the right hand, where the less lofty customers of the house were in the habit of assembling, the parlour on the left being reserved for the more select society in which Squire Cass frequently enjoyed the double pleasure of conviviality and condescension. But the parlour was dark to-night, the chief personages who ornamented its circle being all at Mrs. Osgood's birthday dance, as Godfrey Cass was. And in consequence of this, the party on the high-screened seats in the kitchen was more numerous than usual ; several personages, who would otherwise have been admitted into the parlour and enlarged the opportunity of hectoring and condescension for their betters, being content this evening to vary their enjoyment by taking their spirits-and-water where they could themselves hector and condescend in company that called for beer.

The conversation, which was at a high pitch of animation when Silas approached the door of the Rainbow, had, as usual, been slow and intermittent when the company first assembled. The pipes began to be puffed in a silence which had an air of severity ; the more important customers, who drank spirits and sat nearest the fire, staring at each other as if a bet were depending on the first man who winked ; while the beer-drinkers, chiefly men in fustian jackets and smock-frocks, kept their eyelids down and rubbed their hands across their mouths, as if their draughts of beer were a funereal duty attended with embarrassing sadness. At last, Mr. Snell, the landlord, a man of a neutral disposition, accustomed to stand aloof from human differences as those of beings who were all alike in need of liquor, broke silence, by saying in a doubtful tone to his cousin the butcher—

" Some folks 'ud say that was a fine beast you druv in yesterday, Bob ? "

The butcher, a jolly, smiling, red-haired man, was not disposed to answer rashly. He gave a few puffs before he spat and replied, " And they wouldn't be fur wrong, John."

After this feeble delusive thaw, the silence set in as severely as before.

George Eliot.

A SUNDAY ORDINARY

AT the conclusion of this colloquy we had arrived at the Gate House, Highgate, just in time to hear the landlord proclaim that dinner was that moment about to be served up. The civic rank of the alderman did not fail to obtain its due share of servile attention from Boniface, who undertook to escort our party into the room, and having announced the consequence of his guests, placed the alderman and his family at the head of the table.

I have somewhere read that there is as much valour expected in feasting as in fighting ; and if anyone doubts the truth of the axiom, let him try with a hungry stomach to gratify the cravings of nature at a crowded ordinary— or imagine a well disposed group of twenty persons, all in high appetite and eager for the fray, sitting down to a repast scantily prepared for just half the number, and crammed into a narrow room, where the waiters are of necessity obliged to wipe every dish against your back, or deposit a portion of gravy in your pocket, to say nothing of the sauce with which a remonstrance is sure to fill both your ears. Most of the company present upon this occa- sion appeared to have the organs of destructiveness to an extraordinary degree, and mine host of the Gate House, who is considered an excellent physiognomist, looked on with trembling and disastrous countenance as he marked the eager anxiety of the expectant gourmands sharpening their knives, and spreading their napkins, at the shrine of Sensuality, exhibiting the most voracious symptoms of desire to commence the work of demolition.

"Could you make room for three more gentlemen ? " said the waiter, ushering in three woe-begone knights of the trencher, who, having heard the fatal clock strike when at the bottom of the hill, and knowing the punctuality of the house, had toiled upwards with breathless anxiety to be present at the first attack, and arrived at the end of the second course, just in time to be too late. " Confound all clocks and clockmakers ! set my watch by Bishopsgate church, and made sure I was a quarter too fast." " Very sorry, gentlemen, very sorry, indeed," said Boniface ; " nothing left that is eatable—not a chop or a steak in the house ; but there is an excellent ordinary at the Spaniards, about a mile further down the lane ; always half an hour later than ours." " Ay, it's a grievous affair, landlord ; but, howsomdever, if there's nothing to eat, why we must go : we meant to have done you justice to-day—but never mind, we'll be in time for you another Sunday, old gentleman, depend upon it " ; and with this significant promise the three *hungarians* departed. "Those three men are no *ordinary* customers," said our host ; " they have done us the honour to dine here before, and what is more, of leaving nothing behind ; one of them is the celebrated Yorkshireman, Tom Cornish, whom General Picton pitted against a Hanoverian glutton to eat for a fortnight, and found, at the end of a week, that he was a whole bullock, besides twelve quartern loaves, and half a barrel of beer ahead of his antagonist ; and if the Hanoverian had not given up, Tom would have eaten the rations of a whole company." " Ay, that's a very good joke, landlord," said the alderman ; " but you know I am up to your jokes : you think these long stories will save your mutton, but there you're wrong—they only give time to take breath ; so bring in the sirloin and the saddle of mutton, waiter ; and when we've done dinner I'll tell you an anecdote of old Tattersall and his beef-eater, which occurred at this house in a former landlord's time. Come, Mr. Blackmantle, let me send you a slice of the sirloin, and tell us what you think of good eating."

Edward Westmacott.

A TEMPLE OF COMMERCE

THE Banks of Jordan was a public-house in the city, which from its appearance did not seem to do a very thriving trade ; but as it was carried on from year to year in the same dull, monotonous, dead-alive sort of fashion, it must be surmised that some one found an interest in keeping it open.

Charley, when he entered the door punctually at two o'clock, saw that it was as usual nearly deserted. One long, lanky, middle-aged man, seedy as to his outward vestments, and melancholy in countenance, sat at one of the tables. But he was doing very little good for the establishment : he had no refreshment of any kind before him, and was intent only on a dingy pocket-book in which he was making entries with a pencil.

You enter the Banks of Jordan by two folding doors in a corner of a very narrow alley behind the Exchange. As you go in, you observe on your left a little glass partition, something like a large cage, inside which, in a bar, are four or five untempting-looking bottles ; and also inside the cage, on a chair, is to be seen a quiet-looking female, who is invariably engaged in the manufacture of some white article of inward clothing. Anything less like the flashy-dressed bar-maidens of the western gin palaces it would be difficult to imagine. To this encaged sempstress no one ever speaks unless it be to give a rare order for a mutton chop or pint of stout. And even for this she hardly stays her sewing for a moment, but touches a small bell, and the ancient waiter, who never shows himself but when called for, and who is the only other inhabitant of the place ever visible, receives the order from her through an open pane in the cage as quietly as she received it from her customer.

The floor of the single square room of the establishment is sanded, and the tables are ranged round the walls, each table being fixed to the floor, and placed within wooden partitions, by which the occupier is screened from any inquiring eyes on either side.

Such was Mr. Jabesh M'Ruen's house-of-call in the city, and of many a mutton chop and many a pint of stout had Charley partaken there while waiting for the man of money. To him it seemed to be inexcusable to sit down in a public inn and call for nothing ; he perceived, however, that the large majority of the frequenters of the Banks of Jordan so conducted themselves.

Anthony Trollope.

THREE CHOICE SPIRITS

CHEERILY, though there were none abroad to see it, shone the Maypole light that evening. Blessings on the red—deep, ruby, glowing red—old curtain of the window ; blending into one rich stream of brightness, fire, and candle, meat, drink, and company, and gleaming like a jovial eye upon the bleak waste out of doors ! Within, what carpet like its crunching sand, what music merry as its crackling logs, what perfume like its kitchen's dainty

breath, what weather genial as its hearty warmth ! Blessings on the old house, how sturdily it stood ! How did the
vexed wind chafe and roar about its stalwart roof ; how
did it pant and strive with its wide chimneys, which still
poured forth from their hospitable throats great clouds of
smoke, and puffed defiance in its face ; how, above all,
did it drive and rattle at the casement, emulous to extin-
guish that cheerful glow, which would not be put down
and seemed the brighter for the conflict.

The profusion too, the rich and lavish bounty, of that
goodly tavern ! It was not enough that one fire roared
and sparkled on its spacious hearth ; in the tiles which
paved and compassed it, five hundred flickering fires burnt
brightly also. It was not enough that one red curtain shut
the wild night out, and shed its cheerful influence on the
room. In every saucepan lid, and candlestick, and vessel of
copper, brass, or tin that hung upon the walls, were count-
less ruddy hangings, flashing and gleaming with every
motion of the blaze, and offering, let the eye wander
where it might, interminable vistas of the same rich
colour. The old oak wainscoting, the beams, the
chairs, the seats, reflected it in a deep, dull glimmer.
There were fires and red curtains in the very eyes of
the drinkers, in their buttons, in their liquor, in the pipes
they smoked.

Mr. Willett sat in what had been his accustomed place
five years before, with his eyes on the eternal boiler ; and
had sat there since the clock struck eight, giving no other
signs of life than breathing with a loud and constant snore
(though he was wide awake), and from time to time putting
his glass to his lips, or knocking the ashes out of his pipe,
and filling it anew. It was now half-past ten. Mr. Cobb
and long Phil Parkes were his companions, as of old, and

for two mortal hours and a half, none of the company had pronounced one word.

Whether people, by dint of sitting together in the same place and the same relative positions, and doing exactly the same things for a great many years, acquire a sixth sense, or some unknown power of influencing each other which serves them in its stead, is a question for philosophy to settle. But certain it is that old John Willett, Mr. Parkes, and Mr. Cobb, were one and all firmly of opinion that they were very jolly companions—rather choice spirits than otherwise ; that they looked at each other every now and then as if there were a perpetual interchange of ideas going on among them ; that no man considered himself or his neighbour by any means silent ; and that each of them nodded occasionally when he caught the eye of another, as if he would say " You have expressed yourself extremely well, sir, in relation to that sentiment, and I quite agree with you."

Charles Dickens.

PRINTED IN GREAT BRITAIN BY THE WHITEFRIARS PRESS, LTD., LONDON AND TONBRIDGE.

for two small leaves under bark roots of the cork-pine, and pronounced one word.

Whether people, by that or along together in the same place, and the same relative position, and doing such the same things to a great many years, acquire a sort of some, or communicate lower of influence, each of that which aces a llama to them on his opinion of ought and so many. But certain was, that old John Wilcox, Mr. ----, and Mr. Crabb, were, almost all manner of opinion -- if they were taught to go conclusions -- in that month

And otherwise with a long I would notion there even now so that ... If there were to implied too remains at once drawn almost, here could be no nail besides, at hand, that

And other to call something, a tired character so great medical assistance, when here cannot be ... We the ... as we asked ... I do hope ... the advantage of extreme right. To remember that a moment of living are

Edward Burns